COLORED SYMMETRY

COLORED SYMMETRY

BY

A. V. SHUBNIKOV, N. V. BELOV
and others

A Series of Publications from the
Institute of Crystallography
Academy of Sciences of the U.S.S.R.
Moscow, 1951–1958

TRANSLATED FROM THE RUSSIAN

BY

JACK ITZKOFF AND JACK GOLLOB
Translavic Associates
Los Angeles, California.

EDITED BY

WILLIAM T. HOLSER
California Research Corporation
La Habra, California.

PERGAMON PRESS
OXFORD · LONDON · NEW YORK · PARIS
1964

PERGAMON PRESS LTD.

Headington Hill Hall, Oxford
4 and 5 Fitzroy Square, London W.1

PERGAMON PRESS INC.

122 East 55th Street, New York 22, N.Y.

GAUTHIER-VILLARS ED.

55 Quai des Grands-Augustins, Paris 6

PERGAMON PRESS G.m.b.H.

Kaiserstrasse 75, Frankfurt am Main

Distributed in the Western Hemisphere by
THE MACMILLAN COMPANY · NEW YORK
pursuant to a special arrangement with
Pergamon Press Incorporated

The first part of this book is a translation based on A. V. Shubnikov's
"Симметрия и антисимметрия конечных фигур (Simmetriya i
antisimmetriya konechnykh figur)" published by the U.S.S.R.
Academy of Sciences. The second part consists of several articles
by N. V. Belov et al., which are appropriately acknowledged in
footnotes to each.

Set in Monotype Baskerville 11 on 12 pt.
and printed in Great Britain by
THE PITMAN PRESS, BATH

Contents

	PAGE
EDITOR'S PREFACE	xi
AUTHOR'S PREFACE TO PART I	xv

PART I

SYMMETRY AND ANTISYMMETRY OF FINITE FIGURES

A. V. SHUBNIKOV

THE SYMMETRY OF FINITE FIGURES	3
Introduction	3
Basic Concepts and Definitions of Symmetry	3
General definition of symmetry	3
The figure	4
The uniform distribution of equal domains of a figure	4
Reflection in a plane	5
Rotations around an axis	6
Mirror rotations (rotary reflections)	7
Singular points, lines and planes. Transformations of space	8
Particles and media, in view of the broadened concept of figures	9
Equivalent and non-equivalent operations	11
Inversion	11
Reflection in a straight line, or reversal	13
Identification	13
Comparison of the operations of identification, reflection, reversal and inversion	14
The reduction of all symmetrical transformations to reflections in planes	15
Consecutive reflection in three or more planes intersecting at one point	16
Consecutive reflection in three arbitrarily selected planes, intersecting at one point	17
Euler's theorem	19
Congruent and mirror equality	20
Symmetrical transformations of the first and second kind	22
Reflection as a fundamental operation of symmetry	23
On the equality of objects in general	24

PAGE

Repetition of operations and powers of operations 25

The designation of operations by components of a figure 26

The product of operations 27

Symmetry Groups 27

General concept of a symmetry group 27

The order of a group 28

The asymmetric figure 28

Fundamental properties of symmetry groups 29

Point groups 31

Point groups determined by rotation through an n-th part of a revolution 31

Groups determined by rotation through any given rational part of a full revolution 35

Groups determined by rotation through an irrational part of a complete revolution 37

Groups determined by one mirror rotation through an angle equal to an even part $1/(2n)$ of a complete revolution 38

Groups determined by one mirror rotation through an angle equal an odd-numbered part $1/(2n + 1)$ of a revolution 40

Groups determined by one arbitrary mirror rotation 43

Concluding remarks on the derivation of symmetry groups determined by one operation 43

Sub-groups 44

Elements of symmetry and their designation 45

Arrangement of a plane of symmetry relative to axes of symmetry 45

Groups determined by one rotation and reflection in a transverse plane 46

Groups determined by one rotation and reflection in a longitudinal plane 47

Groups determined by two rotations 50

On the impossibility of groups existing which require more than two axes for their determination 61

Groups determined by two rotations and reflection 62

Concluding observations on the derivation of point groups 71

Types of symmetry groups 74

Limiting groups 75

Crystallographic groups 76

The Symmetry of Plane Figures 76

Neutral and polar plane figures 76

Plane figures of mixed polarity 77

PAGE

Operations of symmetry of plane figures   77
Symmetry groups of finite plane figures   84
Symmetry groups of finite polar plane figures   86

ANTISYMMETRY OF FINITE FIGURES   88
  Basic Concepts and Definitions of Antisymmetry   88
    The representation of symmetrical operations of three-dimensional
    figures by matrices of cosines   88
    Symmetrical operations of three-dimensional figures as afine
    orthogonal transformations   92
    Symmetrical operations of plane figures in two-dimensional and
    three-dimensional space   93
    Operations of antisymmetry in three-dimensional figures   96
    Reverse equality or anti-equality of figures   97
    Polar and neutral figures   98
    The asymmetrical figure   99
    Operation of the change of sign of a figure   100
    Operations of antireflection in a plane   104
    The operation of 180° antirotation   106
    The operation of anti-inversion   107
    The general case of antirotation   108
    The general case of mirror antirotation   109
  Groups of Antisymmetry of Finite Figures   112
    Three types of groups of antisymmetry   112
    Groups of mixed polarity   114
    Groups of mixed polarity determined by one operation   115
    Groups of mixed polarity determined by two mutually parallel or
    perpendicular elements of symmetry   119
    Groups of mixed polarity determined by one axis and two planes—
    longitudinal and transverse   126
    Groups of mixed polarity, derived from series XIII and XIV 132
    Groups of mixed polarity, derived from series XV and XVI   136
    Limiting groups of mixed polarity   141
    Survey of point groups of mixed polarity   141
    Simple forms of groups of mixed polarity   144

APPENDIX
  The Division of Symmetrical Figures into Equal Domains   148

PAGE

Examples of Antisymmetrical Figures from the Field of Physical
Crystallography   150

The Symmetry of Vectors and Tensors   153

Antisymmetry of Textures (Limiting Groups)   161

On the Terms: "Dissymmetry," "Asymmetry," and "Antisymmetry"   171

PART II

INFINITE GROUPS OF COLORED SYMMETRY

N. V. BELOV AND OTHERS

THE 1651 SHUBNIKOV GROUPS [DICHROMATIC SPACE GROUPS]—N. V.
Belov, N. N. Neronova and T. S. Smirnova   175

    Introduction   175

    Bravais Lattices for Shubnikov Groups   176

    Symbolism. General Theorems   185

    The Derivation of Shubnikov Groups   188

DICHROMATIC PLANE GROUPS—N. V. Belov and T. N. Tarkhova   211

    Introduction   211

    Derivation of the Groups   211

       An alternate derivation   218

MOSAICS FOR THE DICHROMATIC PLANE GROUPS—N. V. Belov and
E. N. Belova   220

ON ONE-DIMENSIONAL INFINITE CRYSTALLOGRAPHIC GROUPS—N. V.
Belov   222

    Introduction   222

    Line Groups in a Plane   222

    Two-sided or Dichromatic Line Groups in a Plane   223

    Rod Groups   226

POLYCHROMATIC PLANE GROUPS—N. V. Belov, E. N. Belova and
T. N. Tarkhova   228

    Derivation   228

    Mosaics for "Crystallographic" Groups   228

    Non-crystallographic Mosaics   234

PAGE

THREE-DIMENSIONAL MOSAICS WITH COLORED SYMMETRY—N. V. Belov 238

    Introduction 238

    Cubic Mosaics 238

    Pseudo-cubic Mosaics 239

    Mosaics with Polychromatic Translation 243

LITERATURE ON SYMMETRY 249

SUPPLEMENTARY REFERENCES 253

INDEX 261

Editor's Preface

THE study of symmetry theory in its classical sense might fairly have been called complete 70 years ago when Fedorov, Schoenflies and Barlow finished the description of the 230 space groups. Research since then has been mainly elaboration and variation, and of course very extensive application to the solution of crystal structures by X-ray diffraction. But during the past ten years there has been growing interest in broader definitions of symmetry, in which strict equivalence of points is replaced by a change of sign, of color, or by even more general changes. Although this idea had been explicitly stated and substantially developed by Heesch in 1930[43a]*, the current interest in the subject can certainly be traced to the appearance in 1951 of A. V. Shubnikov's book on *Symmetry and Antisymmetry of Finite Figures*[93]. Shubnikov's development of the dichromatic three-dimensional point groups was followed by the derivation of the dichromatic three-dimensional space groups, first published by N. V. Belov, N. N. Neronova and T. S. Smirnova in the *Trudy* of the Institut Kristallografii, Akademiia Nauk, in 1955[101]. In the following year Belov and his colleagues appeared in the new journal *Kristallografiia* with several papers on two-dimensional and three-dimensional polychromatic space groups and related subjects[104-108]. Since that time a large number of papers by various authors have appeared in *Kristallografiia*, and in translation in *Soviet Physics—Crystallography*, to be joined by numerous papers in Western journals. The supplementary bibliography at the end of this volume is ample evidence that interest has continued, and increased, in both the theoretical aspects of symmetry theory and in its applications. Color symmetry has been applied to a wide variety of problems: projections for crystal structure determination[94,95,103,110,155,156,161,167,185,189],

* For references to the literature see the numbered list in the back of this volume.

twinning[119,122,131,147,157,175,177],   morphology   and   crystal
growth[115,140,157,158,168,170,176,177], magnetic structures and transformations[111, 121, 126–128, 132, 133, 136, 137, 143, 149, 160, 163, 166, 173, 183,
193,194,195], ferroelectric structures[137,138,179,184,193], general physical
properties and transformations[148,159,164,165,168], and ornamental
patterns[88,105,145].

The basic work on color symmetry by Shubnikov and Belov
has remained inaccessible to many of the growing number of
Western crystallographers who have become interested in the
subject. The purpose of this volume is to make available in
English the complete derivation of the dichromatic and polychromatic symmetry groups. For this reason I decided to
combine in a single volume the translations of Shubnikov's
book and the papers published by Belov and his students
before 1957. This combination will make the volume more
generally useful, at some sacrifice of consistency in style and
point of view. Professors Belov and Shubnikov have not only
agreed to this plan, but have been most helpful in supplying
corrected texts of their works.

Shubnikov's work gives a complete and clear development
from first principles of the ideas of classical symmetry and
dichromatic or antisymmetry, and their application to point
groups. From this the reader can move easily to Belov's
development of dichromatic space groups, and his generalization to polychromatic groups. Some readers may prefer,
however, to begin with one of the reviews of the general subject
that have been published by Mackay[114], Le Corre[124], Niggli[139],
Nowacki[154,] Holser[169], or Neronova and Belov[171].

Nomenclature for color groups has been a matter of some
controversy—resulting, for example, in about ten systems of
naming the dichromatic plane groups. Some of these reflect
a real and useful difference of viewpoint, but the result is
confusion if not misunderstanding. This volume adheres to a
system analogous to that of the International Tables for
X-ray Crystallography[96]. This has resulted mainly in retaining
Belov's notation as originally published, and correcting
Shubnikov's notation. However, complete elimination of
Shubnikov's notation would have destroyed the sense of his
careful and systematic development of the groups, so the

International symbol for an operation or a group is always given in square brackets[] immediately after the Shubnikov symbol. Comparing Shubnikov with the International notation, we see that he not only uses different symbols for orientation (dot · for parallel, colon : for perpendicular, and slash / for other angles, with the direction of a plane instead of its normal indicated), but he uses as a basic symmetry operation the reflection axis (denoted by an overline) instead of the inversion axis. Shubnikov uses an underline for a dichromatic operation, but the prime ′ substituted for good reason by Belov seems to have gained general acceptance by everyone except Shubnikov and his students. Tables I and VI correlate the Shubnikov and International symbols for the classical and dichromatic point groups, respectively. Other concordances were published by Nowacki[154] (with some errors), and Niggli[139].

Some changes to the original papers have been made by the authors: these are principally the substitution of a new section on the antisymmetry of textures that had subsequently been published by Shubnikov, and the deletion of a discussion of Zamorzaev's work from Belov's paper on dichromatic space groups. In general I have made no attempt to change the style and presentation of the original papers. However, after considerable study of the material on polychromatic groups, I have taken the liberty of correcting, rearranging and integrating the several published papers. This now makes a single more or less consistent story, and it is still Belov's story, not mine. It should be more useful in this form, at least until a definitive text can be written by Belov or someone else.

Shubnikov's general bibliography on symmetry has been placed near the end of the volume. To this I have added a list of papers published since 1951. This includes all publications through 1962 that deal specifically with color symmetry or its applications, and a few other publications on symmetry referred to by Belov. Both lists have been put in a uniform notation, discrepancies checked, and translations listed where known.

We would like to thank the American Institute of Physics

for permission to incorporate their translations of materials that appeared in *Soviet Physics—Crystallography*, **2,** 16–18, **3,** 263–268, 625–626.

WILLIAM T. HOLSER

Ann Arbor, Michigan

Author's Preface to Part I

THE study of symmetry, which is basic to crystallography, may be developed in two essentially different ways, just like any mathematical discipline: (1) by speculative, logical exposition of the various conclusions potentially inherent in its basic premises, and (2) by introducing changes in these same premises.

Up to the present the study of symmetry has primarily been developed by the first, logical approach. Its basic premises have not been changed essentially. This first approach appears to us to be basically completed and further development of the indicated discipline, which is the task of the present work, seems to be possible only by the second approach.

Let us note that in the present case one cannot speak of radically substituting completely new principles for old, obsolete ones in the study of symmetry, but only of expanding and improving principles so that the old premises occupy a suitable position among the more general new ones.

Before discussing further development of the study of symmetry by the indicated approach, let us turn to its sources—to a definition of the concept of symmetry. According to E. S. Fedorov, "symmetry is the property of geometrical figures to repeat their parts, or more precisely, their property of coinciding with their original position when in different positions. Such self-coincidence may be of two types: either the figure shows self-coincidence as a result of a certain movement, or the self-coincidence results from a mirror reflection." (Brief Course in Crystallography, 1910.)

Let us dwell at length on this definition of symmetry. According to E. S. Fedorov, symmetry is a property of *geometrical figures*. Does this mean that E. S. Fedorov did not know that not only geometrical figures but also a great number of the most varied things can be symmetrical; crystals, plants, animals, many man-made articles, pictures, etc? Certainly not, but this obviously should signify that the symmetry observed in nature and in man-made articles may be reduced to and successfully replaced by the symmetry of geometrical figures.

Everyone knows that this is actually true, but for one exception: the above replacement is not possible in all cases.

One can substitute a square section of a plane figure for square sheets of cardboard, glass or tin inasmuch as their symmetry is the same; however the same square section of a plane figure cannot be substituted for the square face of a crystal of rock salt, since the crystal face has no plane of symmetry coinciding with it, as one side of the face faces the inside of the crystal while the other faces out. For this purpose a planar section with different sides is necessary. The tension of a stretched rubber band may be represented by a segment of a geometrically straight line located along the axis of the rubber band and having a length proportional to the tension, because both the tension under consideration and the straight line segment have the same symmetry; however, the very same segment cannot be substituted for the rate of uniform movement. For this purpose a segment with an arrow showing the direction of movement is necessary. A stationary brass or steel disc may be represented by a geometric circle, which has the same symmetry, but a rotating disc has a completely different symmetry and cannot be represented by any geometric figure since such geometric figures generally do not exist. For this purpose one needs either a rotating circle or something equivalent to it with respect to symmetry, but by no means any circle known to geometry. A geometric cube can be substituted for a cube of rock salt since both cubes have one and the same symmetry, but a cube of pyrites crystal, which has a completely different symmetry, cannot be substituted for the same geometric cube. Crystallographers know that for this purpose a cube of definite form with striated faces is suitable.

It is clear from what has been stated that the symmetry realizable in practice and accessible to direct observation in natural objects cannot actually be reduced entirely to the symmetry of only geometric figures. For this purpose figures of a broader class are needed, and in particular, such as have been termed in one of our works—happily or not—*material figures.* The *non*-geometric figures mentioned above also pertain to them: the unidirectional straight line segments (rectilinear arrows), the planar figures with unequal sides, the rotating figures, etc.

Such is the essence of one of the innovations in the study of symmetry upon which we shall dwell. Strictly speaking, perhaps one may not call it an innovation in that it has already been used in crystallography for a long time, but on an elementary level, not knowledgeably or in accordance with its actual importance. As an example we point out that in not one textbook on crystallography is a word spoken about right and left cubes, whereas such cubes are not only theoretically conceivable but actually are found in crystals belonging to the pentagonal-trioctahedral [m3]* and pentagonal-tri-tetrahedral classes [23] of the cubic system.

According to E. S. Fedorov, in a symmetrical figure the parts are *repeated*. It is clear that only the parts which are in some sense *equal* among themselves can be repeated. *Unlike* objects cannot repeat one another. In the study of symmetry it has long been the accepted practice to consider as being equal not only such figures as may be brought into self-coincidence with one another by simple superposition, but also those which coincide as a result of mirror reflection. Both of these *aspects* of equality—*congruent equality* and *mirror equality*—may be reconciled by the *generic* concept of equality which Möbius proposed in his time: figures are equal if the distances between any given points on one figure are equal to the distances between the corresponding points on another figure. It is important to note that this concept of the equality of figures, which is broader than the one accepted in geometry, in no way excludes the duality mentioned above, since we can always distinguish if two figures are shown—e.g. two gloves—whether both are right-handed or one is right-handed and the other left-handed.

The duality in the concept of equality, which is accepted in the study of symmetry, is justified by experience and there is not the slightest doubt as to its expediency. Does this mean that

* Equivalent International (Hermann–Manguin) symmetry symbols are shown in brackets. See Editor's Preface.

2

the concept of equality of figures is closed once and for all and that it cannot change in the future? Of course not, and later on we intend to substantiate this.

Upon comparison of two mirror-equal *enantiomorphic* figures it is impossible not to note that their observed likeness is a likeness which arises in the compared objects from a certain *oppositeness* in their properties. The right one has no more or less equality with the left one than a positive has with a negative. This is apparent, incidentally, from the fact that the right-hand figure is transformed into the left-hand one by changing the sign of one or three (but not two) coordinates of all its points. Hence it must be considered pure chance that the right-hand figure has not been called positive and the left-hand one negative, and mirror equality was not called *reverse equality* or *anti-equality*, which gives us the opportunity to use these terms for our newly-introduced view of the equality of figures, which we will proceed to explain.

We have arrived at the necessity of introducing this view of the equality of figures in the study of symmetry as a result of comparing natural phenomena and material formations in which this aspect of equality is actually observed. Let us give examples.

Let us make a photographic positive and negative image of the very same object. If we term the positive, in accordance with the sense of this very word, a *positive figure*, then we simply will have to term the negative a *negative figure*. We are obliged to do this by the complete oppositeness of their properties, and in particular by the fact that upon superposition of these figures one on the other, they both disappear, producing something *neutral*, analogous to a number without a sign or a number with two signs—in this case, zero. One could introduce at will any number of other examples of figures anti-equal or *polar* to one another: a droplet of water in the air and a bubble of air in water, a medal and its mold, corrosion pits and growth mounds on crystal faces, snowflakes and "ice-flowers" (little star-shaped formations of water inside ice, resulting from melting of the ice near inclusions, due to the action of the sun's rays), a crystal and a "negative crystal" (a many-faced liquid inclusion inside a crystal), forms of growth and solution of crystals, positrons and electrons, the conductor in a dielectric and the dielectric in a conductor, a screw and a nut, an engraving and engraving plate, etc. In all these examples we are dealing with a pair of figures which differ in *sign*. This provides a basis for introducing the abstract idea of positive, negative and neutral figures into the study of symmetry.

In order to make the concept of anti-equality of figures more definite, let us consider the following problem. Given a piece of leather which is white on one side and black on the other. One glove must be made from it. It is not difficult to grasp that the problem has four solutions. The glove may be: (1) right-hand white, (2) right-hand black, (3) left-hand white, (4) left-hand black. We note that the right-hand glove may be turned inside out at will and put on the left hand. In this sense the glove is simultaneously both right-handed and left-handed, and both black and white. From here the idea follows quite naturally of considering equal any two gloves of the same size, made from the same material that has two different sides. Thus four aspects of congruence are established instead of the previously recognized two: (1) congruent equality, (2) mirror equality, (3) congruent anti-equality, and (4) mirror anti-equality. The right-hand black glove has congruent equality with a right-hand black one; the right-hand white glove has mirror equality with a left-hand white glove; the right-hand white glove has congruent anti-equality with a right-hand black one; the right-hand black glove has mirror anti-equality with the left-hand white one.

Not every figure comprised of equal parts is symmetrical. In a symmetrical figure the equal parts are not placed at will, but according to definite laws which arise from the requirement that the figure be able to be superposed on itself in different positions. It is evident that during such superpositions the equal parts of the figure must change places. In order for congruently equal parts to change places one motion is sufficient. In order for mirror-equal parts to change places, one motion is not sufficient: it must be combined with reflection. In former studies of symmetry, two kinds of symmetrical operations were consequently established: *operations of the first kind (movements)*, and *operations of the second kind (mirror movements)*.

Having taken four views of the equality of figures, we now must also sanction four types of symmetrical transformations: (1) movements, (2) mirror movements, (3) *anti-movements*, and (4) *mirror anti-movements*, understanding anti-movement to mean movement accompanied by a *change of sign* of the figure, and mirror anti-movement to mean mirror movement accompanied by a *change of sign* of the figure. As far as the change of sign itself is concerned, it can be understood as the transformation of the positive (white) figure into a congruently equal negative (black) figure. It is evident that the operation of changing a sign of a figure may be an independent operation of symmetry only for neutral figures, since changing the sign of a figure without changing the figure itself is possible only if the figure carries both signs at the same time or, which amounts to the same thing, if it does not carry them at all.

In order not to confuse the old terminology with the new, we shall term the symmetry expanded in the above sense *antisymmetry* and the corresponding figures *antisymmetrical*. Antisymmetrical figures may obviously be of two types: (1) figures consisting of congruently anti-equal parts (right-hand white and right-hand black figures, or conversely, left-hand white and left-hand black figures) and (2) figures consisting of parts of all four types.

It is demonstrated in this book that antisymmetry is possessed not only by figures into whose composition positive and negative parts enter, i.e., *figures of mixed polarity*, but also by neutral figures. Nevertheless, all such views of antisymmetry lead to previously known views of symmetry and therefore do not merit special attention.

In previous studies of symmetry it was demonstrated that the symmetrical operations of closed figures are made up of *rotations*, which pertain to movement, and *mirror rotations*, which pertain to mirror movement. For antisymmetrical figures there must be added: *antirotations*, i.e., rotations accompanied by a change of sign of all the components of the figure and consequently of the figure as a whole, and *mirror antirotations*, i.e., mirror rotations, accompanied by a change of sign of the figure.

Operations of symmetry which transfer the figure into the same new position from its initial position are considered *equivalent*. The following may serve as examples of equivalent operations: the 90° clockwise rotation of a figure and its 270° counter-clockwise rotation; the 180° reflected rotation of a figure around any given axis and the inverse (reflection around a point—a center of symmetry).

The entire aggregate of operations of symmetry of any given figure, which are *nonequivalent* in themselves, constitutes a *group*. The number of such operations determines the *order* of the group. The order of the group is equal at the same time to the maximum number of *equal* components into which a symmetrical or antisymmetrical figure may be geometrically divided. Non-equivalent operations constitute *elements* of a group. The fundamental property of any mathematical group, as is known, is that the *product* of any two of its elements (the result of the consecutive application of two operations of symmetry) is equal to some element of that same group. For example, the product of two 90° rotations about the same axis (the *square* of a 90° rotation) is equal to an 180° rotation about the same axis. The product of a 90° rotation and the inverse rotation operation is an *identity*—the operation of a stationary figure. This last operation inevitably fits into any group.

Crystallographers prefer to deal with *elements of symmetry* rather than with elements of a group. It is surprising to say that this concept to which crystallographers are so accustomed has not been accurately defined until now; consequently it is not considered possible even to enumerate all of the elements of symmetry of any given figure. For example, no one knows how many elements of symmetry an ordinary cube has. In order to settle this confusion we propose in this work to call an element of symmetry a group defined by one operation, i.e., a group comprised of all the non-equivalent *steps* of a given operation (products of two, three, etc. identical operations). For example, the four-fold axis is the group which contains the following four operations: a 90° counterclockwise rotation, an 180° counterclockwise rotation, a 270° counterclockwise rotation and a 360° counterclockwise rotation (identity). All the other steps and inverse operations do not count as operations which are equivalent to any of the fore-mentioned four rotations.

If this definition of an element of symmetry is accepted, then for closed symmetrical figures there remain no other elements of symmetry besides *ordinary* and *mirror* axes. For antisymmetrical figures with elements of symmetry there will also be *ordinary antiaxes* and *mirror antiaxes*.

Let us agree to designate ordinary axes by whole numbers which show the multiplicity of the axis; mirror axes by numbers with a line above, simple antiaxes by numbers with a line below, and mirror antiaxes by numbers with lines above and below. Then there will only be the following ten elements of symmetry for crystalline polyhedra:

$$1, 2, 3, 4, 6, \quad [1, 2, 3, 4, 6]$$

$$\bar{1}, \bar{2}, \bar{3}, \bar{4}, \bar{6}. \quad [\bar{2}, \bar{1}, \bar{6}, \bar{4}, \bar{3}]$$

If crystalline polyhedra could be antisymmetrical (a question we will not touch upon in our investigation), then it would be necessary to add to these elements of symmetry the following elements of antisymmetry:

$$\underline{1}, \underline{2}, \underline{3}, \underline{4}, \underline{6}, \quad [1', 2', 3', 4', 6']$$

$$\underline{\bar{1}}, \underline{\bar{2}}, \underline{\bar{3}}, \underline{\bar{4}}, \underline{\bar{6}}. \quad [\bar{2}', \bar{1}', \bar{6}', \bar{4}', \bar{3}']$$

From the mathematical point of view, any symmetrical operation may be viewed as the transformation of one rectangular system of coordinates into another one (right or left) on the condition that the relative positions of the figure and the system of coordinates remain as before. If we refer to the operations of symmetry of finite figures, then the origin of the coordinates remains fixed.

The operation of symmetry will be known if the angles between the old axes X_1, X_2, X_3 and the new axes X_1', X_2', X_3' are known. There are nine such angles in all. In place of them their cosines are taken, designated by the small letter c with two indexes, the first being the number of the old axis and the second being the number of the new axis. For example, $c_{11} = \cos{(X_1 X_1')}$, $c_{32} = \cos{(X_3 X_2')}$.

The system of cosines is shown by the table

$$
\begin{array}{ccc}
c_{11} & c_{12} & c_{13} \\
c_{21} & c_{22} & c_{23} \\
c_{31} & c_{32} & c_{33}
\end{array}
$$

In this book it is proved in detail that all previously known operations of symmetry of finite three-dimensional figures may formally be considered to be similar to special operations of symmetry in four-dimensional space, namely operations of the form

$$
\begin{pmatrix}
c_{11} & c_{12} & c_{13} & 0 \\
c_{21} & c_{22} & c_{23} & 0 \\
c_{31} & c_{32} & c_{33} & 0 \\
0 & 0 & 0 & +1
\end{pmatrix}
$$

inasmuch as all such operations leave the fourth axis x_4 in place, along which the coordinates of all points of a three-dimensional figure are equal to zero.

Taking this into account we easily conclude that all the new operations of symmetry which we introduced and termed operations of antisymmetry, may be represented by the general table

$$
\begin{array}{cccc}
c_{11} & c_{12} & c_{13} & 0 \\
c_{21} & c_{22} & c_{23} & 0 \\
c_{31} & c_{32} & c_{33} & 0 \\
0 & 0 & 0 & -1
\end{array}
$$

On the whole, our proposed extended treatment of symmetry leads to the equivalence of both signs attached to the 1 in the preceding tables of cosines. From the geometrical point of view this means that all the operations of anti-symmetry do not change the absolute value of the fourth coordinate of all the points of a figure, i.e., of the coordinate which equals zero. However, they change its sign—they transform -0 into $+0$ and back again.

In order to make such transformations more clear, they may be compared with corresponding transformations in space of one less dimension, i.e., with the transformations of two-dimensional figures in three-dimensional space. All such

transformations, as is easily realized, may be described by
the table

$$
\begin{array}{ccc}
c_{11} & c_{12} & 0 \\
c_{21} & c_{22} & 0 \\
0 & 0 & \pm 1
\end{array}
$$

where the plus sign by the 1 refers only to those operations
which, although they are operations in three-dimensional
space, may also be considered operations in two-dimensional
space according to the table

$$
\begin{array}{cc}
c_{11} & c_{12} \\
c_{21} & c_{22}
\end{array}
$$

whereas the operations with a minus sign by the unit cannot
be considered operations in two-dimensional space. The first
operations are not associated with the "turning over" of a
figure on its reverse side; the second operations are so associated. The first operations are inherent in finite plane figures
with two different sides and in figures with two like (equal)
sides, the second ones are inherent only in figures with two
like sides. To the first operations belong only rotations around
an axis normal to the plane of the figure, and reflections in
planes normal to that same plane. To the second operations
belong 180° rotations around axes located in the plane of
the figure, reflection in the plane of the figure and mirror
rotations about an axis normal to the plane of the figure.
These second operations play the same role for plane figures
that operations of antisymmetry play for three-dimensional
figures. The usual operations of symmetry of three-dimensional
figures are not related to their "turning over," i.e. to the
change of sign of the figure. The turning inside out of the
glove—with the white outside and the black inside—is an
antioperation consisting of reflection in a plane (inasmuch as
the right-hand glove during this process changes into the
left-hand one) and a change in sign (inasmuch as the white
face replaces the black one).

The present work is dedicated to the antisymmetry of finite
figures. Of course infinite systems of finite figures may also
be antisymmetrical. An open chessboard made up of black

and white squares may serve as an example of plane infinite antisymmetrical systems. Here we may also consider figures of various vibrating membranes. During the process of vibration they divide at nodes into convex $(+)$ and concave $(-)$ parts, rhythmically transforming into each other. It is appropriate to note here that the transformation of positive figures into negative ones is considered to be important in all cases where we are dealing with free vibration and with periodic processes in general. In our opinion this circumstance serves as one of the arguments for introducing the operations of a change in sign into the study of symmetry.

A direct transition can be made from infinite plane antisymmetrical figures like the chessboard to infinite space systems consisting of equal white $(+)$ and black $(-)$ polyhedra occupying space. Such systems may obviously be utilized in the interpretation of ionic structure. However, considering that we are not obliged to relate the concept of the sign of a figure to the sign of an electric charge only, and going further, it is possible to believe that any other crystalline structure may also be interpreted using positive and negative figures in space, it seems to us that such an interpretation may prove to be especially useful in the future for the study of the *dynamics of crystalline structures*, i.e., in those cases where similar adjacent elements of structure alternately arrive at opposite positions during vibration, or change their sign.

All these and similar questions nevertheless go beyond the province of this work and may serve as the theme for further investigations. It is clear to us that the study of symmetry is by no means a closed field of knowledge; it will continue to exist and develop along with the development of related sciences and primarily with the development of crystallography.

A. V. SHUBNIKOV

PART I

Symmetry and Antisymmetry
of Finite Figures

by A. V. SHUBNIKOV

The Symmetry of Finite Figures

INTRODUCTION

THE study of symmetry is concerned with the investigation of laws concerning the regular disposition of figures or components of figures in space. Figures may be finite or infinite, differentiated by the number of dimensions, and conceived of as being set in a space which is of the same or of a higher dimension than the figures themselves. Obviously, it should be the province of the study of symmetry first of all to determine the selection of figures and the space in which the figures will be examined. The first half of our work is dedicated to the symmetry of three-dimensional finite figures in three-dimensional space; that is, to the study of the symmetry of finite figures in its classic sense. During the exposition of this part, attention will be paid to a number of important details of the subject which were by-passed by our predecessors. We will conclude this part with a consideration of the symmetry of finite plane figures, in order to facilitate the transition to the second part, which is devoted to the antisymmetry of finite, three-dimensional figures.

BASIC CONCEPTS AND DEFINITIONS IN SYMMETRY

General Definition of Symmetry

By a symmetrical figure we mean, in the broadest sense, a figure made up of equal and uniformly spaced components. As we can see, the concept of *symmetry* has been assembled from concepts of the *figure*, the *equality* of figures and the *uniformity* of their spacing. It is clear that the study of symmetry will have a different content, depending upon the meaning of these basic concepts.

3

The Figure

This part of our work is devoted to the symmetry of *finite, three-dimensional figures*. We note, however, that the study of symmetry, which has been developed for these figures, can be extended without any changes or additions as a whole to a larger group of figures: to figures with a singular point, the figures being finite or infinite.

Further, we shall apply the concept of symmetry in accordance with the requirements of crystallography, physics, and every-day practice not only to purely geometrical figures, but also, as was explained in the preface, to figures to which we ascribe certain additional properties beyond the ordinary metric ones. The following may serve as examples of such *material* figures: a segment of a directional straight line, generally represented by an arrow; a plane, both sides (the face and the back) of which are assumed to differ; polyhedra with different colored faces; rotating figures; etc. To this list we must also add the ideal forms of crystals, since many of the more important inconsistencies of geometric crystallography could not otherwise be eliminated. It is very important to consider that these figures are just as abstract as purely geometrical figures, and they must under no circumstances be identified with physical bodies, although our figures in a number of cases may quite successfully be represented by real bodies, for example crystals, rather than as purely geometrical figures.

The Uniform Distribution of Equal Domains of a Figure

The laws of uniform distribution of domains of a figure, and also, to a considerable degree, their equality are determined by *operations of symmetry* or *symmetrical transformations*. Equal domains of a figure are transformed into each other by operations of symmetry, while the figure as a whole is transformed into itself (coincides with itself in various positions).

Further on, (pp. 16, 17) we will develop the conditions which will make it clear that the symmetrical transformations of three-dimensional figures can only include: *reflection in a plane, rotation around an axis of symmetry,* and *mirror rotation.* Let us examine these operations individually.

Reflection in a Plane

To reflect a figure in a plane means to transfer all of its points onto the other side of the plane along perpendiculars to the plane, in such a way that the new distance of the points from the plane will be equal to the old. Let us consider the figure

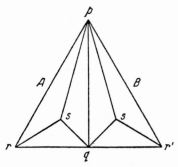

FIG. 1. Reflection in the plane *pq*. Tetrahedra *A* and *B* exchange places, while the figure *AB* as a whole is transformed into itself.

composed of two irregular tetrahedra *A* and *B* turned with one of their apices toward the observer, and with their bases, which are right triangles, in the plane of the diagram (Fig. 1). If we reflect the figure in the plane *pq*, then the point *r* moves to the position *r'*, the point *s* to the position *s'*; conversely, the points *r'*, *s'* to the positions *r*, *s*. All the other points of the figure also undergo analogous transpositions, with the exception of the points lying in the reflection plane itself, which remain fixed upon reflection. As the result of the reflection of all points of the figure, the latter attains a new position but in this new position it will not differ in any way from the figure in the original position. Consequently we can and will consider the operation of reflection of the figure *AB* in the plane *pq* to be a symmetrical transformation of this figure. Nevertheless this operation will not be a symmetrical transformation for each tetrahedron individually since both tetrahedra may differ from one another, if only by their position in space. The plane *pq* is called *the plane of symmetry of the figure.*

Rotations around an Axis

Examples of figures which may be transformed into themselves by rotation through rational parts of a circle are shown in Fig. 2.

All these figures consist of irregular tetrahedra with one of their apices turned toward the observer. The first of these

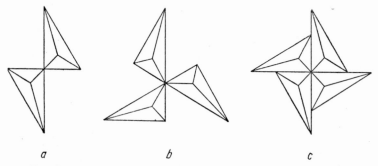

a   *b*   *c*

FIG. 2. Examples of figures with one two-fold (*a*), three-fold (*b*) and four-fold (*c*) axis.

figures coincides with itself by rotations in multiples of a half-turn about the axis which is normal to the plane of the diagram; the second figure coincides with itself by rotations in multiples of 1/3 of a complete turn about an analogous axis and the third by rotations in multiples of 1/4 turn. It is evident that the number of these figures could be carried to infinity. The axes of rotation of these figures are called *axes of symmetry of n-th order**, where *n* is the number of coincident figures during a complete turn. Consequently the first figure possesses a two-fold axis; the second figure a three-fold axis; etc. During each rotation the tetrahedra of a given figure exchange places but the points on the axis remain fixed. In the new position, the figure differs in no way from the figure in the old, initial

* Hereafter translated as "*n*-fold axes"—see Preface.

position. Consequently, the forementioned rotations also can and will be considered symmetrical transformations.

Mirror Rotations (rotary reflections)

For examples of an operation of mirror rotation it is simplest to use the figures shown in Fig. 3. Each of these figures is composed of an even number of tetrahedra. These tetrahedra alternately turn one of their apices toward the observer and

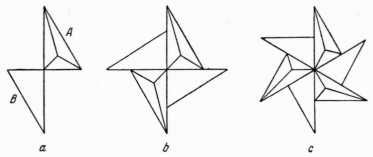

FIG. 3. Examples of figures with a two-fold (*a*), four-fold (*b*) and six-fold (*c*) mirror axis.

one away from him. The tetrahedra which are turned toward the reverse side appear as empty triangles to the observer. Let us examine the first of these figures, shown in the left-hand diagram. If we give it a half-turn around the axis normal to the diagram, the projection of tetrahedron *A* in the new position will coincide with the projection of *B* in the old position and vice versa; but the whole figure in the new position still will not coincide with the figure in its old position since the tetrahedron *A* in the new position will be turned with its apex toward the observer, while for the coincidence of tetrahedron *A* with *B* it is necessary that this apex should be turned toward the opposite side. Coincidence will, however, be attained if after the rotation the figure is reflected in the plane of the diagram. A mirror rotation is also a complex operation of rotation accompanied by reflection in a plane normal to the axis of rotation. In this case we have a 180° mirror rotation. It is easy to see that the second figure in the diagram is capable of self-coincidence by mirror rotations in multiples of 90°, and the third figure by mirror rotations in multiples of 60°. An axis of mirror rotations is called *a mirror axis of n-th order* [*n-fold axis*]. The order of the axis *n* is equal to the number of coincident figures obtained during a complete turn; in the figures under consideration we have mirror axes of the second, fourth and sixth order. It is obvious that the order of an axis may be any even and, as we shall see later, any odd number.

During mirror rotations the components of the figure (the tetrahedra) change place, but one point, namely the point of intersection of the axis and the reflection plane, remains fixed. With respect to the axis itself and the plane itself, they also remain in place *as a whole*, that is, all of their points, with the exception of the forementioned, although changing places, do not exceed the limits of the axis or the plane.

Singular Points, Lines and Planes. Transformations of Space

Points, lines, and planes which remain fixed during all the symmetrical transformations of a given figure are called *singular*. Every finite figure—a cube, parallelepiped, sphere, ellipsoid, etc., has at least one singular point. The center of gravity of a figure, for example, is always such a point; a finite figure cannot have two centers of gravity. A singular point does not necessarily have to be located inside a figure; for example the singular point of a ring, that is, its center, lies outside the figure (Fig. 4). In both this and in similar cases it is expedient to assume that symmetrical operations are carried out simultaneously on both the figure and the space closely related to it. Hence the finite figure, strictly speaking, is considered as an infinite figure. From this point of view any symmetrical transformation is a transformation of infinite space. We, however, will be interested primarily in only those transformations of space which are at the same time transformations of one finite figure even though it consists of separate components. The study of symmetry of finite figures may be considered in this sense as the study of symmetrical transformations of space which leave at least one fixed point in place. It is obvious that when one considers the symmetry of any isolated three-dimensional figure, this figure itself must be considered formally as a *singular* geometrical element (similar to a point, line or plane), inasmuch as it must remain completely fixed during all symmetrical transformations. It is clear that the three-dimensional figure and also with it all three-dimensional

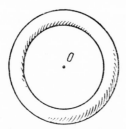

FIG. 4. An example of a figure with its singular point *O* lying out-side the figure.

space, may cease playing the role of singular geometrical elements only when they become part of the figures and space of higher dimension.

*Particles and Media, in View of the Broadened Concept of Figures**

Let us agree to define a *particle* as any finite, material form, whether a star, planet, crystal, plant, animal, molecule or atom. We will call a particle having a definite regular shape an *individual*. We cannot imagine the existence of a particle outside of its surrounding *medium*. For every particle there is a characteristic line of division between it and the medium. This boundary line may be distinct or indistinct but it must exist. If it becomes too diffuse, the particle blends with the medium, dissolves in it and ceases to exist as a particle. When we speak of a medium, we do not think about its boundary lines; we consider them to be inessential to the medium and

---

* This paragraph should be considered as a philosophical digression from the method of exposition of the subject adopted by the author. Analogous digressions will be encountered further on in the text.

as though nonexistent. An ideal medium is infinite and *homogeneous*, that is, composed uniformly throughout. Any disruption of the uniformity of the medium is the basis for the formation of a particle. An ideal particle is *non-homogeneous* in principle, if only because we are able to distinguish external and internal parts in it. The concepts of the ideal medium and the ideal particle are useful to abstract science; there are no ideal media or particles in nature just as there is no ideal *chaos*, which we think of as being a completely disordered combination of non-homogeneous media and amorphous particles. Knowledge of nature commences where man's intellect begins to distinguish particles and media from the chaos of the unknown. The following may serve as typical examples of the unity of the particle and the medium: (1) a crystal existing in interreaction with its own surrounding melt or solution, that is, a growing crystal dissolving or existing in active equilibrium with the liquid or gas surrounding it; (2) a droplet of moisture in its own vapor; (3) a cosmic body in material space, etc.

The same physical form may, depending on conditions, be considered at times a particle and at times a medium, under theoretical conditions or approximations of reality as is always done in exact science. To the mineralogist the crystal is above all "an individual of inorganic nature", "a crystalline individual", "indivisible"; a heterogeneous body, composed of pyramids of growth, distinguishable from one another by their physical properties and chemical composition; a body having a specific internal structure in which the center of formation of the crystal, the boundaries of the pyramids of growth, the layers of growth, the inclusions, etc., may be distinguished physically; a body having a definite external form which is studied with a great deal of attention. To the physicist the crystal is primarily a regularly constructed medium in which one or another phenomenon may occur, an infinite medium, an anisotropic medium with different properties in different directions, a medium with non-continuous or continuous periodic structure, depending on the circumstances. The Earth's sphere is an individual, the earth—a medium; a drop of water is an individual, water—a medium, etc.

In view of the above-mentioned notions it appears as though the broadened concept of the figure is especially suitable for describing natural forms. Also in keeping with these ideas is the fact that symmetrical transformations of finite figures are considered as simultaneous transformations of all space, since figures cannot exist outside of space. If, however, there is a figure in space, it is expedient to think of it as being composed of a different material than the one of which space itself is composed, since the boundary between the figure and the medium must otherwise disappear, and together with it the figure itself, as a glass body disappears when it is placed in a medium with an index of refraction equal to the index of refraction of the glass.

Equivalent and Non-equivalent Operations

Symmetrical transformations are considered *equivalent* or *identical* if they lead to the same regrouping of a figure's components. Otherwise they are considered *non-equivalent* or *different*. In order to judge whether two comparable operations lead to the same or different regrouping of a figure's components, the equal components of the figure must be made *conditionally unlike*, renumbering them or designating them by different letters. Otherwise all symmetrical operations would be equivalent to one another, inasmuch as they all transfer the figure into positions which are completely indistinguishable from the basic position. 180° clockwise and counterclockwise rotations must, consequently, be considered as equivalent operations; 60° clockwise rotations and 120° counterclockwise rotations also represent the same operation. As we see, in questions of symmetry the importance does not lie in the operation itself or in the means by which it is accomplished, but in its *results*.

Inversion

Among our above-mentioned operations, we met with the operation of a 180° mirror rotation. Let us again follow this operation on a figure familiar to us (Fig. 5). We already know that this figure comes into self-coincidence if we subject it to a 180° mirror rotation about the axis normal to the diagram. It is easy to see directly that this same result is obtained if the figure undergoes that same angle of mirror rotation about axis *ab* or *cd*, and not only about these axes but also about any straight line passing through the center of the figure. All these operations are similar. They make tetrahedron *A*

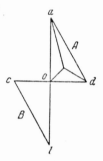

FIG. 5. 180° mirror rotations about axes passing through the center of the figure *o*, equivalent to inversion (reflection at the point *o*).

coincide with tetrahedron *B*, and, inversely, *B* with *A*, whereupon the point *a* is transferred to position *b*, which is diametrically opposite it in relation to the center, and inversely, point *b* is transferred to position *a*; furthermore, the point *c* is transferred to the position *d*, and inversely, *d* to the position *c*, etc. In other words, the 180° mirror rotation about any axis passing through the point *o* does not differ in its results from the operation of transferring all the points of a figure along straight lines through the point *o* onto its opposite side, in such a way, that the new distances of all the points of the figure from the point *o* will equal the old. Such an operation is called an *inversion*. If the figure coincides with itself by inversion at the given point *o*, the latter is called the *center of symmetry**. In this instance, it is said that the figure has a center of symmetry.

* E. S. Fedorov calls the point *o* the center of inversion, and calls the point of intersection of the axes of symmetry the center of symmetry.

If we compare inversion with reflection in a plane, we find characteristics common to both operations. During inversion, all the points of the figure move in a straight line beyond the center of symmetry, just as they move beyond the plane perpendicular to it during reflection. It may therefore be said that inversion is *reflection in a point.*

Reflection in a Straight Line, or Reversal

Of the previously described operations, the ordinary 180° rotation requires additional comment. It is quite clear that the result of such a rotation may be achieved by the transference of each point of the figure along a perpendicular to the axis at an equal distance from the axis. As we see, the result of a rotation around a two-fold axis may be described as reflection in a straight line. We will call this operation in short, *a reversal.*

Identification

The study of symmetry was able to assume a strict and final form only after the introduction into it of the formal operation of self-transformation of a figure by means of remaining fixed. We call this operation *identification* [отождествление]. The standard term "identity", [идентичность] designating this operation, seems unfortunate to us since grammatically it does not signify action, and any operation is an action. Just as with all other operations, identification may be interpreted variously, for example, as the rotation of a figure in a full turn around any straight line, which therefore may be considered as a one-fold axis of symmetry. Identification may be viewed as the result of two consecutive reflections in the same, completely arbitrary plane, etc. Identification is sometimes called a *unit operation.* Later on (p. 30), a basis for this designation will be given. The important theoretical significance of the operation of identification will be gradually revealed.

Comparison of the Operations of Identification,
Reflection, Reversal and Inversion

The operation of identification leaves all the points of the figure fixed. This means if we select in the figure any point with the coordinates x_1, x_2, x_3, they will not change after identification. This may be represented by the matrix

$$\begin{Bmatrix} x_1 & x_2 & x_3 \\ x_1 & x_2 & x_3 \end{Bmatrix},$$

in which the old coordinates are shown in the upper line and the new coordinates are shown in the lower line.

The operation of reflection in a plane of symmetry may also be represented by a bracket. For this we will place the two axes X_1 and X_2 of a rectangular system of coordinates in a plane of symmetry; the third, X_3, will be perpendicular to it. After reflection the coordinates of the points along the two former axes obviously do not change, while the coordinate along the third axis only reverses its sign. Thus, reflection in a plane may be represented by the matrix

$$\begin{Bmatrix} x_1 & x_2 & x_3 \\ x_1 & x_2 & -x_3 \end{Bmatrix}.$$

The operation of reversal, obviously, may be represented by the matrix

$$\begin{Bmatrix} x_1 & x_2 & x_3 \\ x_1 & -x_2 & -x_3 \end{Bmatrix},$$

if the first axis is placed along a two-fold axis.

During inversion each of the three coordinates of any point of the figure reverses its sign:

$$\begin{Bmatrix} x_1 & x_2 & x_3 \\ -x_1 & -x_2 & -x_3 \end{Bmatrix}.$$

Since the upper lines of the previous brackets are all written the same, while in the lower lines only the signs of the coordinates are essential, the comparison of all four operations may be written in abbreviated form as follows:

Name of the operation	Its interpretation as a "reflection"	Signs of the new coordinates		
Inversion . . .	In a point	—	—	—
Reversal . . .	In a straight line	+	—	—
Mirror reflection . .	In a plane	+	+	—
Identification . .	In a space	+	+	+

Note the last line of this table, where identification is treated as *reflection* in *space*, and naturally enters the family of the three other simplest symmetrical transformations.

The Reduction of all Symmetrical Transformations to Reflections in Planes

It has been previously mentioned that the operation of identification is equivalent to two-stage reflection in one arbitrary plane.

It is not difficult to ascertain from an examination of Fig. 6, that the rotation of figure A about the axis o through an angle 2α is equivalent to its consecutive reflection in the two planes which intersect on the axis and form an angle α between each other, where one of these planes may be selected arbitrarily. The first reflection in plane I transfers figure A to position A', the second reflection in plane II transfers figure A' to final position B. As we see, both planes are bound by condition to function only jointly. This means that if the rotation about axis o is a symmetrical transformation, then on the whole the reflections taken separately in the planes I and II are not symmetrical operations and the indicated planes are not planes of symmetry.

If a simple rotation is equivalent to double reflection, then a mirror rotation, consisting of rotation and reflection, is obviously equivalent to triple reflection.

Thus all the symmetrical transformations we have described up to now may be considered as reflections in one, two, or three planes, although the latter may not in themselves be planes of symmetry.

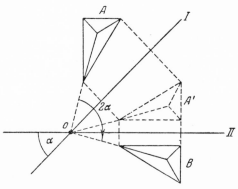

FIG. 6. Rotation of the figure A about the axis o through an angle 2α is equivalent to consecutive reflection in planes I and II, which form the angle α between each other.

Consecutive Reflection in Three or More Planes Intersecting at One Point

We demonstrated that a mirror rotation is equivalent to consecutive reflection in three planes intersecting at one point. Two of them pass along the mirror axis of symmetry and the third is perpendicular to the first two. It may be demonstrated (see the following paragraph) that consecutive reflection in three planes which intersect at one point will be equivalent to mirror rotation for any reciprocal arrangement of these planes.

It is easy to demonstrate also that consecutive reflection in four planes intersecting at one point, (in other words, two rotations about two intersecting axes) is equivalent to one rotation (see Euler's Theorem below) and that generally, consecutive reflection in an odd number of planes intersecting at one point is equivalent to mirror rotation, while consecutive reflection in an even number of planes intersecting at one point is equivalent to simple rotation. If one takes into account the fact that the point of intersection of all the reflecting planes is a singular point of a figure, and if one accepts consecutive reflections in planes as determining a symmetrical operation, then it follows from the forementioned that there exist no other point- (those which leave specific points fixed) symmetry operations besides the ones considered above. The final definition of a symmetrical figure may now be given in the following form: a symmetrical figure is a figure which may self-coincide by consecutive reflections in planes. This definition is suitable for both finite and infinite figures. In the latter instance the requirement of the intersection of planes at one point is removed.

Consecutive Reflection in Three Arbitrarily Selected Planes, Intersecting at One Point

Let a, b, c, represent arbitrarily selected, reflecting planes intersecting at one point (at the center of the sphere), which are compelled by condition to act in the indicated sequence (the result of consecutive reflection depends upon the sequence of the operation) (Fig. 7). Consecutive reflection in the first two planes is equivalent to rotation about axis C through an angle equal to double the angle α between these planes. This rotation may be replaced by double reflection in planes d and g which form the very same angle α between each other. We have the right to draw the second of these planes through C arbitrarily; we will draw it at a 90° angle to plane c. Thus we have replaced the original planes a, b, c with planes d, g, c. The two latter planes, intersecting along axis D at a right angle, may in turn be replaced by planes f and e which intersect along the same axis D at the same right angle. We will draw plane f perpendicular to plane d. Thus we have at present replaced the three planes a, b, c with planes d, f, e. The two latter planes intersect at right angles. Consecutive reflection in such planes is equivalent to a $2 \times 90°$ or 180° rotation and therefore does not depend on the sequence of reflection. We may therefore replace the sequence of reflection

d, f, e with the sequence d, e, f. Thus, finally, consecutive reflection in planes a, b, c is equivalent to consecutive reflection in planes d, e, f. The first and the second planes intersect at

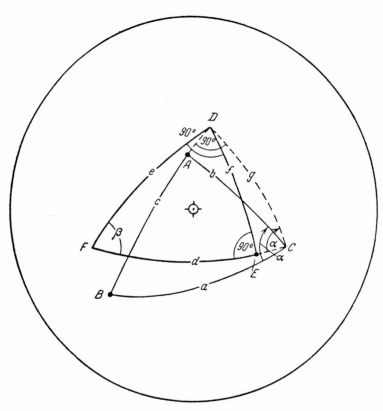

Fig. 7. Consecutive reflection in planes a, b, c, equivalent to mirror rotation of axis F through the angle 2β.

a certain angle β, which may, if desired, be calculated by the laws of spherical trigonometry, and they intersect the third plane f at right angles. From this it follows that axis F is perpendicular to plane f; that is, the triple reflection in planes a, b, c is equivalent to the mirror rotation around axis F through an angle 2β.

Euler's Theorem

Let A_1 and A_2 be the points of emergence on the surface of a sphere of two rotation axes intersecting at the center of the sphere (Fig. 8). Let us connect points A_1 and A_2 by an arc

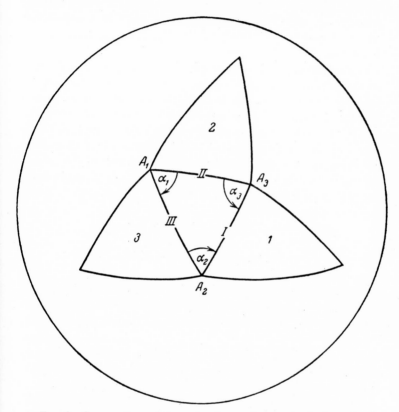

FIG. 8. Consecutive rotation of a figure about axis A_1 through angle $2\alpha_1$ and about axis A_2 through $2\alpha_2$ is equivalent to a rotation about axis A_3 through $2\alpha_3$.

of the great circle *III*. From this arc, at the point A_1 we lay off the angle α_1, with a magnitude of half the given angle of rotation about the axis A_1, and a direction opposite to the rotation (shown by the arrow in the drawing). We obtain the arc of the great circle II. We further lay off the angle α_2 from the arc III at the apex A_2, with a magnitude of half the angle of rotation about axis A_2, and a direction the same as the rotation of A_2. We obtain the arc of the great circle I. Let us show that point A_3 at the intersection of arcs I and II is the point of emergence of the third axis, about which rotation through an angle $2\alpha_3$ is equivalent to the two consecutively executed rotations through angles $2\alpha_1$ and $2\alpha_2$ around axes A_1 and A_2.

Let us construct the three spherical triangles 1, 2, 3 which are reflection congruent to the triangle $A_1A_2A_3$. Carrying out the first rotation about axis A_1 through angle $2\alpha_1$, we transfer triangle 2 to position 3; the second rotation about axis A_2 through angle $2\alpha_2$ transfers that same triangle 2, which now coincides with triangle 3, to position 1. It is clear from the drawing that the double rotation produced in this way is equivalent to one rotation about the axis A_3 through angle $2\alpha_3$, transferring triangle 2 then and there to position 1, which required demonstration.

Congruent and Mirror Equality

We have previously examined two of the basic concepts of the study of symmetry: the expanded concept of the finite figure and the concept of symmetrical transformation. The concept of equality of figures and their components has played an important part in the theory of symmetry during the past and should continue to do so in the future. In a broad sense this concept is closely associated with the representation of various transformations of figures. If it is a question of the *components of a symmetrical figure*, then just those components which are transformed into one another will be *equal*, or, just those which exchange places during symmetrical transformations (which amounts to the same thing).

It follows from this definition that not only may the finite components of a figure be equal, but also the infinite regions of figures, as well as planes, straight lines and even points. For example, in Fig. 1 not only the tetrahedra A and B will be equal, but also the points r and r', s and s', inasmuch as they are transformed into one another by reflection*.

It is essential to distinguish between the two aspects of the equality of components of a symmetrical figure: *mirror equality* and *congruent equality*. Mirror-equal components of a figure are transformed into each other by *odd-numbered operations*, that is, by operations equivalent to an odd number of reflections in planes. Of these operations we as yet know only simple reflection in a plane of symmetry, and mirror rotations. Congruently equal components of a symmetrical figure are transformed into each other by *even-numbered operations*; of these, we as yet know only simple rotations.

We have applied the concept of equality only to the components of a symmetrical figure, but it may also be extended to *separate figures* or to components of a non-symmetrical figure. Of course such an extension of concept will be accompanied by some modification of its content which should be apparent without explanation. We will consider separate figures to be equal if they can be transformed into each other by those same operations of reflection in a plane, rotations and mirror rotations, which nevertheless will not be symmetrical operations in this case. If figures can be made to coincide with

* Some authors prefer to call the equal components of a symmetrical figure "equivalent" [эквивалентными], which means "equal in value", "of equal worth". We selected the universal term "equal" [равные] for many reasons. Let us point out some of them. (1) We have already employed the word "equivalent" to designate equivalent operations. (2) In the study of symmetry and in crystallography the terms "mirror-equal" and "congruent-equal" have been accepted. Having called the equal components of a symmetrical figure equivalent, we would have had to call some of them "mirror equivalent", others—"congruent-equivalent", which is difficult to accept. (3) In the Russian language, there is the word "to equate" [сравнивать] having the same root as the word "equal" [равные]. Both of these words, by their joint-usage—as will be shown later, permit the expression with the utmost simplicity of what we consider most essential. (4) Other Russian words which we attempted to use in place of the word "equal" do not express appropriate derivatives of verbs. Among such words we tested are: ["одинаковыи," "одноэначный," "равночен-ный," "равнозначный," "соответственный," "похожий,"] etc. We make this extensive footnote in order to show that the selection of the term "equal" was made not by chance but after long consideration, although it is obvious that we are not dealing here with the word, but with its meaning.

each other by simple superimposition (an even number of reflections), then they are congruently equal to one other; if for the coincidence of two figures it is still necessary, besides the transposition of one figure in space, to have reflection, that is, a total of an uneven number of reflections, then the figures are mirror-equal to each other.

It is obvious that figures may exist which simultaneously are both congruently equal and mirror-equal to each other. If two figures are only mirror-equal to each other, they are called *enantiomorphic* in relation to each other. One of the enantio-

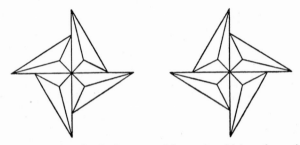

FIG. 9. An example of mirror-equal figures in which each consists only of right or only of left components.

morphic figures, it makes no difference which, is called the *right*, the other—the *left*.

Figures with one simple axis of symmetry (Fig. 9) either consist only of right or only of left components. Figures with one mirror axis or one plane of symmetry (Figs. 1 and 3) consist of both right and left components. We shall say that the figure possesses *congruent symmetry* if it consists only of congruently equal components, and *mirror symmetry* if it consists of left and right components.

Symmetrical Transformations of the First and Second Kind

Even-numbered and odd-numbered operations are otherwise called operations of the *first* and *second kind*. Identification, which is equivalent to two consecutive reflections in one plane, is an even-numbered operation, an operation of the first kind.

It reduces the components of a figure to one sort of component, to only one, congruent to itself. Simple rotations are also operations of the first kind. Mirror reflection leads to figures consisting of right and left components (Fig. 3); this is an operation of the second kind. Simple reflection, which may formally be interpreted as 360° mirror rotation about a one-fold mirror axis, is also an operation of the second kind. It is related to the existence of two enantiomorphic components in a figure (Fig. 1).

Reflection as a Fundamental Operation of Symmetry

We saw earlier that all symmetrical transformations may be formally reduced to consecutive reflections. This point of view, which was first advanced by Vulf, has many advantages.

In the first place it eliminates ambiguity in determining symmetrical operations of the first and second kind. All the operations are part of a natural sequence and, although the distinction between operations in relation to their being even-numbered and odd-numbered is preserved, their unit is not destroyed, just as unity is not destroyed in the case of whole numbers, which although forming a single series, still are divisible into even and odd numbers.

In the second place, just as it is impossible to make odd numbers out of even ones, it is also impossible to make odd-numbered operations (mirror movements) out of even-numbered operations (movements).

In the third place, in setting forth reflection in a plane as a fundamental symmetrical transformation, we give recognition to the original concept of symmetry, which arose historically from the observation of figures with one plane of symmetry.

We saw previously that the simplest symmetrical operations may differ from each other by the number of changes of signs of the coordinates. Identification is characterized by no change, reflection in a plane by one change, reversal by double changes, inversion by triple changes. From the foregoing it is also clear that identification may be considered as reflection in zero planes, reflection in a plane may be considered as reflection in one plane, rotation as consecutive reflection in two planes, mirror rotation as consecutive reflection in three planes. Which of these four numbers—0, 1, 2, 3, is to be considered basic? Of course, not 0 and not 2, but specifically 1. Having taken the operation of reflection for a basis, we proceed in this fashion, which serves as an extra confirmation of the expediency of Vulf's ideas.

On the Equality of Objects in General

If we take any two objects, we may always find one or another characteristic of similarity and characteristics of difference in them. "To equalize" objects means to make them equal, artificially extracting, and ignoring all characteristics of difference, and leaving or emphasizing the characteristics of similarity. "To distinguish" between objects, on the contrary, means to make objects different, consciously extracting all the characteristics of similarity in the compared objects. Objects which are *absolutely equal*, identical in all characteristics, do not exist. In nature only *relatively equal* objects may exist, identical only in a limited number of characteristics. Absolute equality is possible only among abstract, hypothetical objects. Let us take, for example, one of the symmetrical figures shown in Fig. 2. Let us imagine it to be completely isolated in empty space. Under these conditions we cannot differentiate the tetrahedra composing the figure. These tetrahedra will actually be absolutely equal among themselves. The same figure placed on the page of a book will now not consist of absolutely equal components, since we are in a position to distinguish between them, if only by their position on the sheet of paper. Our previously given definition of the equality of figures in a limited sense—a definition especially adapted to the study of symmetry in its classic form—we associated with the concept of *transformation*. There is no contradiction of the broad concept of the equality of objects that has just been explained. Since there are no absolutely equal objects, we are naturally obliged to have recourse to the transformation of a figure in order to make it equal to another figure. The elimination of all the accepted differences between compared objects is that same necessary transformation in its most general aspect, to which we have recourse in order to make objects equal.

Repetition of Operations and Powers of Operations

If a symmetrical figure is subjected to any symmetrical transformation, it comes into self-coincidence, that is, it arrives at a new position, which is indistinguishable from the original one. From this it follows that any symmetrical transformation may be repeated any number of times, and this in turn means that if any operation M is a symmetrical transformation, then the operation equivalent to two, three, and any given number of operations M carried out consecutively will also be a symmetrical transformation. If, for example, the figure self-coincides by a 30° rotation about a certain axis, then it must also self-coincide by 60, 90, 120°, etc., rotations about the same axis. The operations produced by the repetition of operations 2, 3, 4 . . . , n times, are called *powers* of operation M, and are designated correspondingly $M^2, M^3, M^4, . . . , M^n$. For example, the operation of a 90° rotation is equal to the "square" of the operation of a 45° rotation, and the "cube" of an operation of a 30° rotation.

Not all the powers of an operation are necessarily dissimilar operations; many of them may be equivalent to each other. For an example, let us examine a figure with one four-fold axis of symmetry (Fig. 9). This figure self-coincides by 90°, $2 \times 90°$, $3 \times 90°$, $4 \times 90°$, $5 \times 90°$, etc., rotations and, of course, by the operation of identification (0° rotation). Of all these operations, the only ones non-identical to each other are the 0, 90, 180 and 270° rotations. As far as 360, 450°, etc., rotations are concerned, they are not independent symmetrical operations since they are equivalent in result to rotations of 0, 90°, etc. The figure under consideration has, consequently, only four different operations.

The Designation of Operations by Components of the Figure

Let us examine any symmetrical figure, for example the figure with one six-fold mirror axis (Fig. 10). We have already encountered it earlier. Let us designate its equal components (tetrahedra) by the letters, A, B, C, D, E, F. Let us conditionally call component A the *first*. It is assumed that we have divided the figure into the maximum number of equal components,

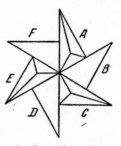

FIG. 10. An example of a figure brought into self-coincidence by six operations.

that is, in the given instance, into six tetrahedra and not into three pairs or two sets of three tetrahedra. If the figure undergoes one or another symmetrical transformation, its first component is transferred to the position of some other component. We may therefore designate any operation by the symbol of that component into which the first component is transformed. How many independent transformations may the given figure undergo? Obviously, as many as it has equal components, that is, six. Let us enumerate all these operations: (1) operation B is a 60° clockwise mirror rotation (or 300° counterclockwise); (2) operation C is a simple 120° clockwise rotation (or a double clockwise 30° mirror rotation, or a simple counterclockwise 240° rotation, etc.); (3) operation D is an inversion (or a 180°, 360° + 180°, etc., mirror rotation); (4) operation E is a simple clockwise 240° rotation or 120° counterclockwise; (5) operation F is a 300° clockwise mirror rotation (or 60° counterclockwise); (6) finally, operation A, which by definition transfers A to A, or, simply, leaves A in place, is identification.

The Product of Operations

An operation equivalent to two consecutively carried out operations is called the *product* of these *operations* and is designated as in algebra, by the two symbols of the operations placed side by side; for this it is essential that the first operation should be placed in the first position (to the left), since the result of the two consecutively carried out operations may depend on the order of the operations. Some authors prefer to call the product of operations, the *sum of operations*, and to designate BC by $B + C$, B^2 by $2B$, etc. The main point remains unchanged. In accordance with this, some authors consider the above-mentioned Theorem of Euler as a theorem of addition of rotations, others as a theorem of multiplication of rotations.

Let us introduce several examples of products on the figure just examined. What is the product BC, comprised of the operations B and C? Operation B transfers A to B. Operation C is a 120° rotation of the figure; by this rotation, A is transferred to C, and B to D. Consequently, by both consecutively carried out operations, A will be transferred to D. We may therefore write

$$BC = D.$$

The previously considered powers of operations represent particular cases of products. It is easy to see, for example, that repeating operation B twice transfers A to C, therefore we may write

$$BB = B^2 = C.$$

Repeating operation C three times brings the figure to the original position, consequently,

$$C^3 = A.$$

SYMMETRY GROUPS

General Concept of a Symmetry Group

A combination of all the different operations by which a given symmetrical figure may be brought into self-coincidence,

4

constitutes a *symmetry group*. The symmetry group of any figure
with one plane of symmetry (Fig. 1) consists of two operations:
identification, A, and reflection, B. The symmetry group of a
figure possessing only a center of symmetry (Fig. 5) also
consists of two operations: identification A, and inversion B.
The symmetry group of a figure having only one six-fold
mirror axis (Fig. 10), consists of six operations: A, B, C, D, E, F.

The Order of a Group

The number of non-equivalent operations constituting a
symmetry group is called *the order of the group*. Since each
operation determines identically one of the equal domains
of a figure which are not divisible into smaller equal domains,
then the order of a symmetry group obviously must be equal
to the maximum number of equal domains of the figure into
which it may be divided. The maximum number of equal
domains of a figure is otherwise called *the value of symmetry*
of a figure. The value of symmetry of a figure with one plane
of symmetry (Fig. 1) is equal to two. The order of the symmetry group of the figure shown in Fig. 10, is equal to six, etc.

The Asymmetric Figure

Any figure may be brought into self-coincidence by the operation of identification. If the operation of identification is the
sole symmetric transformation of the figure, then the figure
is called *asymmetric*. From the formal point of view an asymmetric figure would be more correctly called a figure with a
minimum value of symmetry. The value of symmetry of an
asymmetrical figure is equal to one. The minimum order of
the group is also one. If a symmetrical figure is divided into
the maximum possible number of equal components, then
each component taken separately is an asymmetric figure
(see Appendix, p. 148).

Fundamental Properties of Symmetry Groups

It is easy to prove the correctness of the following four conditions on any of the previously introduced symmetrical figures.

1. The product of any two operations M and N, in a symmetry group, is equal to a certain operation P, in that same group:

$$MN = P. \qquad (a)$$

Actually, the preceding operation M, according to agreement, brings the figure into self-coincidence. So does the latter operation N. It follows from this that the composite operation MN should also bring the figure into self-coincidence. Such is the first property of product MN. Any operation taken individually is either a rotation or a mirror rotation. According to the foregoing, their product must also be either a rotation or a mirror rotation. Such is the second property of MN. Both properties taken together signify that MN is one of the symmetrical operations of a figure, which was to be demonstrated.

2. The product of an operation of identification A and any other operation M of a group of symmetry is equivalent to the reverse product of this operation and identification, or, which amounts to the same, to the operation itself:

$$AM = MA = M. \qquad (b)$$

This position does not require special clarification. If from the outset we leave the figure fixed, that is, we do nothing with it, but subsequently transform it by operation M, then the result will be obtained just the same as if we had from the outset transformed the figure by operation M and subsequently had done nothing with it; and, of course, the result would be the same as if we had subjected it to only the one operation M in all, without A.

3. In order to formulate the third, also obvious, case it is necessary to introduce the concept of *inverse operation*. If operation M transfers the first component A of the figure to position M, then the inverse operation in relation to M will

be the operation M^{-1}, which transfers the component M back to the position of the first component A and this first component to a certain new position, occupied by a certain component N. Say, for example, we have a figure with one six-fold mirror axis (Fig. 10). Operation B is a 60° clockwise mirror rotation. Its inverse operation, B^{-1}, is the same angle of mirror rotation in the opposite direction. It transfers B to A, and A to F; consequently

$$B^{-1} = F.$$

An inverse operation is, obviously, one of the operations entering into a group.

Moreover, since the product of the direct operation M and the inverse operation M^{-1} leaves the figure fixed, that is, transfers A to A, it is equivalent to identification

$$MM^{-1} = A. \tag{c}$$

4. It is also easy to be convinced from examination of the individual examples that the product of any three symmetrical operations of a given group satisfies the associative law

$$(MN)P = M(NP). \tag{d}$$

These four conditions, completely obvious for groups of symmetry, lie mathematically at the basis of the definition of an *abstract group*, that is, a group not necessarily composed of symmetrical operations, but of any sort of elements—letters, numbers, mathematical operations, etc.

It was previously stated (p. 13), that the operation of identification A is sometimes called a unit operation. This is brought about by the fact that the product of M and A and, conversely, of A and M, is equal to M just as the algebraic product of one and any given number n equals n.

If the product of operations is viewed and designated as their *sum*, then the operation of identification will be, obviously, *zero*. Later on we shall see twice (pp. 31 and 88) that the term "unit operation" has certain advantages over the term "zero operation".

Point Groups

Symmetry groups formed only by operations which leave at least one point fixed, are called *point groups*. All the previously introduced figures possessed the symmetry of point groups. It now becomes our task to enumerate all the conceivable point groups of symmetry. We shall begin with the simplest groups determined by one operation; subsequently we shall examine the groups determined by two and more operations.

Point Groups Determined by Rotation through an n-th Part of a Revolution

Since any symmetrical transformation of a figure may be repeated any number of times, and since from the repetition of an operation new operations generally arise, then a certain group of operations is always determined by one operation. It is now our task to enumerate all the groups which are determined by one point operation of the first kind; to put it differently, by one rotation (including a 360° rotation; that is, identification).

Let us begin with the simplest operation of the first kind— with identification. The repetition of this operation, in contrast to all the other cases examined below, does not produce new operations; therefore, the group determined by one operation of identification, consists only of one of this type of operation. This is a first order group. Let us designate it by the symbol *1* [1]*.

Every symmetry group may be represented by some kind of a sample figure. To do this, it is quite suitable to use figures which consist of asymmetrical tetrahedra, like the figures which we met with earlier. Group *1* [1] under consideration may be depicted in this case by one tetrahedron. Any asymmetrical figure may exist in two enantiomorphic

---

* Throughout the text Shubnikov's symmetry symbols are followed by International Hermann–Mauguin symbols in brackets. See preface to this volume.

modifications: a right and a left (Fig. 11). Each of them may serve as a model for representing group *1* [1].

Point symmetry groups may also be quite graphically depicted

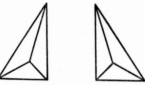

FIG. 11. An example of right and left asymmetrical figures.

by spheres with small, asymmetrical triangles drawn on their surface. One of the singular points which remains fixed during all operations of a group is assumed to coincide with the center

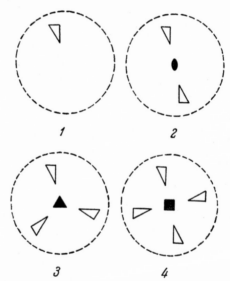

FIG. 12. Depiction of groups *1, 2, 3, 4* [1, 2, 3, 4] by elements of symmetry on a sphere.

of the sphere. The sphere itself is imagined as being transparent. The triangles are colored white on the front and black on the reverse side. It is always assumed that they are affixed to the sphere by the black side. This means that if the observer sees a white triangle then it is located on the half of the sphere which is turned toward the observer; if, on the contrary, we see a black triangle then it is located on the reverse half of the sphere. With these assumptions group *1* [1] may be depicted by a sphere with one white triangle (Fig. 12). Group *1* [1] may be formally considered as a group determined by one full revolution.

Group *2* [2], which follows, is determined by one half-revolution. The double repetition of this operation is equivalent to identification; triple repetition is equivalent again to

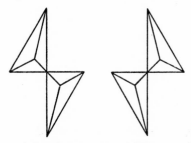

FIG. 13. Figures belonging to group *2* [2] may exist in two enantiomorphic modifications.

a 180° rotation, etc. Obviously, the whole group must consist only of these two operations. Group *2* [2] is, consequently, a second-order group. This group may be depicted by a figure which we have already met (Fig. 2*a*). It consists of two asymmetrical tetrahedra connected by a two-fold axis of symmetry. Since the figure is formed only of tetrahedra congruently equal to each other, two enantiomorphic modifications are possible: right and left (Fig. 13).

Another interpretation of group *2* [2] is given in Fig. 12. We see a sphere with two white triangles and a two-fold axis, directed toward the observer and conventionally depicted by a small, black two-angle figure. It is easy to see that a 180° rotation of the sphere will bring the figure into self-coincidence. It is also customary to depict group *2* [2] in another projection (Fig. 14). The two-fold axis in this diagram is located on the plane of the drawing. Therefore both of its ends can be seen. The white triangle on the front hemisphere is transferred by a 180° rotation to the rear hemisphere, into the position of the black triangle.

Group *3* [3], which follows, is determined by one rotation through one-third of a full revolution. A double 120° revolution is equivalent to a 240° rotation; a triple revolution to a full revolution, or identification. There are no other operations in the group which differ among themselves besides these three.

Fig. 14. Another method of depicting group 2 [2].

Group *3* [3] is, consequently, a third-order group. Just as the preceding group, *2* [2], it may be depicted by one of the enantiomorphic figures consisting of three mirror-equal tetrahedra. We have already encountered this figure earlier

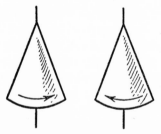

Fig. 15. An example of enantiomorphic figures belonging to one limit group ∞ [∞] (rotating cones).

(Fig. 2*b*). Another depiction of this group is given in Fig. 12.

The following fourth-order group, *4* [4], is analogous to the preceding one; it also is shown in Fig. 12.

Obviously, when once begun, this series of groups which are called *cyclic* may be extended to infinity. The last member in this series is a group determined by an infinitely small rotation about an infinite-fold axis. Let us designate this group by the symbol ∞ [∞]. The rotating cone (Fig. 15) may serve as a figure which characterizes the given group. Like all the figures of the series under consideration, such a cone may exist in two enantiomorphic modifications: right and left.

This group of symmetry is interesting in that it may not be illustrated by the usual geometrical figures. Here, in practice, we encounter the necessity of introducing into the study of

FIG. 16. Another example of figures belonging to group ∞ [∞]
(striated cones).

symmetry figures which we called material. Besides rotating cones, also suitable for the depiction of group ∞ [∞] are stationary cones, to all of whose points we attribute the properties of infinitely small striations, oriented obliquely in relation to the structure of the cone (Fig. 16). An example of a graphic model of such a cone could be a wooden cone with glued on plush, brushed in a slantwise direction.

We have examined all the groups determined by one rotation through an integral fraction $1/n$ of a revolution. Let us proceed to groups determined by any rotation through a rational part of a revolution.

Groups Determined by Rotation Through any Given Rational Part of a Full Revolution

First of all let us note that any rotation through an angle greater than 360° is equivalent to a rotation through an angle α which is less than 360°; therefore, as a determining angle one may always take the angle equal to $(m/n) \cdot 360°$ where m/n is a proper fraction.

Thus, let a rotation through the fractional part m/n of a circle be a symmetrical transformation of a figure. It is required to find all the remaining symmetrical operations of this figure according to the conditions, $m < n$; furthermore, one may always assume that m and n do not have a common denominator, otherwise the fraction m/n may be reduced. If the operation of rotation through the m/n part of a circle is a symmetrical operation, then all the multiple rotations through the $2(m/n)$; $3(m/n)$; $4(m/n)$, . . ., $n(n/m)$ part of a circle also must be symmetrical operations. The last operation of a rotation through an angle equal to $n(m/n) = m$ revolutions is equivalent to one full revolution, or identification. The following operation of a rotation through an angle equal to $m + (m/n)$ revolutions is equivalent to rotation through an angle equal to m/n revolutions; that is, to the first, original operation. The operation following this will be equivalent to the second operation with an angle equal to $2(m/n)$, etc. In short, there will be n different operations; all of them must be equivalent to rotations through angles less than 360°, and each of them is a step of least rotation. All of these requirements may be maintained only under the condition that the minimum angle of rotation is equal to the $1/n$ part of a circle. That is, the group determined by an angle of rotation equal to the m/n part of a circle is that same group which is determined by rotation through the $1/n$ part of a circle.

In order to clarify what has been stated, let us introduce a concrete example. Say it is required to find the group determined by a rotation through 2/7 of a revolution. The operations of this group will be multiple rotations through the following parts of a full revolution: 2/7, 4/7, 6/7, 8/7, 10/7, 12/7, and 14/7. But the last four rotations through angles equal to 8/7, 10/7, 12/7, and 14/7 parts of a revolution are equivalent to rotations through the 1/7, 3/7, 5/7, 7/7 part of a revolution. Consequently the whole complex of operations consists of rotations through angles equal to 1/7, 2/7, 3/7, 4/7, 5/7, 6/7, 7/7 parts of a revolution, that is, those same operations which are determined by rotation through 1/7 part of a circle.

Groups Determined by Rotation through an Irrational
Part of a Complete Revolution

If a given rotation is equal to the irrational part *o1* of a circle (Fig. 17), then as the result of repeating this operation a

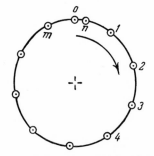

FIG. 17. Diagram to demonstrate that besides the cyclic groups *1, 2, 3* . . ., ∞ [1, 2, 3 . . ., ∞], there exist no other groups determined by one rotation.

limited number of times, it is impossible to bring the figure to the original position, since by multiplying an irrational number by a whole positive number it is impossible to get a whole positive number, that is a whole number of complete revolutions. Nevertheless, this may be achieved by an endless repetition of the given rotation. Actually, by repeating the given rotation over and over again, we will transfer the end of arc *o1* consecutively into positions *2, 3, 4* . . . After one revolution (with some excess) is completed by this method, the given segment of the arc will occupy such a position *mn*, that the zero point *o* will appear inside the arc. Segments *on, om*, will be, consequently, less than the given arc. Each of these segments, in turn, may now be taken, on the basis of the foregoing, for the original. Having repeated for one of them, let's say for *on*, the same reasoning as for arc *o1*, we come to the conclusion that along with the operation of rotation on arc *on* the operation of rotation on an arc less than *on* should also exist in the group of rotations under consideration. It is clear that under these conditions for an elementary rotation one should use a rotation which is smaller than any given rotation;

that is, an infinitely small rotation. Hence we conclude that the group under consideration is the cyclic group ∞ [∞].

Thus we consider it established that besides the cyclic groups *1, 2, 3,* . . ., ∞, [1, 2, 3, . . .,∞] there do not exist any other groups determined by one rotation.

Groups Determined by One Mirror Rotation through an Angle Equal to an Even Part $1/(2n)$ of a Complete Revolution

The simplest mirror rotation in this category is a 180° ($n = 1$) mirror rotation, or inversion. The square of inversion is identification. Higher powers do not produce new operations

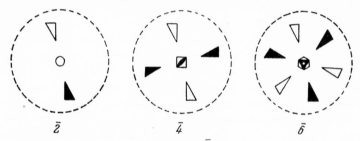

$\bar{2}$ $\bar{4}$ $\bar{6}$

FIG. 18. Depiction of groups $\bar{2}$, $\bar{4}$, $\bar{6}$ [$\bar{1}$, $\bar{4}$, $\bar{3}$] by elements of symmetry on a sphere.

beyond these two. We have, therefore, a second-order group previously represented by the figure shown in Fig. 5. Let us designate this group by the symbol $\bar{2}$ [$\bar{1}$]. Another depiction of this group is shown by two small triangles on a sphere: black and white (Fig. 18). As was previously explained, the white triangle is located on the forward hemisphere, the one turned toward the observer, and the black triangle on the rear hemisphere. The center of symmetry is conventionally depicted in the drawing by a small, white circle.

The next in complexity ($n = 2$) is a 90° mirror rotation. The square of this operation is equivalent to a simple 180° rotation; the cube is equivalent to a 270° mirror rotation, and the fourth power is equivalent to identification. Neither higher powers nor various products of indicated operations produce new operations. The group under consideration is consequently a fourth-order group; let us designate it by the symbol $\bar{4}$ [$\bar{4}$]. We previously encountered (Fig. 3b) the figure illustrating this group. Another depiction of it is shown in Fig. 18. A four-fold mirror axis is shown in it by a small, white quadrangle. The fact that a simple 180° rotation enters into the given group as one of its elements shows that the four-fold mirror axis is simultaneously a simple two-fold axis (the black two-angle figure inside the white quadrangle).

The next representative of these groups will be group $\bar{6}$ [$\bar{3}$] (where $n = 3$), which is a sixth-order group. Its elements are: a 60° mirror rotation; a 120° simple rotation (the square of a 60° mirror rotation); an inversion (the cube of a 60° mirror rotation); a 240° simple rotation, or what amounts to the same thing; a 120° rotation on the reverse side (the fourth power of a 60° mirror rotation); a 300° mirror rotation, or, what amounts to the same thing, a 60° mirror rotation on the reverse side (the fifth power of a 60° straight mirror rotation); and identification (the sixth power of a 60° mirror rotation). The presence in the group of a 120° simple rotation testifies to the fact that the six-fold mirror axis depicted in the diagram (Fig. 18) by a small white hexagon is simultaneously a simple, three-fold axis. The presence of inversion signifies that the six-fold mirror axis always passes through the center of symmetry of the figure. We previously represented the group under consideration by the figure shown in Fig. 3b.

Group $\bar{8}$ [$\bar{8}$] following in turn is analogous to $\bar{4}$ [$\bar{4}$]; it does not have inversion in its make-up, but group $\overline{10}$ [$\bar{5}$] which follows later is analogous to $\bar{6}$ [$\bar{3}$] and has inversion. Generally, if n is an odd number (as in groups, $\bar{2}, \bar{6}, \overline{10}$ [$\bar{1}, \bar{3}, \bar{5}$], etc.), then the group will contain inversion; if it is an even number (as in groups $\bar{4}, \bar{8}, \overline{12}$ [$\bar{4}, \bar{8}, \overline{12}$], . . .), then the corresponding group will not contain inversion. As we see, the series of groups under consideration may be extended to infinity and divided into two sub-series: the first is characterized by the presence of inversion (through the center of symmetry) in its groups, the second by the absence of this operation.

*Groups Determined by One Mirror Rotation through an Angle
Equal to an Odd-numbered Part* $1/(2n + 1)$ *of a Revolution*

The simplest operation of this kind is simple reflection in a plane, which may be formally considered as mirror rotation about an axis normal to the reflecting plane through an angle

FIG. 19. Depiction of groups $\bar{1}$, $\bar{3}$, $\bar{5}$ [$\bar{2}$, $\bar{6}$, $\overline{10}$] by elements of symmetry on a sphere.

equal to a complete revolution $(n = 0)$. The square of reflection is identification. Other operations of the group, determined by one reflection, are not included; consequently, this is a second-order group. Let us designate it by the symbol of a plane of symmetry, m [m]. This group may be represented

FIG. 20. Depiction of group $m = \bar{1}$ [$m = \bar{2}$] by a vertical plane of symmetry on a sphere.

by the previously considered figure with one plane of symmetry (Fig. 1). Two other drawings of this group are shown in Figs. 19 and 20. In the first of them the plane of symmetry coincides with the plane of the drawing. Let us agree to depict such planes by an unbroken circle—up to now, we traced out the circle of the projection with a dotted line and it simply

depicted a sphere. The white triangle on the forward hemisphere, having been reflected in the plane of symmetry, is
transferred to the rear half of the sphere and is located exactly
under it, so that it cannot be seen. Having made an opening
in the white triangle, we see the second triangle through it,
which should appear black. Such is the meaning of the black
dot placed in the center of the triangle. We will make wide
use of this means of designation in those cases where we must
show that a symmetrical figure has a plane of symmetry
coinciding with the plane of the drawing. In particular, if we

FIG. 21. Depiction of group $m = \bar{1}$ [$m = \bar{2}$] by two tetrahedra
shielding each other.

desired to depict a figure consisting of two irregular tetrahedra
shielding each other and having one plane of symmetry
coinciding with the plane of the drawing, then we would
simply get a triangle with a dot in the center (Fig. 21).

In the second drawing (Fig. 20) of group $m = \bar{1}$ [$m = \bar{2}$],
the plane of symmetry (unbroken straight line) is oriented
perpendicularly to the plane of the drawing.

The next group of the series under consideration ($n = 1$),
is determined by the operation of a mirror rotation through
an angle equal to 1/3 of a revolution about a three-fold axis (Fig.
19). The square of this operation is equivalent to a 240° simple
rotation, the cube is equivalent to simple reflection in a plane
normal to the axis; the fourth power is equivalent to a simple
120° rotation, the fifth power to a 240° mirror rotation, the
sixth power to identification. Higher powers do not yield new
operations. We have, consequently, a six-fold group. The
presence in it of a 120° simple rotation signifies that the group
is characterized by a simple three-fold axis of symmetry, and
simple reflection attests to the presence of one plane of symmetry.
We shall designate this group by the symbol of a three-fold

mirror axis, $\bar{3}$ [$\bar{6}$], or by the symbol $3:m$ [$\bar{6}$]. The number in this symbol signifies a three-fold axis; the m signifies the plane of symmetry; and the colon signifies their mutual perpendicularity. This sign mnemonically reminds us that the plane

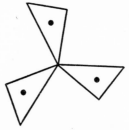

Fig. 22. A figure belonging to group $3:m$ [$\bar{6}$].

"divides" the axis in half (we consider the standard sign of perpendicularity to be inconvenient for a number of reasons). An example of a figure belonging to this group is given in Fig. 22. The figure consists of six tetrahedra. In the drawing, three of the tetrahedra are shielding three others.

The next group ($n = 2$) is determined by a mirror rotation

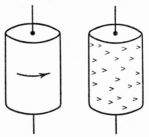

Fig. 23. Figures belonging to the group $\infty:m$ [$\bar{\infty}$].

through one-fifth part of a revolution (Fig. 19). This group, which we designated by the symbol $\bar{5}$ [$\overline{10}$] or by the symbol $5:m$ [$\overline{10}$], is completely analogous to the previous one.

The series of groups under consideration obviously may be carried out to infinity. The limiting group $\infty:m = \bar{\infty}$ [$\bar{\infty}$] must possess one infinite-fold axis and a plane of symmetry perpendicular to it. As an example of a figure which may by itself reflect the properties of this group, we may use a rotating cylinder or a cylinder completely covered by very tiny "marks", as shown in Fig. 23. These figures do not have enantiomorphic modifications, since group $\infty:m$ $[\overline{\infty}]$ contains operations of the second kind. A cylinder rotating clockwise is not distinguished from a cylinder rotating counterclockwise, since they may be brought into coincidence with each other by simple super-imposing, for which one of them must be first turned upside down. Expressing it freely, figures brought into self-coincidence by operations of the second kind may not have right and left forms because rightness and leftness are simultaneously contained in them.

Groups Determined by One Arbitrary Mirror Rotation

We already know that any symmetrical operation may be performed on a figure any number of times. The double repetition of any mirror rotation is equivalent to a simple rotation through twice the angle. This means that any group determined by mirror rotation includes in its make-up a group determined by one simple rotation. We know, however, that all groups determined by one rotation are exhausted by groups determined by an integral part $1/n$ of a rotation. It follows from this that the groups derived from one mirror rotation are exhausted only by groups derived from mirror rotations through an integral part of a revolution. In other words, there do not exist other groups, besides the already examined point symmetry groups, that are determined by one mirror rotation.

Concluding Remarks on the Derivation of Symmetry Groups Determined by One Operation

We established the existence of two series of symmetry groups which are determined by one operation—the series with the general symbol N, and the series with the general symbol $\overline{N}$:

$$1, 2, 3, \ldots, \infty \quad [1, 2, 3, \ldots, \infty]$$
$$\overline{1}, \overline{2}, \overline{3}, \ldots, \overline{\infty} \quad [\overline{2}, \overline{1}, \overline{6}, \ldots, \overline{\infty}]$$

The first of them may in turn be broken down into two series

$$1, 3, 5, \ldots, \infty \quad [1, 3, 5, \ldots, \infty] \tag{I}$$

$$2, 4, 6, \ldots, \infty \quad [2, 4, 6, \ldots, \infty] \tag{II}$$

The groups of series (I) are characterized by the absence of reversal in their operations. This operation is included in the groups of series (II). Such a division of the groups of series N is of great importance in crystallophysics.

Series $\overline{N}$ is divided into three series

$$\overline{2}, \overline{6}, \overline{10}, \ldots, \overline{\infty} \quad [\overline{1}, \overline{3}, \overline{5} \ldots, \overline{\infty}] \tag{III}$$

$$\overline{4}, \overline{8}, \overline{12}, \ldots, \overline{\infty} \quad [\overline{4}, \overline{8}, \overline{12}, \ldots, \overline{\infty}] \tag{IV}$$

$$\overline{1}, \overline{3}, \overline{5}, \ldots, \overline{\infty} \quad [\overline{2}, \overline{6}, \overline{10}, \ldots, \overline{\infty}] \tag{V}$$

In the groups of series (III) there is a center of symmetry, but not a transverse plane of symmetry. In the group of series (IV) there is neither a center nor a plane of symmetry. In groups (V) there is no center, but there is a plane of symmetry.

For the groups of series (V) we use the symbols:

$$1{:}m, \quad 3{:}m, \quad 5{:}m, \ldots, \infty{:}m. \quad [\overline{2}, \overline{6}, \overline{10}, \ldots, \overline{\infty}] \tag{V}$$

The first of these groups, containing one plane of symmetry, may of course be designated by the symbol m inasmuch as one-fold axes are contained in infinite quantity in all groups.

Sub-groups

Before proceeding to the enumeration of groups of symmetry determined by two and three operations, let us introduce the concept of the *sub-group*. We call the sub-group of a given group the combination of several of the operations of the given group, that in turn form a group. The order of a sub-group of a given group is always lower than the order of the latter. Group *6* [6] is a sixth-order group; its sub-groups are groups *1*, *2*, *3* [1, 2, 3]; first, second and third order. All the operations of these sub-groups are part of the make-up of group *6* [6].

Elements of Symmetry and their Designation

Any symmetry group consists of symmetrical operations, which are *elements* of the group. A group which is produced by one operation will be an *elementary group*. Every elementary group corresponds to one *element of symmetry*, that is, a conditionally selected point, straight line, or plane of a figure with which the existence of the elementary group is in some way associated. Up to now, our elements of symmetry have been: the center of symmetry, the plane of symmetry, and simple and mirror axes of symmetry.

We will designate elements of symmetry by the same symbols which we designated the corresponding elements of a group and elementary groups; for example the symbol *2* [2] will designate a 180° rotation, a group of rotations about a two-fold axis, and the two-fold axis itself; the symbol *m* will designate reflection in a plane, a plane of symmetry and the group of operations (reflection and identification) associated with it; the symbol *4̄* [4̄] will designate a four-fold mirror axis of symmetry, a group of mirror rotations through angles in multiples of 90° about this axis, and also one 90° mirror rotation. In this system of designation, ambiguity is avoided by the clarifying word placed before the symbol. Thus, for example, the meaning of the term *axis 2* [2] can in no way be confused with the meaning of the terms *group 2* [2] or *operation 2* [2].

Every point group may be represented and depicted as a combination of elements of symmetry.

Arrangement of a Plane of Symmetry Relative to Axes of Symmetry

It is now important to establish how a plane of symmetry may be arranged relative to axes of symmetry.

If *P* (Fig. 24) is a plane of symmetry and *L* is an axis of symmetry intersecting the plane at any angle, then there must also exist a second axis *L'* obtained from the first mirror reflection in the plane, otherwise the latter would not be a plane of symmetry. It is easy to be convinced by the construction that a plane of symmetry must divide the angle between the axes in half or else miss it. In a particular case the axis may coincide with the plane (the angle of intersection of the axis with the plane is equal to zero) or be perpendicular

FIG. 24. Drawing to demonstrate the theorem that the plane of symmetry must divide in half the angle between axes of symmetry.

to it (90° angle). There can be no other mutual arrangement of a plane of symmetry with a pair of axes of symmetry which intersect at a point on the plane of symmetry.

Groups Determined by One Rotation and Reflection in a Transverse Plane

We have already described some of the groups of this kind as groups determined by one odd-fold mirror axis. There remain the groups determined by one even-fold simple axis and plane of symmetry normal (tranverse) to it (Fig. 25).

The simplest of these groups is given by one two-fold axis and a transverse plane of symmetry. Let us designate this group by the symbol $2:m$ $[2/m]$. This group is shown in another projection in Fig. 26. The following four operations serve as elements of the group: a 180° rotation about an axis, reflection in a plane of symmetry, inversion (that is, the product of the first two operations), and identification (the square of the rotation or the square of the reflection). Group $2:m$ $[2/m]$, consequently, is a fourth-order group. No single element in itself determines the whole group; at least two of them are

necessary for this: rotation and reflection, inversion and reflection, inversion and reflection, or rotation and inversion.
The first pair is easier to interpret geometrically than to express
in the symbol of a group.

The next group, $4:m$ [$4/m$], is an eighth-order group (8
triangles on the surface of a sphere). Inversion also enters

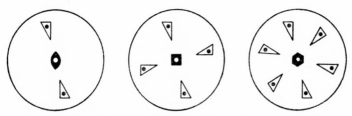

Fig. 25. Depiction of groups $2:m$, $4:m$, $6:m$, [$2/m$, $4/m$, $6/m$]
by elements of symmetry on a sphere.

into the make-up of its elements. The groups of the series
under consideration differ in this respect from the groups
of the previously considered series V (Fig. 19), which were
characterized by an odd-numbered axis and plane of symmetry,
and did not have a center of symmetry.

The next group $6:m$ [$6/m$] repeats all the basic features of
the two preceding ones; it is a twelfth-order group, having
a center of symmetry in the make-up of its elements of symmetry.
It is obvious that this series of groups

$$2:m, \quad 4:m, \quad 6:m, \ldots, \quad \infty:m \quad [2/m, 4/m, 6/m, \ldots, \infty/m]$$
$$\text{(VI)}$$

may be carried out to infinity. Its limiting group will be
group $\infty:m$ [∞/m] which we already considered. Examples
of figures of series $N:m$ [N/m] are shown in Fig. 27.

*Groups Determined by One Rotation and Reflection in a
Longitudinal Plane*

If we take any group determined by one rotation, for example,
group 4 [4], which is characterized by the arrangement of
triangles on a sphere (Fig. 28a) that we are familiar with,

and we add to it one reflection in plane *m*, which passes along the four-fold axis (*the longitudinal plane*), then the number of triangles will double (Fig. 28*b*), and in their new arrangement

Fig. 26. Another depiction of group 2:*m* [2/*m*].

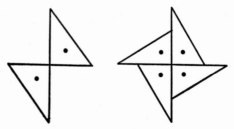

Fig. 27. Figures belonging to groups 2:*m*, 4:*m* [2/*m*, 4/*m*].

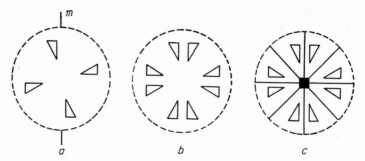

Fig. 28. Construction of group 4·*m* [4 *mm*] from group 4 [4], by the addition to it of a longitudinal plane of symmetry.

we shall discover not only the given elements of symmetry—one four-fold axis and a plane of symmetry—but also three new planes of symmetry which also pass along the axis. The mutual arrangement of all these elements of symmetry is shown in Fig. 28c. We shall designate this group by the symbol *4·m* [4mm]. In this symbol, the point dividing the symbol of axis *4* from the symbol of plane *m* is a sign of parallelism*; it simultaneously indicates that the total number of planes of symmetry is obtained by "multiplication" of the given number of planes (one) by the number characterizing the order of the axis.

All the other groups of this infinite series of groups may also be constructed analogously (Fig. 29).

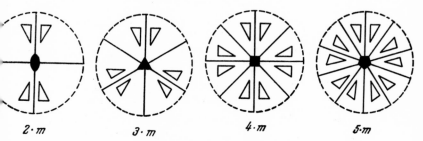

2·m   *3·m*   *4·m*   *5·m*

Fig. 29. Groups of the series *2·m*, *3·m*, *4·m*, . . ., ∞·m
[2mm, 3mm, . . ., ∞m].

The series of groups of symmetry under consideration fall naturally into two constituent series

2·m, *4·m*, *6·m*, . . ., ∞·m, [2mm, 4mm, 6mm, . . ., ∞m]
                                                        (VII)

1·m, *3·m*, *5·m*, . . ., ∞·m, [1m, 3m, 5m, . . ., ∞m = ∞m]
                                                        (VIII)

according to the following important characteristic: in each group with an even-numbered axis of symmetry, we have two sorts of qualitatively different planes of symmetry. Having taken group *4·m* [4mm] for an example, we notice that two planes of symmetry are arranged differently in it, with respect to the triangles on the sphere, than are the two others. That is, for the concrete case shown in Fig. 29, two of the planes occupy a closer position to the triangles and pass parallel to the legs

* [The plane itself (not its normal) is parallel to the axis.]

of the triangles, while the other two planes stand further from the triangles and are not parallel to their legs. In the groups with the odd-numbered axes, all the planes of symmetry are non-equivalent to one another.

Series (VIII) begins with group $1 \cdot m = m = \bar{1}\,[1m = m = \bar{2}]$, which is simultaneously the first member of previously considered series (V).

Examples of figures of series (VII) and (VIII) are shown in Fig. 30.

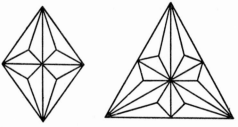

Fig. 30. Figures belonging to groups $2 \cdot m$, $3 \cdot m$ $[2mm, 3m]$.

Fig. 31. Figure belonging to group $\infty \cdot m$ $[\infty m]$.

The limiting group $\infty \cdot m$ $[\infty m]$ has an infinite number of longitudinal planes of symmetry and one infinite-fold axis. It may be graphically depicted by a stationary cone (Fig. 31).

Groups Determined by Two Rotations

The previously demonstrated Theorem of Euler is the basis for derivation of these groups. As applied to our problem this theorem means the following: If A_1 (Fig. 32) is an n_1-fold axis of symmetry with an elementary angle of rotation $2\alpha_1 = \dfrac{360°}{n_1}$, and A_2 is an n_2-fold axis of symmetry with an angle of rotation $2\alpha_2 = \dfrac{360°}{n_2}$, then the axis A_3 passing through the apex A_3 of the spherical triangle $A_1A_2A_3$, constructed along

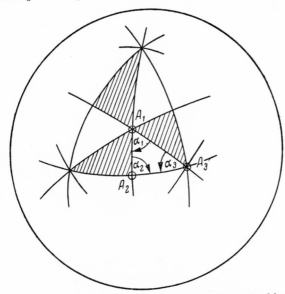

FIG. 32. Diagram for the derivation of groups determined by two rotations.

the given side A_1A_2 and the two adjacent angles α_1 and α_2, must also be a quite definite n_3-fold axis of symmetry with an angle of rotation $2\alpha_3$. On the other hand, if A_1 is an n_1-fold axis, then the triangle $A_1A_2A_3$ must repeat itself on the sphere by consecutive rotation around it n_1 times through an angle $2\alpha_1$. The same may also be said with respect to axes A_2 and A_3: around each of them the triangle $A_1A_2A_3$ must repeat itself an integral number of times corresponding to the order of the axes. Since the rotations about A_1 are completed each time through the angle $2\alpha_1$ which is twice as large as the angle of triangle $A_1A_2A_3$ at apex A_1, then during the repetition of the triangle on the surface of the sphere, there must remain areas (shaded on the diagram) which are not occupied by the recurrent triangles. These areas, as can easily be seen, will be mirror-equal to triangle $A_1A_2A_3$. The whole surface of the sphere will be completely covered by shaded and non-shaded triangles. Through their apices, axes of symmetry will pass which are equivalent (equal) to the axes A_1, A_2, A_3.

Thus the problem of finding all the groups of symmetry determined by the two axes A_1 and A_2, or, in other words, by two rotations about these axes, leads to the consideration of all the cases of filling in the surface of the sphere with triangles congruently equal and mirror-equal to the triangle $A_1A_2A_3$, and also leads to the study of the properties of the latter.

Before proceeding to the derivation of these groups, let us recall that the sum of the angles of any spherical triangle is less than $3 \times 180 = 540°$, and more than $180°$. Actually, if we deform any given spherical triangle, displacing one of its apices along the surface of the sphere, then in a particular case, all three apices may appear to be arranged on one great circle. Formally considering this great circle as a spherical triangle, we find that each of its angles is equal to $180°$, and their sum will be $540°$. In any obvious spherical triangle, the sum of the angles must be less. On the other hand, if we gradually bring together all three apices of a spherical triangle, it will increasingly resemble a flat triangle; the sum of its angles will approach $180°$ and at the limit, when all three apices meet at one point, the sum of the angles will equal $180°$ exactly but then the triangle itself will degenerate into one point. In all clearly spherical triangles, the sum of the angles should obviously be more than $180°$. Previously we saw that for angles of rotation about axes, the following relations take place:

$$2\alpha_1 = \frac{360°}{n_1}, \quad 2\alpha_2 = \frac{360°}{n_2}, \quad 2\alpha_3 = \frac{360°}{n_3}.$$

It follows from this that the angles of the spherical triangle $A_1A_2A_3$ may only be equal to the integral parts of the semicircle:

$$\frac{180°}{2} = 90°; \quad \frac{180°}{3} = 60°; \quad \frac{180°}{4} = 45°; \quad \frac{180°}{5} = 36° \text{ etc.}$$

If each of two angles of a spherical triangle equals 90°, then
the third angle may be any integral part of a semicircle since
the sum of the angles under these conditions will always be
more than 180° and less than 540°. Consequently, we may
have an infinite series of triangles with the angles

$$
\begin{array}{ccc}
90° & 90° & 90° \\
90° & 90° & 60° \\
90° & 90° & 45° \\
90° & 90° & 36° \\
90° & 90° & 30°
\end{array}
$$

. . . .

The series of symmetry groups shown in Fig. 33 correspond
to these triangles. The first fourth-order group, which is
determined by two rotations about two mutually perpendicular

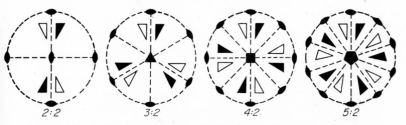

2:2   3:2   4:2   5:2

FIG. 33. Groups of the series 2:2, 3:2, 4:2, . . . , ∞:2 [222, 32,
422, . . . , ∞2].

two-fold axes and is designated by the symbol 2:2 [222],
emerges with a kaleidoscopic repetition of a spherical triangle
with three right angles (of one octant of the surface of the
sphere). The total number of such triangles is eight. The
group has three two-fold axes in all. The fact that it is completely determined by only two of them is apparent from the
following consideration. Let us assume that we are given only
an axis normal to the plane of the diagram, and an axis directed
from left to right. Let us take the small white triangle on the
surface of the sphere, located in the upper left octant (see
group 2:2 [222] in Fig. 33). By a 180° rotation about the first
axis this triangle is transferred to the position of the second white
triangle in the lower right octant. A 180° rotation about the

second axis transfers both white triangles onto the rear half of the sphere to the position of the two black triangles. By these two rotations we obtain all four triangles on the surface of the sphere. A 180° rotation about the third axis, which passes along the plane of the diagram from top to bottom, does not create new positions of a triangle on the surface of the sphere, but brings about only their mutual exchange of places. This signifies that such a rotation is a symmetrical transformation, that the third axis is also a two-fold axis and

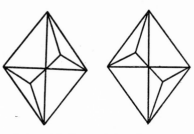

Fig. 34. Enantiomorphic figures belonging to group 2:2 [222].

that group 2:2 [222] is a fourth-order group. The group has no other operations besides the three 180° rotations about the axes, and the operation of identification. All these operations are of the first kind; therefore all the small triangles equal one another.

The second group of the series under consideration is also determined only by two axes, that is, either by a pair of two-fold axes intersecting each other at a 60° angle, or by a three-fold axis and a two-fold axis normal to it. In the symbol 3:2 [32] which we assign to this group, a second point of view is reflected. The group under consideration is a six-fold group, which is easy to verify, given one small asymmetrical triangle on the surface of a sphere, by repeating it with all the rotations of the given axes. As may be seen from the diagram, the group has a total of one three-fold axis and three two-fold axes normal to it which intersect each other at angles of 60°.

The third, eight-fold, 4:2 [422], repeats all the basic features of the first two groups. Obviously, this series of groups may be carried out to infinity. The limiting group of infinite order will have the symbol $\infty:2$ [$\infty 2$], and will possess one infinite-fold *main axis* of symmetry and an infinite number of *two-fold transverse (lateral) axes*.

One may see from what has been stated, that all figures belonging to the given groups of symmetry (such as figures

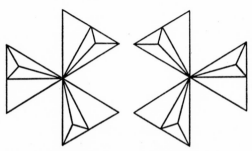

FIG. 35. Enantiomorphic figures belonging to group $3:2$ [32].

consisting only of right or left components) may exist in two enantiomorphic modifications. In Fig. 34 an example is given of enantiomorphic figures belonging to group $2:2$ [222],

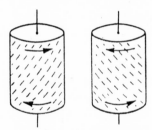

FIG. 36. Enantiomorphic figures belonging to group $\infty:2$ [$\infty 2$].

and in Fig. 35 an example of enantiomorphic figures belonging to group $3:2$ [32].

The cylinders turning on a right-hand or left-hand screw (Fig. 36) may serve as an example of right and left forms, belonging to the limiting group $\infty:2$ [$\infty 2$]. Here again it is appropriate to recall that among purely geometrical figures we do not find such figures which may represent group $\infty:2$ [$\infty 2$].

The series of groups we described breaks down into two constituent series

$$2:2, \quad 4:2, \quad 6:2, \ldots, \quad \infty:2, \quad [222, 422, 622, \ldots, \infty 2] \quad \text{(IX)}$$

$$1:2, \quad 3:2, \quad 5:2, \ldots, \quad \infty:2. \quad [12, 32, 52, \ldots, \infty 2] \quad \text{(X)}$$

Into the first series enter groups with an even-fold main axis. In the groups of the first series, the lateral axes are of two sorts; this may be seen by the difference in their arrangement relative to the small triangles on the surface of the sphere. In the groups of the second series, the lateral axes are equivalent. The first group of this series, $1:2 = 2$ [$12 = 2$], we already encountered earlier, in series (II).

Let us proceed to other groups, determined by two rotations. It is not difficult to show that only three such groups exist. We previously saw that if two angles of a spherical triangle, which is suitable for construction of desired figures, each equal to 90°, then the third angle may be equal to any integral part $1/n$ of a semicircle, since the sum of the three angles in this case will be, as is usual for any spherical triangle, $>180°$ and $<540°$. In order to find all the other possibilities, let us retain the value of 90° for the first angle, and to the second angle let us assign the following value according to the quantity $1/3$ of a half-revolution, that is, 60°. In order that the sum of the three angles be more than 180°, the third angle must be equal to one of the following three values: $1/3 \cdot 180° = 60°$; $1/4 \cdot 180° = 45°$; $1/5 \cdot 180° = 36°$. If it is equal to a still smaller part of a semicircle, for example $180°/6 = 30°$, then the sum of the angles will not be more than 180°. Thus, because of this characteristic, only three spherical triangles are suitable for the construction of the desired groups; these have the angles:

$$
\begin{array}{ccc}
90° & 60° & 60° \\
90° & 60° & 45° \\
90° & 60° & 36°
\end{array}
$$

In order to be finally convinced that the three groups actually correspond to these triangles, we must carry out the actual construction of the groups. This will be done later, but let us now show that there are no other combinations of angles of a spherical triangle which meet the necessary demands.

If the first and largest angle is equal to 90°, the second will equal 45° (the next value after 60°), so that whatever the third angle in order of value is, their sum may not exceed 180°. Finally, if the largest angle equals 60°, then in addition to other like or smaller angles, it will not exceed 180°, which it was also necessary to demonstrate.

Let us proceed to the construction of groups. Kaleidoscopic repetition of a spherical triangle with 90°, 60° and 60° angles on the surface of a sphere is shown in Fig. 37. It can be seen

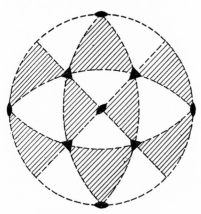

Fig. 37.   Group *3/2* [23].

from the diagram that the group under consideration, which we shall designate by the symbol *3/2* [23], belongs to twelfth-order groups; it contains three mutually perpendicular two-fold axes and four three-fold axes which intersect the two-fold axes at identical angles, equal to the angle that a diagonal of a cube makes with its edges. This angle is close to 55°; its exact value is expressed by an irrational number of degrees. This group is fully determined either by two three-fold axes, or by one three-fold axis and one two-fold axis. In the symbol *3/2*, the slanting arrangement of the axes in regard to one another is expressed by the slanting line between the numbers *3* and *2*. In group *3/2* [23], shown in Fig. 37, we depart from the previously accepted method of depicting groups by using small asymmetrical triangles on a sphere, in order not to complicate the diagram. This departure from the rule will be further extended to all groups having four three-fold axes.

The pentagonal-tritetrahedron depicted in Fig. 38 may serve

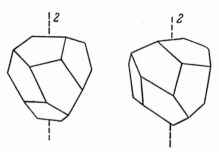

Fig. 38. Enantiomorphic figures belonging to group *3/2* [23].

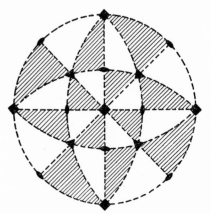

·Fig. 39. Group *3/4* [43].

as an example of figures belonging to this group. As is to be expected, the figure under consideration may exist in two enantiomorphic modifications.

The following group *3/4* [43] is related to the preceding in the sense that the spherical triangle, with the 90°, 60° and 30° angles which form its basis, represents half of the corresponding triangle of the preceding group. Two-fold, three-fold, and four-fold axes pass through the angles of the triangle. The group contains: three four-fold axes, four three-fold axes, and six two-fold axes (Fig. 39).

The order of the group is 24. The pentagonal-trioctahedron depicted in two enantiomorphic modifications in Fig. 40 may serve as an example of figures belonging to this group.

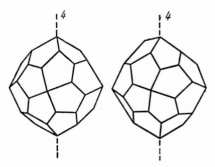

Fig. 40. Enantiomorphic figures belonging to group *3/4* [43].

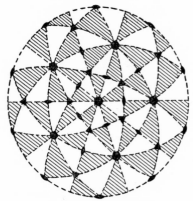

Fig. 41. Group *3/5* [53].

The last of the three groups, group *3/5* [53], determined by a spherical triangle with 90°, 60° and 36° angles, contains six five-fold axes, ten three-fold axes, and fifteen two-fold axes; their arrangement on a sphere is shown in Fig. 41. The order of the group is 60. This group may be represented by a 60-hedron with pentagonal faces. One of the two possible

6

modifications of this figure is shown in Fig. 42. It may be constructed from a rectilineal dodecahedron with each of its five-angled faces replaced by five pentagons.

Our derivation of symmetry groups determined by two rotations would be incomplete if we did not include in these groups still another group, which plays an important role in many matters of crystallography. Taking a primary pair of

FIG. 42. One of the enantiomorphic figures belonging to group *3/5* [53].

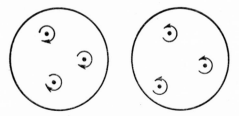

FIG. 43. Conventional depiction of enantiomorphic spheres.

axes for the determination of one or another group of a category under consideration, we assumed their multiplicity to be limited. This did not prevent us from going to the limit to establish several groups determined by one finite and one infinite axis. If, for the construction of a group, we now take two infinite-fold axes intersecting at an arbitrary angle, then, applying Euler's Theorem, we come to the conclusion that a group of symmetry ∞/∞ [$\infty\infty$] exists, consisting of an infinite number of infinite-fold axes, directed to all sides. Let us note that this group does not contain one plane of symmetry. A sphere whose surface consists completely of points rotating in one direction may serve as an example of figures reflecting all the characteristics of group ∞/∞ [$\infty\infty$]. Such a sphere may exist in two enantiomorphic modifications—right and left, depending upon the direction in which the points rotate (Fig. 43). Another, less artificial, example of a figure belonging to group ∞/∞ [$\infty\infty$] is a sphere which is made of isotropic material, rotating the plane of light polarization right and left, for example, amorphous *d-* or *1-*tartaric acid.

We have investigated all the groups of symmetry determined by two axes of symmetry; it turned out that all these groups contain more than two axes. From this it may be assumed that there are no groups of symmetry which require more than two axes for their determination. The following sections are given to the consideration of this question.

On the Impossibility of Groups Existing which Require More than Two Axes for their Determination

Let us assume that such groups exist. This means that in these groups, besides a combination of axes determined by two out of three given axes, there exist special auxiliary axes. These latter may be distributed in a quite definite manner among the given axes, namely: each two-fold axis must divide the angle between a pair of one-fold axes in half; each three-fold axis must pass through the center of a rectilineal spherical triangle whose apices serve as exit points of the one-fold axes, etc. Let us consider how the new axes in groups of the type $N:2$ [N2] may be arranged. Axes of identical multiplicity, that is, two-fold axes, are arranged in these groups in one plane, normal to the main axis. Under these conditions, only the two-fold axes, dividing the angles between the given two-fold axes in half, may be new axes. However, the groups constructed by this means will not be new, since they are already included in groups of the type under consideration. The first group, $2:2$ [22], of this type, occupies a special position. The two-fold axes are arranged in it along the apices of a rectilineal triangle with 90°, 90° and 90° angles; consequently, the new three-fold axis may be located only in the center of this triangle. Having carried out the corresponding construction, we again obtain group *3/2* [32], which we already know.

It remains to be considered whether it is impossible to add new axes to the three remaining groups: *3/2*, *3/4*, *3/5* [32, 42, 52]. In group *3/2* [32], there are triangles through whose apices pass three-fold axes. The only place where the new axis may be located, namely, the two-fold axis, is the center of the side of the triangle, joining both three-fold axes. If such a construction is made, group *3/4* [43] will be obtained, which again is not new. In groups *3/4* [43] and *3/5* [53], the spherical triangles are asymmetrical; different kinds of axes are arranged in their apices and therefore it is impossible to place a new axis here.

Thus, summing up, the previously derived groups determined by two rotations exhaust all groups containing single rotations as elements (considering identification as a rotation).

Groups Determined by Two Rotations and Reflection

It was previously shown that a plane of symmetry may occupy a completely determinate position relative to a certain axis, namely: it may either pass along it or intersect it transversely. It may also occupy only two positions in relation to two intersecting axes: it may divide the angle between them in half, or pass simultaneously along both axes. In any other arrangement of a plane relative to axes, it will either not be a plane of symmetry or it will give rise to new axes as the result of reflection in it. Since we have already determined all the combinations of axes, the addition of a plane of symmetry in order to obtain new groups should not give rise to new axes, that is, a plane of symmetry may be added to axes only by the previously shown methods.

In groups of type *N:2* [*N2*], an additional plane of symmetry may either pass simultaneously along the main and lateral axes, or pass along the main axis and divide the angle between the laterals in half, or, finally, pass simultaneously along all the lateral axes. Let us consider all these possibilities in turn.

Let us take group $4:2$ [42] as an example and add to it one plane of symmetry, m [m] (Fig. 44a).

As the result of only one reflection in this plane, we obtain

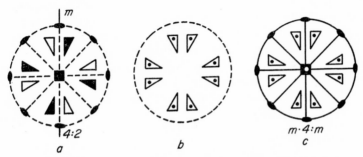

FIG. 44. Construction of group $m \cdot 4:m$ [4/mmm] from group $4:2$ [42] by the addition of a longitudinal plane of symmetry passing along a two-fold axis.

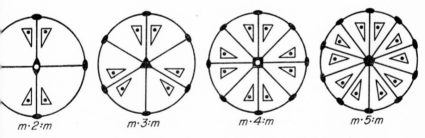

FIG. 45. Groups of the series $m \cdot 2:m$, $m \cdot 3:m$, $m \cdot 4:m$, . . . , $m \cdot \infty:m$ [2/mmm, $\bar{6}m2$, 4/mmm, . . . , ∞/mm].

on the surface of the sphere the new distribution of small triangles shown in Fig. 44b. It is clear from this distribution that the addition of one plane of symmetry has given rise to the appearance of three other longitudinal and one transverse plane of symmetry (Fig. 44c). We have obtained the sixteen-fold group $m \cdot 4:m$ [4/mmm], consisting of one four-fold axis, four two-fold axes, four longitudinal planes of symmetry, one transverse plane of symmetry and a center of symmetry.

In the given instance, the four-fold simple axis is simultaneously a mirror axis of the same multiplicity, of course.

An analogous result is also obtained with all the other groups of type $N:2$ [$N2$]. We shall designate the new groups by the symbol $m \cdot N:m$, inasmuch as they also may be treated as groups determined by one simple axis and two planes of symmetry—a longitudinal and a transverse (Fig. 45). It is easy to verify by using the same method, that the addition of one transverse plane of symmetry to groups $N:2$ [$N2$] will lead to the same result.

The series of groups under consideration falls naturally into two component series

$$m \cdot 2:m, \quad m \cdot 4:m, \quad m \cdot 6:m, \ldots, m \cdot \infty :m$$
$$[2/mmm, \ 4/mmm, \ 6/mmm, \ldots, \ \infty/mm], \qquad \text{(XI)}$$

$$m \cdot 1:m, \quad m \cdot 3:m, \quad m \cdot 5:m, \ldots, m \cdot \infty :m$$
$$[\bar{3}m2, \ \bar{6}m2, \ \overline{10}m2, \ldots, \overline{\infty}m2 = \infty/mm]. \qquad \text{(XII)}$$

The first, consisting of groups with even-fold main axes, is characterized by the presence of a center of symmetry in each group. In groups of the second sub-series with odd-fold main

FIG. 46. A figure belonging to group $m \cdot \infty :m$ [∞/mm].

axes, centers of symmetry are absent. Limiting group $m \cdot \infty :m$ [∞/mm] of this series has the following elements of symmetry: one infinite-fold axis, an infinite number of two-fold transverse axes, an infinite number of longitudinal planes of symmetry, one transverse plane of symmetry and a center of symmetry. This group may be illustrated by the figure of a stationary cylinder (Fig. 46). The first group $m \cdot 1:m$ [$\bar{3}m2$] of series (XII), having two mutually perpendicular planes of symmetry intersecting on axis *2*, was encountered earlier in series (VII) under the symbol $2 \cdot m$ [2mm].

Examples of figures belonging to groups of the series $m \cdot N : m$ are shown in Fig. 47.

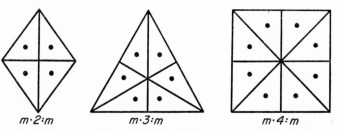

$m \cdot 2 : m$ $m \cdot 3 : m$ $m \cdot 4 : m$

FIG. 47. Figures belonging to groups $m \cdot 2 : m$, $m \cdot 3 : m$, $m \cdot 4 : m$, . . ., $m \cdot \infty : m$ [mmm, $\overline{6}m2$, 4/mmm, . . ., ∞/mm].

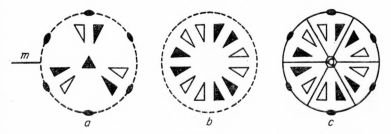

a   *b*   *c*

FIG. 48. Construction of group $\overline{6} \cdot m$ [3m] from group $3 : 2$ [32] by the addition of a longitudinal plane of symmetry, dividing the angle between the transverse axes in half.

Let us now consider groups derived from the groups of type $N : 2$ [N2] by the addition of a plane of symmetry passing along the main axis and dividing the angle between the two lateral axes in half. Let us take group $3 : 2$ [32] as an example, and add to it the plane of symmetry m (Fig. 48a). As the result of reflection in this plane, the number of small triangles on the sphere increases two-fold (Fig. 48b). In the new picture showing the distribution of these triangles, it is easy to see the appearance of two other longitudinal planes of symmetry (Fig. 48c). The group derived by this method will have the following elements of symmetry: a six-fold mirror axis, three two-fold axes normal to it, three longitudinal planes of symmetry and a center of symmetry. We shall designate this group by the symbol $\bar{6} \cdot m$ [$\bar{3}m$], inasmuch as it may equally be considered as a group determined by a six-fold mirror axis [three-fold inversion axis] and a longitudinal plane of symmetry.

By this procedure a whole series of groups of type $\overline{N} \cdot m$ may

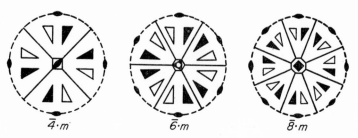

$\overline{4} \cdot m$ $\overline{6} \cdot m$ $\overline{8} \cdot m$

FIG. 49. Groups of the series $\overline{4} \cdot m$, $\overline{6} \cdot m$, $\overline{8} \cdot m$, . . . [$\overline{4}2m$, $\overline{3}m$, $\overline{8}2m$, . . .].

be obtained (Fig. 49). Like the other series, it may be broken down into two component series

$$\overline{4} \cdot m, \quad \overline{8} \cdot m, \quad \overline{12} \cdot m, \ldots, m \cdot \infty:m$$
$$[\overline{4}2m, \overline{8}2m, \overline{12}2m, \ldots, \overline{\infty}2m = \infty/mm]. \quad \text{(XIII)}$$

$$\overline{2} \cdot m, \quad \overline{6} \cdot m, \quad \overline{10} \cdot m, \ldots, m \cdot \infty:m$$
$$[\overline{1}m, \overline{3}m, \overline{5}m, \ldots, \overline{\infty}m = \infty/mm]. \quad \text{(XIV)}$$

In the first of these groups whose main mirror axis is at the same time an even-fold axis, and which therefore have no center of symmetry; in the second are groups whose mirror axis is at the same time an odd-fold simple axis, and which therefore have a center of symmetry. The limiting group of both these series is group $m \cdot \infty:m$ [∞/mm] considered previously. The first group $\overline{2} \cdot m$ [$\overline{1}m$] of series (XIV) was encountered earlier in series (VI) under the symbol $2:m$ [$2/m$]. Examples of figures belonging to groups $\overline{N} \cdot m$, are shown in Fig. 50.

It still remains for us to decide how to place an additional plane of symmetry in groups: $3/2$, $3/4$, $3/5$, ∞/∞ [23, 43,

53, ∞∞]. A plane of symmetry may be placed in group $3/2$ [23] by only two means: either along two-fold axes and simultaneously perpendicular to a third two-fold axis, or along a two-fold axis and simultaneously along the nearest three-fold axis. In the first instance we obtain group $\bar{6}/2$

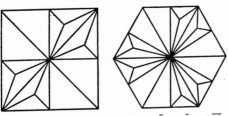

FIG. 50. Figures belonging to groups $\bar{4} \cdot m$, $\bar{6} \cdot m$ [$\overline{42}m$, $\bar{3}m$].

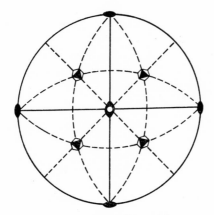

FIG. 51. Group $\bar{6}/2$ [$2/m\bar{3}$].

[$2/m\bar{3} = m3$] (Fig. 51); in the second group $3/\bar{4}$ (Fig. 52). The first of these groups is a group of the twenty-fourth order and contains the following elements of symmetry: three two-fold axes, four three-fold axes (they are, however, six-fold mirror axes), three planes of symmetry and a center of symmetry. The second group is also a group of the twenty-fourth order and contains: three four-fold mirror axes, four three-fold axes and six planes of symmetry. The didodecahedron depicted

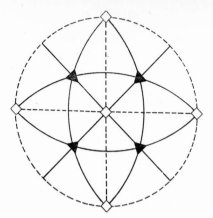

FIG. 52. Group $3/\overline{4}$ [$\overline{4}3m$].

FIG. 53. A figure belonging to group $6/2$ [$2/m3$].

FIG. 54. A figure belonging to group $3/\overline{4}$ [$\overline{4}3m$].

in Fig. 53 may serve as an example of figures belonging to group *6/2* [*2/m3*]. An example of figures possessing symmetry *3/4̄* [*4̄3m*], is given in Fig. 54. This is a hexatetrahedron,

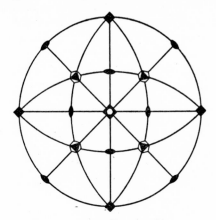

FIG. 55. Group *6̄/4* [*4/m* *3̄2/m*].

FIG. 56. Figure belonging to group *6̄/4* [*4/m* *3̄2/m*].

obtained from a tetrahedron by a six-fold multiplication of each of its faces.

Let us proceed to group *3/4* [*43*]. The first plane of symmetry may be placed in it along any side of the spherical triangle which we used in the construction of this group. In all three instances, however, the same group, *6̄/4* [*4/m* *3̄2/m = m3m*], is derived, as can easily be seen by comparing the three pictures of the distribution of small triangles emerging as the result of one reflection in one, another, or a third plane of symmetry. The new group is shown in Fig. 55. The 48-face polyhedron depicted in Fig. 56 may serve as an example of figures belonging to this group. This figure is derived by a six-fold increase in each of the faces of an octahedron. The order of this group is correspondingly equal to 48. The group contains four six-fold mirror axes, three four-fold axes, six two-fold axes, nine planes of symmetry and a center of symmetry.

Let us proceed to group $3/5$ [53]. As in the preceding group,

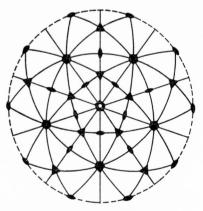

Fig. 57.   Group $3/\overline{10}$ [$\bar{5}3m$].

three positions of an additional plane are possible here—along the three sides of a spherical triangle. In all instances, however, the addition of one plane automatically gives rise to the appearance of two other planes, as the result of which one new group emerges (Fig. 57) from group $3/5$ [53]. Let us designate it by the symbol $3/\overline{10}$ [$\bar{5}3m$]. Besides the elements of symmetry which are part of group $3/5$ [53], the new group contains fifteen planes of symmetry and a center of symmetry. The 120-faced polyhedron obtained from the rectilineal dodecahedron, by the exchange of each of its five-angled faces for ten triangular ones (Fig. 58), may serve as an example of figures belonging to group $3/\overline{10}$ [$\bar{5}3m$]. Its order equals 120.

It remains for us to establish the last of the groups, determined by three operations—spherical group $\infty/\infty \cdot m$ [$\infty \infty m$].

This group may be derived from group ∞/∞ [$\infty\infty$], which has an infinite number of infinite-fold axes, by the addition of one plane of symmetry. By repeating all the possible rotations contained in group ∞/∞ [$\infty\infty$], this plane produces an infinite number of other equal planes of symmetry. We

FIG. 58. Figure belonging to group $3/\overline{10}$ [$\overline{5}3m$].

finally obtain the point group containing all the conceivable elements of symmetry. The ordinary sphere is that figure which fully reflects the characteristics of this group.

Concluding Observations on the Derivation of Point Groups

The spherical group $\infty/\infty\cdot m$ [$\infty\infty m$] concludes the enumeration of all the point groups of symmetry. No other initial combinations of two, three, or more operations lead to new groups. This may be demonstrated.

The only possible point operations are, as we know, simple and mirror rotations. We have considered the following groups: (1) groups determined by one operation of the first and second kind, (2) groups determined by one rotation and reflection, (3) groups determined by two rotations and (4) groups determined by two rotations and reflection. But we have not considered generally: (1) combinations of simple and mirror rotations, and (2) combinations only of mirror rotations, limited only by a particular instance of a combination of rotations with reflections. It is necessary to show, consequently, that these combinations do not yield anything new.

Table 1

Point Groups of Symmetry of Three-dimensional Figures*

I	II	III	IV	V	VI	VII	VIII	IX	X	XI	XII	XIII	XIV	XV	XVI
1 [1]	*2* [2]	*2̄* [1̄]	*4̄* [4̄]	*1:m* [2̄]	*2:m* [2/m]	*2·m* [2mm]	*1·m* [1m]	*2:2* [222]	*1:2* [12]	*m·2:m* [2/mmm]	*m·1:m* [2̄m2]	*4̄·m* [4̄2m]	*2̄·m* [1̄m]	*3/2* [23]	*6̄/2* [2/m3̄]
3 [3]	*4* [4]	*6̄* [3̄]	*8̄* [8̄]	*3:m* [6̄]	*4:m* [4/m]	*4·m* [4mm]	*3·m* [3m]	*4:2* [422]	*3:2* [32]	*m·4:m* [4/mmm]	*m·3:m* [6̄m2]	*8̄·m* [8̄2m]	*6̄·m* [3̄m]	*3/4* [43]	*3/4* [4̄3m]
5 [5]	*6* [6]	*1̄0* [5̄]	*1̄2* [12̄]	*5:m* [1̄0]	*6:m* [6/m]	*6·m* [6mm]	*5·m* [5m]	*6:2* [622]	*5:2* [52]	*m·6:m* [6/mmm]	*m·5:m* [1̄0m2]	*1̄2·m* [12̄.2m]	*1̄0·m* [5̄m]	*3/5* [53]	*6̄/4* [4/m3̄ 2/m]
7 [7]	*8* [8]	*1̄4* [7̄]	*1̄6* [16̄]	*7:m* [1̄4]	*8:m* [8/m]	*8·m* [8mm]	*7·m* [7m]	*8:2* [822]	*7:2* [72]	*m·8:m* [8/mmm]	*m·7:m* [1̄4m2]	*1̄6·m* [16̄.2m]	*1̄4·m* [7̄m]		*3/1̄0* [5̄3m]
∞ [∞]		*∞̄* [∞̄ = ∞/m]		*∞:m* [∞ = ∞/m]		*∞·m* [∞m]		*∞:2* [∞2]		*m·∞:m* [∞̄m = ∞/mm]				*∞/∞* [∞∞]	*∞/∞·m* [∞∞m]

We know that any mirror axis is, at the same time, a simple axis of the same or of half the multiplicity. Hence, it follows from Euler's Theorem that mirror axes may occupy the same positions in space as simple ones. This means that the locating of all groups of symmetry with mirror axes leads only to the consideration of all the possibilities of redesignation of simple axes as mirror axes of the same or twice the multiplicity in groups containing only simple axes.

Let us first take groups of type $N:2$ [$N2$]. If redesignation of the main axis into a mirror axis is not accompanied by a change in its multiplicity, then such redesignation will simply signify the addition of one transverse plane of symmetry, which we have already considered earlier. If redesignation of the main axis into a mirror axis is coupled with an increase of twice its multiplicity, then such a redesignation will cause the appearance of longitudinal planes of symmetry dividing the angles between the transverse axes in half. This may be detected, for example, in group $3:2$ [32]. The distribution of small triangles on a sphere, which corresponds to this group,

---

FOOTNOTE TO TABLE 1

* Only *generating elements of symmetry* are included in the group symbols, i.e. those elements of symmetry which, if given, are sufficient to determine a whole group and all its other elements of symmetry. Numbers without lines signify ordinary axes of symmetry of corresponding multiplicity. Numbers with lines above them signify mirror axes. The letter m signifies a plane of symmetry. A point placed between symbols of elements of symmetry denotes their parallelism; a colon—perpendicularity; a slanted line—their slanted inclination to one another. The symbol of infinity signifies an infinite-fold axis.

[The columns of Table 1 have been rearranged in a somewhat more logical fashion by Shubnikov in a later publication.[175] However, its substitution here would have confused the continuity of Shubnikov's original work.

In the International notation, displayed in brackets in Table 1, numbers without overlines signify ordinary axes of symmetry of corresponding multiplicity. Numbers with overlines signify inversion axes. The letter m signifies a plane of symmetry, whose direction corresponds to its normal, and if this normal is parallel to an axis of symmetry the two symbols are separated by a slant line. The axes in various perpendicular and diagonal directions are displayed in a sequence established by convention (*International Tables for X-ray Crystallography*, vol. 1, p. 28). The symbol of infinity signifies an infinite-fold axis.]

is given in Fig. 48*a*. Redesignating a three-fold axis into a six-fold mirror axis results in an increase in the number of small triangles and leads to the distribution shown in Fig. 48*b*. From this distribution, however, it is clear that three longitudinal planes of symmetry and a center of symmetry appear in the group. Together these elements of symmetry form the previously derived group $\bar{6}:2$ [$\bar{3}$ $2/m = \bar{3}m$] (Fig. 48*c*).

It still remains for us to consider instances of redesignation of mirror axes having two axes at once—main and lateral—in groups of type $N:2$ [$N2$], and also to investigate the remaining four groups $3/2$, $3/4$, $3/5$, ∞/∞ [23, 43, 53, $\infty\infty$]. By applying the above reasoning, it is easy to be convinced that no new groups will be formed.

Types of Symmetry Groups

For a general survey of point symmetry groups it is useful to have a complete catalog of them in view, in the form of Table 1. In the lower line of Table 1 all the groups which we have called limiting are listed, that is, the groups containing infinite-fold axes. Natural series of uniform groups, with Roman numerals, are arranged in vertical columns above the limiting groups. By extending a series to infinity in increasing multiplicity of the main axis, we arrive at the corresponding limiting group. We will say that a given non-limiting group belongs to a *type* of given limiting group if this non-limiting group is in the series ending with the given limiting group. In the composite table of point groups the various types of groups are separated from each other by two vertical lines. Let us note that the first members of certain series may be attached with equal justification to different types, namely: group $m = 1 \cdot m = 1:m$ [$m = 1m = 1/m$] may be attributed with equal correctness to types $\infty:m$, $\infty \cdot m$ [∞m, ∞/m]; group $2 = 1:\bar{2}$ [$2 = 12$] may be attributed to type ∞ [∞] and to type $\infty:2$ [$\infty 2$]; group $2:m = \bar{2} \cdot m$ [$2/m = \bar{1}m$] may be attributed to type $\infty:m$ [∞/m] as well as to type $m \cdot \infty:m$ [∞/mm]; group $m \cdot 1:m = 2 \cdot m$ [$\bar{2}m2 = 2mm$]

may be attributed to type $m \cdot \infty : m$ [∞/mm] and to type $\infty \cdot m$ [∞m].

Limiting Groups

The separation of *limiting groups* into a special category is very significant. Limiting point groups can be represented by the simplest figures with infinite-fold axes, which were

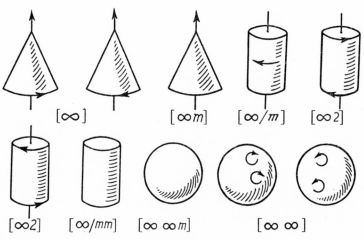

Fig. 59. Figures belonging to limiting groups.

introduced previously. It is expedient to place them together here (Fig. 59).

A diagram of sub-group-relations of limiting groups of symmetry is interesting (Table 2). It is evident from this diagram that group ∞ [∞] is *subordinate*, that is, it is the sub-group of groups $\infty \cdot m$, $\infty : 2$, $\infty : m$ [∞m, $\infty 2$, ∞/m]. These groups are subordinate in turn to group $m \cdot \infty : m$ [∞/mm], while group $\infty : 2$ [$\infty 2$] is also subordinate to group ∞/∞ [$\infty\infty$]; finally groups ∞/∞ [$\infty\infty$] and $m \cdot \infty : m$ [∞/mm] are subordinate to group $\infty/\infty \cdot m$ [$\infty\infty m$]. The latter spherical group is the highest possible point group.

TABLE 2

DIAGRAM OF SUB-GROUP-RELATIONS OF LIMITING POINT
GROUPS OF SYMMETRY

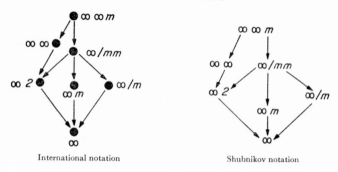

International notation   Shubnikov notation

Crystallographic Groups

By crystallographic groups are usually meant groups which contain only axes (simple and mirror) of 1-, 2-, 3-, 4-, 6-*th* order in one or another combination. Five-fold and higher than 6-fold axes are forbidden to them, since their existence in a crystal is incompatible with the representation of crystallographic lattice. The total number of crystallographic groups is equal to 32. If by crystallographic groups are meant those groups of symmetry which are used to describe various physical properties of crystals, then all limiting groups must also be placed in the forementioned crystallographic groups. The total number of crystallographic groups of symmetry in this case will be equal to 39. A complete survey of crystallographic point groups is given in Fig. 60.

THE SYMMETRY OF PLANE FIGURES

Neutral and Polar Plane Figures

Let us compare two plane figures (Fig. 61*a*, *b*). One (*a*) is a square made of cardboard whose front side is white and rear is black; the other (*b*) is also a square, but made of cardboard which is gray on both sides. Plane figures which, like figure (*a*), have differing sides are called *polar* and figures with like sides *neutral*. We shall consider the white side of the polar figure to be *positive*, the black *negative*. The sides of the neutral figure have no signs, or they simultaneously have both signs, which amounts to the same thing.

Polar and neutral figures of the same geometrical form have different symmetry. The first figure belongs to group $4 \cdot m$ [4mm], that is, it has one four-fold axis normal to the plane of the figure, and four planes of symmetry intersecting each other along axis 4 [4]. The second figure belongs to group $m \cdot 4 : m$ [4/mmm]; besides the indicated elements, it has a plane of symmetry coinciding with the plane of the figure, and a center of symmetry.

Plane Figures of Mixed Polarity

It is necessary to distinguish two kinds of neutral plane figures: figures which as a whole are neutral but consist of polar components, and figures which consist entirely of neutral components. We shall call the first figures *figures of mixed polarity* and the second *completely neutral*, or, when it will not be ambiguous, simply neutral.

Let us agree, furthermore, to depict polar plane figures or components of figures white or black, depending upon which side is turned toward the observer, and completely neutral figures in gray.

An example of a figure with mixed polarity is given in Fig. 62. As we see, it consists of four polar squares arranged as on a chess-board. It is not difficult to establish that the figure possesses $\bar{4} \cdot m$ [$\bar{4}$2m] symmetry, that is, it has one four-fold mirror axis, two longitudinal planes of symmetry, and two transverse two-fold axes.

Operations of Symmetry of Plane Figures

Plane figures may not be brought into self-coincidence by operations of rotation (except for rotation through a complete revolution) about axes which are arranged slantwise relative

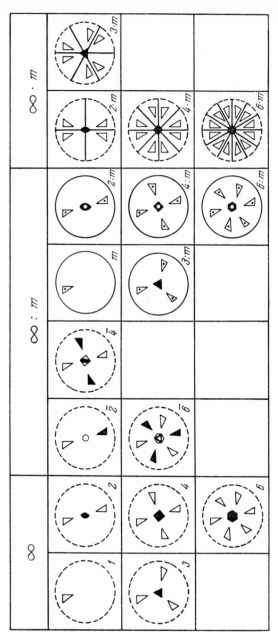

FIG. 60.

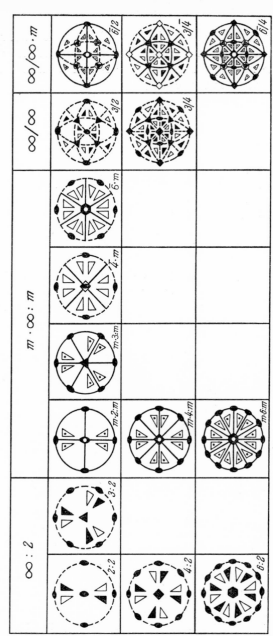

Fig. 60. Crystallographic point symmetry groups [for corresponding International symbols see Table 1].

to the plane of the figure, and also not by operations of reflection in planes of symmetry arranged slantwise relative to the plane of the figures, since the figure is derived from its own plane by all these operations.

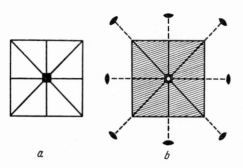

a   b

FIG. 61. Diagram to explain the concept of polar and neutral plane figures.

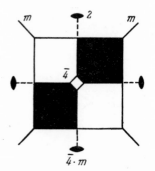

FIG. 62. An example of a plane figure of mixed polarity.

Plane figures may, consequently, be brought into self-coincidence only by the following operations of symmetry:

$+\begin{cases} \text{by operations of identification,} \\ \text{by rotations about axes normal to the plane of the} \\ \quad \text{figure,} \\ \text{by reflections in planes of symmetry normal to the} \\ \quad \text{plane of the figure.} \end{cases}$

> ⌠ by inversions,
> │ by mirror rotations about axes normal to the plane
> │   of the figure,
> — ⟨ by reflection in a plane coinciding with the plane of
> │   the figure,
> │ by 180° rotations about axes lying in the plane of
> ⌡   the figure.

All the enumerated operations of symmetry are operations of plane figures, inasmuch as they leave the plane of figures in place. Some of them, those which we marked with a plus sign, do not lead to the transformation of the front side of the figure into the rear; the others, marked with a minus sign, are accompanied by the indicated transformation. We shall call the first operations as applied to plane figures, *positive*, the second *negative*.

All the previously considered operations of symmetry of three-dimensional figures were positive, inasmuch as we have treated three-dimensional figures as polar figures, although this question was not considered previously. We shall see later how this *a priori* concept of three-dimensional figures may be dropped and replaced by a broader concept.

The expediency of dividing all operations of two-dimensional figures into the indicated two categories may be confirmed by the following considerations. We saw earlier that the order of a point group of symmetry is equal to the maximum number of equal components of the figure—those components which are transformed into each other by symmetrical operations. If we speak of positive operations of plane figures, then the equal *components* of figures will actually be transformed into each other by these operations, that is, those parts of a figure into which the plane figure may be cut by scissors, if it is made of paper or cardboard. If, however, we speak of negative operations, then the components (in the forementioned sense) will not be transformed into each other by the operations, but the *sides* of the components—or, if you like, those components obtained from splitting the cut sections into two parts along their own plane—will be so transformed (see Appendices, p. 148).

FIG. 63.

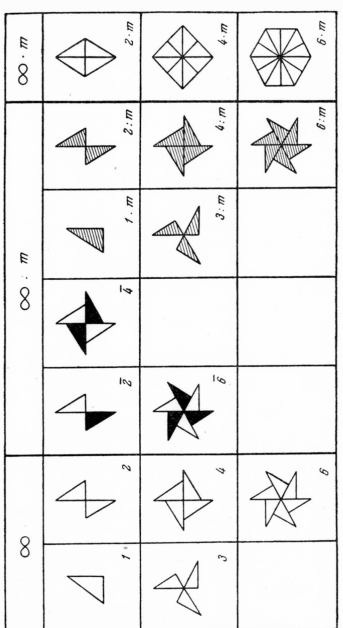

FIG. 63. Crystallographic symmetry groups of finite two-dimensional plane figures [for corresponding International symbols see Table 3].

Symmetry Groups of Finite Plane Figures

It is evident from what has been stated that these groups must be sought among the previously derived point groups. In order to compile a complete summary of them, it is necessary to select from the groups shown in Table 1 those groups whose operations all leave at least one plane in place.

It is not difficult to be convinced that all the groups of Table 1 relate to the sought-for groups, with the exception of the groups in its last two columns. The complete list of groups of symmetry of finite figures is given in Table 3.

In the same way as we used model figures, composed of equal tetrahedra, for depicting symmetry groups of three-dimensional figures, we will use figures composed of equal triangles with unequal edges for depicting symmetry groups of plane figures. For this purpose it is convenient to use neutral and polar triangles, that is, triangles which are gray on both sides, and triangles which have one white side and one black.

It is clear that the gray triangles cannot be completely asymmetrical, since they always possess a plane of symmetry coinciding with their own plane.

Figure 63 shows, by using the method just described, all the *crystallographic* plane figures, that is, those of the groups under consideration in which 5-fold and higher than 6-fold axes are absent. The total number of such groups is equal to 31.

It is essential to note the following. If the three-dimensional figures of groups 2 [2] and $1:2$ [12], $1:m$ [2] and $1 \cdot m$ [1m], $2:m$ [2/m] and $\bar{2} \cdot m$ [$\bar{1}m$], $2 \cdot m$ [2mm] and $m \cdot 1:m$ [$\bar{2}m2$] have been definitely considered equivalent groups, then those same groups for plane figures must be treated as different groups, inasmuch as all the operations of the one are positive, while among the operations of the other there are also negative ones. It is clear that the number of plane crystallographic groups must be decreased from 31 to 27 if this difference in groups is disregarded. Plane crystallographic groups are groups of "dimetric" crystals.

TABLE 3

SYMMETRY GROUPS OF FINITE PLANE FIGURES

∞ [∞]		∞:m [∞/m]				∞·m [∞m]		∞:2 [∞2]		m·∞:m [∞/mm]			
1 [1]	2 [2]	$\bar{4}$ [$\bar{4}$]	$\bar{2}$ [$\bar{1}$]	$1:m$ [$\bar{2}$]	$2:m$ [$2/m$]	$1\cdot m$ [$1m$]	$2\cdot m$ [$2mm$]	$1:2$ [12]	$2:2$ [222]	$\bar{2}\cdot m$ [$\bar{1}m$]	$\bar{4}\cdot m$ [$\bar{4}2m$]	$m\cdot 1:m$ [$\bar{2}m2$]	$m\cdot 2:m$ [$2/mmm$]
3 [3]	4 [4]	$\bar{8}$ [$\bar{8}$]	$\bar{6}$ [$\bar{3}$]	$3:m$ [$\bar{6}$]	$4:m$ [$4/m$]	$3\cdot m$ [$3m$]	$4\cdot m$ [$4mm$]	$3:2$ [32]	$4:2$ [422]	$\bar{6}\cdot m$ [$\bar{3}m$]	$\bar{8}\cdot m$ [$\bar{8}2m$]	$m\cdot 3:m$ [$\bar{6}m2$]	$m\cdot 4:m$ [$4/mmm$]
5 [5]	6 [6]	$\overline{12}$ [$\overline{12}$]	$\overline{10}$ [$\bar{5}$]	$5:m$ [$\overline{10}$]	$6:m$ [$6/m$]	$5\cdot m$ [$5m$]	$6\cdot m$ [$6mm$]	$5:2$ [52]	$6:2$ [622]	$\overline{10}\cdot m$ [$\bar{5}m$]	$\overline{12}\cdot m$ [$\overline{12}2m$]	$m\cdot 5:m$ [$\overline{10}m2$]	$m\cdot 6:m$ [$6/mmm$]
·	·	·	·	·	·	·	·	·	·	·	·	·	·

Symmetry Groups of Finite Polar Plane Figures

In the table of plane groups in Fig. 63, we see figures of three sorts; white (they are black, however, if they are looked at on the reverse side), gray, and two-colored. For each white

TABLE 4

SYMMETRY GROUPS OF FINITE POLAR PLANE FIGURES

∞ [∞]		$\infty \cdot m$ [∞m]	
1	*2*	$2 \cdot m$	$1 \cdot m$
[1]	[2]	[2mm]	[1m]
3	*4*	$4 \cdot m$	$3 \cdot m$
[3]	[4]	[4mm]	[3m]
5	*6*	$6 \cdot m$	$5 \cdot m$
[5]	[6]	[6mm]	[5m]
.	.	.	.
.	.	.	.
.	.	.	.

TABLE 5

SYMMETRY GROUPS OF FINITE NEUTRAL PLANE FIGURES

$\infty : m$ [∞/m]				$\infty : 2$ [$\infty 2$]		$m \cdot \infty : m$ [∞/mm]			
$\overline{2}$	$\overline{4}$	$1:m$	$2:m$	$2:2$	$1:2$	$m \cdot 2:m$	$m \cdot 1:m$	$\overline{4} \cdot m$	$\overline{2} \cdot m$
[$\overline{1}$]	[$\overline{4}$]	[$\overline{2}$]	[2/m]	[222]	[12]	[2/mmm]	[$\overline{2}m2$]	[$\overline{4}2m$]	[$\overline{1}m$]
$\overline{6}$	$\overline{8}$	$3:m$	$4:m$	$4:2$	$3:2$	$m \cdot 4:m$	$m \cdot 3:m$	$\overline{8} \cdot m$	$6 \cdot m$
[$\overline{3}$]	[$\overline{8}$]	[$\overline{6}$]	[4/m]	[422]	[32]	[4/mmm]	[$\overline{6}m2$]	[$\overline{8}2m$]	[$\overline{3}m$]
$\overline{10}$	$\overline{12}$	$5:m$	$6:m$	$6:2$	$5:2$	$m \cdot 6:m$	$m \cdot 5:m$	$\overline{12} \cdot m$	$10 \cdot m$
[$\overline{5}$]	[$\overline{12}$]	[$\overline{10}$]	[6/m]	[622]	[52]	[6/mmm]	[$\overline{10}m2$]	[$\overline{12}.2m$]	[$\overline{5}m$]
.	.	.	.	.	.	.	.	.	.
.	.	.	.	.	.	.	.	.	.
.	.	.	.	.	.	.	.	.	.

figure there is one of the same kind in gray. If it is a question only of crystallographic figures, then the number of white figures (10) equals the number of gray ones. The number of two-colored figures equals 11. The white figures are brought into self-coincidence only by positive operations. The groups depicted by gray figures must include reflections in the figures' own plane, and may also have other negative operations. Groups depicted by two-colored figures do not include negative reflections, but they have other negative operations.

By separating only the "white groups", we will derive a complete list of symmetry groups of finite polar plane figures (Table 4). The remaining groups are listed among symmetry groups of neutral plane figures (Table 5).

Polar crystallographic groups are symmetry groups of crystalline faces.

Antisymmetry of Finite Figures

BASIC CONCEPTS AND DEFINITIONS IN ANTISYMMETRY

The Representation of Symmetrical Operations of Three-dimensional Figures by Matrices of Cosines

LET the three-dimensional symmetrical figures we are considering be referred to a rectilinear system of coordinates whose origin coincides with the singular point of the figure. If we change the old rectilinear system X_1, X_2, X_3 to the new rectilinear system X_1', X_2', X_3', leaving the origin in place, then the transformation may be precisely determined by the angles between the old and new axes. As a rule, the cosines of the angles are given instead of the angles themselves; the cosines are designated by the letter c with two indexes, where the first index is the number of the old axis, and the second index is the number of the new axis.

For example:

$$c_{13} = \cos (X_1 X_3'); \quad c_{23} = \cos (X_2 X_3'); \quad c_{22} = \cos (X_2 X_2').$$

The angles between the axes are understood to mean the angles formed by the positive ends of the axes. The angles between the axes may have any value from 0 to 180°. Under these conditions the cosine of an angle definitely determines the angle, whereas, for example, one sine corresponds to two angles. That is why systems of coordinates use cosines in particular to describe transformations.

Since every old axis forms one angle with every new axis, the total number of cosines is equal to nine. They are usually recorded in a table (matrix) in this fashion:

$$
\begin{matrix}
c_{11} & c_{12} & c_{13} \\
c_{21} & c_{22} & c_{23} \\
c_{31} & c_{32} & c_{33}
\end{matrix}
\tag{1}
$$

In this case the first index of the cosines is the number of the line and the second index is the number of the column of the matrix.

Of the nine cosines only three are completely independent, since the following two groups of relationships always exist between the cosines*.

1. If we take any given line or column of a matrix, the sum of the squares of the cosines separated by this means will equal one. For example:

$$c_{11}^2 + c_{21}^2 + c_{31}^2 = 1 \text{ (separating the first column)}$$
$$c_{21}^2 + c_{22}^2 + c_{23}^2 = 1 \text{ (separating the second line)} \tag{2}$$

2. If any given pair of lines or columns is separated, the sum of the products of similarly arranged cosines will equal zero. For example:

$$c_{11}c_{12} + c_{21}c_{22} + c_{31}c_{32} = 0 \text{ (separating the first two columns)} \tag{3}$$
$$c_{11}c_{31} + c_{12}c_{32} + c_{12}c_{33} = 0 \text{ (separating the first and third lines)}$$

Let us recall that a system is called *right* when the right hand of a person corresponds to the positive end of axis X_1, the left hand to the positive end of X_2, and the head to the positive

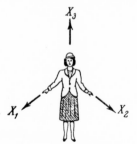

FIG. 64. Right system of coordinates.

end of axis X_3 (Fig. 64). The *left* system is a mirror image of the right. In order to derive the left system, it is sufficient to exchange the places of axes X_1 and X_2 in the right system.

* N. E. Kochin. *Vector computation and the principles of tensor computation,* p. 30, ONTI, Moscow, 1937.

Matrices of cosines are used to describe not only all transitions from one right system to another right and from left to left, but also all transitions from right to left and from left to right. It is known that transitions to similar systems of coordinates are equivalent to rotations, whereas transitions to mirror systems are generally equivalent to mirror rotations, and in particular cases may be equivalent to simple reflection in a plane or inversion.

We have assumed that a system of coordinates, in changing its position, leaves the figure in place. Since only the relative change of the position of the figure and the system of coordinates is important to us, then the same system of cosines may be used to describe all rotations and all mirror rotations of a figure in relation to a fixed system of coordinates. Inasmuch as all symmetrical operations of closed figures are carried out by rotations and mirror rotations, all symmetrical operations of closed figures may be described by the forementioned matrices.

Let us introduce several examples.

Let us suppose that the plane X_1X_2 is the plane of symmetry of a figure; then reflection in this plane will be a symmetrical operation. It is easy to verify that it may be represented by the matrix:

$$\begin{pmatrix} 1 & 0 & 0 \\ 0 & 1 & 0 \\ 0 & 0 & -1 \end{pmatrix} \tag{4}$$

Actually, after the reflection of the figure in plane X_1X_2, axes X_1 and X_2 remain fixed, while axis X_3 reverses its direction; therefore cosines c_{11}, c_{22} as cosines of angles equal to $0°$, will equal unity, while cosine c_{33}, as the cosine of a $180°$ angle, will equal minus one. The remaining cosines of $90°$ angles must equal zero.

If axis X_3 is a two-fold axis, then the operation of a $180°$ rotation about this axis is represented by the matrix:

$$\begin{pmatrix} -1 & 0 & 0 \\ 0 & -1 & 0 \\ 0 & 0 & 1 \end{pmatrix} \tag{5}$$

If the origin of the coordinates is the center of symmetry, the operation of inversion is represented by the matrix:

$$\begin{pmatrix} -1 & 0 & 0 \\ 0 & -1 & 0 \\ 0 & 0 & -1 \end{pmatrix} \qquad (6)$$

The operation of identification is expressed by the *unit matrix*

$$\begin{pmatrix} 1 & 0 & 0 \\ 0 & 1 & 0 \\ 0 & 0 & 1 \end{pmatrix} \qquad (7)$$

consequently this operation itself is often called a unit operation (see p. 13).

Let us consider a more complex case. Let axis X_3 be an axis with an angle of rotation α. We will find the general form of the corresponding matrix of cosines. Let us consider Fig. 65, in which two systems of coordinates are shown; the

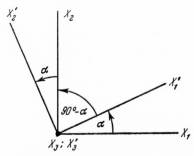

FIG. 65. Diagram for the derivation of matrix (8).

old and the new, where axes X_3, X_3' are arranged normal to the plane of the diagram. It is easy to see from the diagram that in the given case, the following relationships exist:

$$\begin{aligned}
c_{11} &= c_{22} = \cos \alpha, \\
c_{33} &= 1, \\
c_{21} &= \cos (90° - \alpha) = \sin \alpha, \\
c_{12} &= \cos (90° + \alpha) = -\sin \alpha, \\
c_{31} &= c_{32} = c_{13} = c_{23} = 0.
\end{aligned}$$

Having inserted values obtained for the cosines in their place in the matrix, we will obtain it in the form

$$\begin{pmatrix} \cos \alpha & -\sin \alpha & 0 \\ \sin \alpha & \cos \alpha & 0 \\ 0 & 0 & 1 \end{pmatrix} \tag{8}$$

If axis X_3 is a mirror axis with an angle of rotation α, then the corresponding matrix

$$\begin{pmatrix} \cos \alpha & -\sin \alpha & 0 \\ \sin \alpha & \cos \alpha & 0 \\ 0 & 0 & -1 \end{pmatrix} \tag{9}$$

differs from the preceding only by sign of the 1 inasmuch as rotation through angle α is accompanied by reflection in a plane normal to axis X_3, in the given case.

Let us note that the components of our matrices are always cosines of definite angles, although, as in the cases just considered, some of the cosines may be numerically equal to sines.

Symmetrical Operations of Three-dimensional Figures as Afine Orthogonal Transformations

It was previously stated that symmetrical operations may be viewed as transformations which correspond to the translation from one rectilinear rectangular system of coordinates to another of the same kind. During these transformations the coordinates x_1, x_2, x_3 of any given point of a figure are transferred to coordinates x_1', x_2', x_3' according to the following formulae, derived in analytical geometry:

$$\begin{aligned} x &= c_{11}x_1' + c_{12}x_2' + c_{13}x_3', \\ x_2 &= c_{21}x_1' + c_{22}x_2' + c_{23}x_3', \\ x_3 &= c_{31}x_1' + c_{32}x_2' + c_{33}x_3'. \end{aligned} \tag{10}$$

Such transformations are called afine (linear) orthogonal (rectangular). As we see, our previously accepted representation of symmetrical operations by cosine matrices does not differ essentially from representation of them by the equations just introduced, inasmuch as the matrix is only an abbreviated

form for recording these equations. Every symmetrical operation may be expressed by three such equations, and one operation will differ from another only by the values of the
coefficients of c_{ik}.

Symmetrical Operations of Plane Figures in Two-dimensional and Three-dimensional Space

In considering operations of symmetry of plane figures, we
have not specifically posed the question as to whether these
operations are performed in two-dimensional, three-dimensional,
and still higher dimensional space. Even if such a question
had been posed earlier, its solution might have met with
some difficulties inasmuch as we had agreed to characterize
operations by their *result*, and not by which means and in
which space they are performed. And although we could not
avoid paying attention to the fact that, for example, the
rotation of a plane figure about a two-fold axis lying in the
plane of the figure of course takes the figure out of its plane,
nevertheless in the end the plane of the figure remains in place.
Since it is impossible to judge by the final result how the
operation was actually performed, it did not seem possible
to establish whether it was an operation in two-dimensional
or three-dimensional space. Now that it is clear to us that
symmetrical operations may be considered as afine orthogonal transformations, the question posed may be completely
resolved and moreover, not only for plane, but also for three-
dimensional figures.

Since afine orthogonal transformations in two-dimensional
space are expressed by the two formulae.

$$x_1 = c_{11}x_1' + c_{12}x_2',$$
$$x_2 = c_{21}x_1' + c_{22}x_2',$$ (11)

all symmetrical operations in two-dimensional space may be
expressed by matrices of the form

$$\begin{pmatrix} c_{11} & c_{12} \\ c_{21} & c_{22} \end{pmatrix}$$ (12)

It is easy to demonstrate and it is indeed clear from the very outset that all operations of transformation of coordinates of plane figures in which the position of the coordinates' origin is retained, generally lead to rotations of the system of co-ordinates through a certain angle α about the origin, and to reflections in a certain straight line m passing through the origin (Fig. 66).

From this it is evident that only those operations which we termed positive may refer to operations of plane figures in

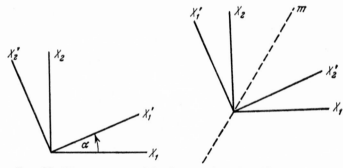

FIG. 66. Diagrams to explain the meaning of positive operations of plane figures.

two-dimensional space. As far as negative operations are concerned, we see that they are operations in three-dimensional space.

In order to proceed further it is necessary to account for the fact that every operation performed in two-dimensional space may be viewed as an operation in three-dimensional space. One does not contradict the other. However, not every operation in three-dimensional space may be viewed as an operation in two-dimensional space.

In order to relate all operations of plane figures to operations in three-dimensional space, it is necessary to express them by matrices of nine components. This may be achieved by the following method. Let us agree to consider axes X_1, X_2 to be set in the plane of a figure, and axis X_3 to be perpendicular to the plane. It is clear that under these conditions all positive operations of plane figures will leave axis X_3 in an unchanged position, and all negative operations will lead only to the change of the positive direction of axis X_3 to the directly opposite negative one. The angles between each of the first two old axes and the third new one and, conversely, between the third old one and each of the two new axes, will remain right angles, while the angle between the old third axis and the new third axis may have only two values: 0° and 180°. In brief, for all operations of two-dimensional figures the equations

$$c_{13} = c_{23} = c_{31} = c_{32} = 0$$

must be observed; moreover, for positive operations,

$$c_{33} = +1$$

and for negative operations,

$$c_{33} = -1$$

In other words, all the operations in which we are interested must be encompassed by the matrix

$$\begin{pmatrix} c_{11} & c_{12} & 0 \\ c_{21} & c_{22} & 0 \\ 0 & 0 & \pm 1 \end{pmatrix} \tag{13}$$

After what has been stated, the terms "positive" and "negative" become understandable as applied to operations of two-dimensional figures. Those operations are positive which do not change the sign of the third, zero, coordinate of the points of the figure, and are described by the coefficient $c_{33} = +1$. Those operations are negative which do alter this sign, and are described by the coefficient $c_{33} = -1$. We should not be surprised that the null coordinate, zero, emerges in two *different* aspects: $x_3 = +0$ and $x_3 = -0$. One may find any number of precedents for this in mathematics; for example, the quantity $\tan\left(\dfrac{\pi}{2} + x\right)$ takes on the value $+\infty$ where $x = -0$, and $-\infty$ where $x = +0$, since when we approach 0 from the positive direction we meet it as the value $+0$, while approaching it from the negative direction we take it as -0.

Operations of Antisymmetry in Three-dimensional Figures

From what has been previously stated, the following conclusions naturally emerge. If positive and negative operations may exist for two-dimensional figures, and if these and other operations may formally be considered as specialized operations in three-dimensional space, then positive and negative operations must also exist for three-dimensional figures, whereupon they may also be formally considered as operations in a higher dimension, in four-dimensional space.

Actually, by analogy with operations of symmetry in two-dimensional and three-dimensional space, it may be assumed that all operations of symmetry in four-dimensional space, may be expressed by matrices of the form

$$\begin{pmatrix} c_{11} & c_{12} & c_{13} & c_{14} \\ c_{21} & c_{22} & c_{23} & c_{24} \\ c_{31} & c_{32} & c_{33} & c_{34} \\ c_{41} & c_{42} & c_{43} & c_{44} \end{pmatrix} \tag{14}$$

where the values c_{ik} are "cosines" of the angles between the old and new axes in the sense that relationships (2) and (3) are also valid for those values, which may be briefly written:

$$\sum_{k=1}^{3} c_{ik}^2 = \sum_{k=1}^{3} c_{ki}^2 = 1, \tag{15}$$

$$\sum_{k=1}^{3} c_{ki} c_{kl} = \sum_{k=1}^{3} c_{ik} c_{lk} = 0. \tag{16}$$

Having assumed this, one may demonstrate without difficulty that all previously considered operations of symmetry of three-dimensional figures in three-dimensional space become part of the *positive* operations in four-dimensional space; that is, operations of the form

$$\begin{pmatrix} c_{11} & c_{12} & c_{13} & 0 \\ c_{21} & c_{22} & c_{23} & 0 \\ c_{31} & c_{32} & c_{33} & 0 \\ 0 & 0 & 0 & +1 \end{pmatrix} \tag{17}$$

This is evident from the fact that the afine orthogonal transformations (9) in three-dimensional space, which describe all previously considered operations of symmetry of three-dimensional figures, do not differ from the transformations

$$
\begin{aligned}
x_1 &= c_{11}x_1' + c_{12}x_2' + c_{13}x_3' + c_{14} \cdot 0, \\
x_2 &= c_{21}x_1' + c_{22}x_2' + c_{23}x_3' + c_{24} \cdot 0, \\
x_3 &= c_{31}x_1' + c_{32}x_2' + c_{33}x_3' + c_{34} \cdot 0, \\
x_4 &= c_{41} \cdot 0 + c_{42} \cdot 0 + c_{43} \cdot 0 + 1 \cdot 0.
\end{aligned} \tag{18}
$$

But just as in the case where in order to describe the symmetry of neutral plane figures, which undoubtedly exist, we were obliged to introduce negative operations, so for the description of symmetry of *neutral three-dimensional figures* we must introduce negative operations of the form

$$
\begin{pmatrix}
c_{11} & c_{12} & c_{13} & 0 \\
c_{21} & c_{22} & c_{23} & 0 \\
c_{31} & c_{32} & c_{33} & 0 \\
0 & 0 & 0 & -1
\end{pmatrix} \tag{19}
$$

What these still unknown polar and neutral three-dimensional figures and new operations are, which we shall call *operations of antisymmetry*, and what *antisymmetry* itself is, we shall learn from the following paragraphs which will be devoted to the explanation of these and certain other new concepts.

Reverse Equality or Anti-equality of Figures

Let us compare the four figures shown in Fig. 67 with each other. Each of them is an oblique hollow tetrahedron made

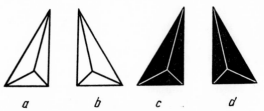

a b c d

FIG. 67. Four equal asymmetrical tetrahedra.

according to the same pattern (Fig. 68) from the same material —cardboard, colored white on one side and black on the other.

The white figures *a*, *b* (rather, those which appear white) have, consequently, a black back side; the black figures *c*, *d* have a white back side. In classical symmetry, the white figures are not considered equal to the black ones. Adopting a broader view of symmetry, we shall consider all four figures equal to one another and, correspondingly, we shall distinguish not

FIG. 68. Pattern for making the tetrahedra shown in Fig. 67.

two, as before, but four kinds of congruence of three-dimensional figures: (1) *congruent equality*, (2) *mirror equality*, (3) *congruent anti-equality*, and (4) *mirror anti-equality*. By anti-equality or *reverse equality* we shall mean the equality between the black and the white figures. Thus, figures *a*, *b* are mirror-equal to each other, figures *a*, *c* congruently anti-equal to each other, figures *a*, *d* mirror anti-equal to each other, and two figures of *a* are congruently equal to each other.

Polar and Neutral Figures

All the four figures just considered are *polar* figures, differing according to sign. Let us agree to consider the white figures *positive*, the black *negative*.

Once polar figures exist, *neutral figures* must also exist. By neutral figures we shall mean figures with equal sides. Hollow tetrahedra made from cardboard with both sides the same color may serve as examples of neutral figures. Let us agree to depict figures or components of figures in gray, if their sides are the same color (Fig. 69).

Neutral figures of two types must be distinguished: *completely neutral figures, and figures of mixed polarity;* that is, figures, neutral as a whole, but consisting of polar components. The gray tetrahedra just mentioned may serve as examples of completely neutral figures. An octahedron with four white and four black faces may serve as an example of a figure of mixed polarity (Fig. 70).

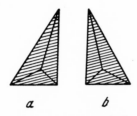

a   *b*

FIG. 69. Neutral tetrahedra.

FIG. 70. Example of a three-dimensional figure of mixed polarity.

Neutral figures have no sign, or, to put it differently, they have two signs at the same time. It is appropriate to imagine the gray figures as two anti-equal figures *enclosed* in each other, and the figure of mixed polarity as two anti-equal figures *joined* into one figure.

The Asymmetrical Figure

By an asymmetrical figure we previously meant a figure which could not be divided into equal components that could be transformed into one another by symmetrical operations. The polar tetrahedra shown in Fig. 67 satisfy this condition, whether we examine them by the classical or the new, broader concepts of symmetry. All four polar tetrahedra are, consequently, asymmetrical figures, which can be brought into self-coincidence by only one single operation of symmetry—identification.

The case is somewhat different with respect to the neutral tetrahedra depicted in Fig. 69. Just as in classical symmetry the neutral oblique-angled triangle cannot be asymmetrical owing to the presence of a plane of symmetry in it, in the expanded view of symmetry the neutral tetrahedron consisting of two anti-equal polar tetrahedra also cannot be an asymmetrical figure owing to the presence of a certain new element of symmetry in it. We shall learn later what this new element of symmetry is.

Operation of the Change of Sign of a Figure

By the operation of the change of sign of a figure we mean the operation transforming any given figure into a coincident anti-equal figure: for example, figure *a* into figure *c* or figure *d* into figure *b* (Fig. 67). It follows from this definition that the operation of change of sign of a figure may be clearly considered as an operation of "repainting" the white side of the figure black and the black side white.

It is essential from the very outset to account for the fact that the operation of change of sign of a figure only becomes an operation of symmetry when it, in conformance to the previously adopted definition of a symmetrical operation, brings a figure into self-coincidence. It is therefore evident that the examples just introduced of the transformation of a white tetrahedron to a black one and a black one to a white one are not examples of symmetrical operations.

It is a somewhat different matter if a neutral tetrahedron is taken for the original figure. As has already been mentioned, a neutral tetrahedron has both signs at the same time (such as ± 0), therefore the change of sign of the figure cannot produce any alterations in it: the figure must be transformed into itself by this operation. Having designated the exterior of the neutral tetrahedron (or one of the polar tetrahedra forming the given neutral tetrahedron) by the letter A, and the interior (or other polar tetrahedron) by the letter B, we may represent the operation of a change of sign, in conformity with the previously adopted system of designation, by the symbol B. As always, the operation of identification A will be another symmetrical operation.

Thus the entire group of symmetrical operations of the neutral tetrahedron under consideration consists of two operations, and is therefore a second-order group. Under these conditions the figure itself, however, must be considered clearly symmetrical, not asymmetrical.

We shall call all negative operations of three-dimensional figures *antioperations of symmetry* or *operations of antisymmetry* and designate them by the symbol of the corresponding positive operation with a line underneath*. The operation of a change of sign, which may be considered as *anti-identification*, must consequently be designated by the symbol $\underline{1}$ [1'].

The matrix designation of this operation takes the form

$$\begin{pmatrix} 1 & 0 & 0 & 0 \\ 0 & 1 & 0 & 0 \\ 0 & 0 & 1 & 0 \\ 0 & 0 & 0 & -1 \end{pmatrix} \tag{20}$$

and is distinguished from the matrix designation of identification

$$\begin{pmatrix} 1 & 0 & 0 & 0 \\ 0 & 1 & 0 & 0 \\ 0 & 0 & 1 & 0 \\ 0 & 0 & 0 & 1 \end{pmatrix} \tag{21}$$

only by the sign of the 1 in the lower right corner of the matrix.

Correspondingly, the operation of anti-identification may be formally considered as reflection in a plane normal to the fourth coordinate axis X_4,—a reflection during which the fourth coordinate of each point of the three-dimensional figure remains equal to zero and changes its sign. We have already become acquainted with operations of the change of sign of a zero (p. 95), during the consideration of symmetry of plane figures.

---

* [Designated by a prime in the bracketed International symbols—see Preface.]

At first glance it seems paradoxical that the operation of anti-identification, being reflection in some imaginary plane, leads to a completely different result than does the commonly known reflection of any given figure in a mirror. Actually, if we place any given white right figure before a mirror, we will see a left figure of the same color in the mirror. This means that reflection in a plane transforms a given figure into a figure enantiomorphic to it, without changing its sign. The operation of anti-identification, conversely, changes only the

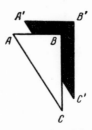

Fig. 71. Reflection in a plane placed behind the white triangle transforms it into a black triangle.

color of the figure and does not transform it into an enantio-morphic figure. Where, then, is the analogy between these two operations?

It is not difficult to discover this analogy, if both operations are compared under corresponding conditions. Let us take the white triangle *ABC* (Fig. 71). Let the reader be so placed that he is compelled to observe this triangle from only one side, and therefore does not know what color this triangle is on the reverse side. The triangle appears white to such an observer. Furthermore, he may conventionally call it right, if only because rotation of its apexes *A*, *B*, *C*, corresponds to the rotation of the hands of a clock and distinguishes it from a left triangle with an opposite arrangement of the correspond-ing apices. Let us now assume that after having placed a mirror behind the triangle, we see the black triangle *A'B'C'* in it. How should this phenomenon be described? The reader, deprived of the opportunity to observe the reverse side of the triangle *ABC* directly, has a right to describe the reflection in the mirror as the transformation of a right white triangle into a right black one; that is, as the operation of anti-identification. The observer who is informed that the reverse side of triangle *ABC* is black will say that the reflection in the mirror transforms the triangle *ABC*, which from the white side appears to be right, into the enantiomorphic triangle *A'B'C'*; that is, into the triangle which from the white side appears to be left. Obviously, both descriptions of the phenomenon are correct, but the first is made from the point of view of an imaginary two-dimensional observer, and the second from the point of view of a more informed three-dimensional observer.

As we see, there is no contradiction in what we know about reflection of three-dimensional figures in one of the planes of three-dimensional space, and in how we obtain reflection of a three-dimensional figure in the imaginary plane of four-dimensional space. But if we are more inclined to consider the reflection of plane figures in a mirror parallel to them as the transformation of a given figure into an enantiomorph without a change in sign, because this point of view is more natural to three-dimensional beings, which we ourselves are, then for the same reason we are more inclined to consider reflection of a three-dimensional figure in an imaginary plane normal to the fourth axis X_4 as the change of sign of a figure without its simultaneous transformation into an enantiomorphic form.

In conclusion let us again note what we said in connection with operations of symmetry of plane figures in three-dimensional space. Although we utilized concepts of operations in four-dimensional space for the thorough investigation of anti-identification, these concepts are not compulsory, inasmuch as every symmetrical transformation is characterized not by the means and the place by which it is accomplished, but by the result to which it leads. The result of an operation of anti-identification, however, is a change of sign of a figure, which is easy to interpret directly as the repainting of both sides of a figure in opposite colors, which may be accomplished without special excursions into four-dimensional space.

Operations of Antireflection in a Plane

Ordinary (positive) reflection in a plane normal to axis X_3 may, as we already know (4), be represented by the matrix:

$$\begin{pmatrix} 1 & 0 & 0 \\ 0 & 1 & 0 \\ 0 & 0 & -1 \end{pmatrix}$$

or, by using four-dimensional symbolism, by the matrix:

$$\begin{pmatrix} 1 & 0 & 0 & 0 \\ 0 & 1 & 0 & 0 \\ 0 & 0 & -1 & 0 \\ 0 & 0 & 0 & 1 \end{pmatrix}$$

The corresponding negative operation of *antireflection* must therefore be represented by the matrix

$$\begin{pmatrix} 1 & 0 & 0 & 0 \\ 0 & 1 & 0 & 0 \\ 0 & 0 & -1 & 0 \\ 0 & 0 & 0 & -1 \end{pmatrix} \tag{22}$$

This operation may be considered as the product of reflection in plane X_3 and the change of sign of the figure. Since we earlier depicted simple reflection (in a plane) by the symbol of a 1 with a line above it, and we agreed to depict an additional

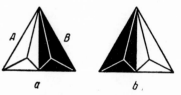

FIG. 72. Enantiomorphic figures with one antiplane of symmetry.

operation of a change of sign by a 1 with a line under it, then the symbol of antireflection will be $\underline{\bar{1}}$ [$\bar{2}'$].

Examples of figures for which antireflection is a symmetrical operation are shown in Fig. 72. Figure *a* consists of two tetrahedra: positive tetrahedron A and negative tetrahedron B. Reflection in a vertical plane transfers A to B and, conversely, B to A without changing the color of the transformed tetrahedra. Consequently, after reflection, the figure as a whole does not come to the original position; that is, one reflection is not a symmetrical operation. In order to transfer the figure to the original position, it is necessary either: (1) to repeat this operation a second time, or (2) change the signs of A and B after the first reflection or change the sign of the figure as a whole, which is the same thing. In the first instance, the twice-repeated operation yields identification. In the second instance, the product of the operation of reflection and the operation of change of sign yields antireflection, in which we are interested. As a whole, the group of symmetry of the figure under consideration consists of two operations: the operation of identification A and the operation of antireflection B. The latter operation transforms the white tetrahedron A into the black tetrahedron B, and simultaneously, black tetrahedron B into white tetrahedron A, while the whole figure AB is transformed into itself.

It is essential to note that figure a has the enantiomorphic modification b. Figure a is transformed into figure b by mirror reflection. In this there is an essential difference between figures a, b having one *antiplane* of symmetry and the corresponding figure (Fig. 1) with one plane of symmetry, which has no enantiomorphic modifications.

The comparison of figures with one plane of symmetry and figures having one antiplane of symmetry, has, in our opinion, very great importance in the understanding of the fundamental principles of the study of symmetry. There is scarcely any doubt that the classical study of symmetry arose from the observation and investigation of forms with one plane of symmetry, which are widely distributed in nature. At the same time an important role, apparently, was played by the fact that in these forms two unique opposite characteristics of figures are quite graphically and instructively combined: their right-handedness and left-handedness. In figures with one antiplane of symmetry, this combination of alternatives is raised to the next degree, inasmuch as in these figures there

are combined in a singular fashion not only the right-handedness and left-handedness of the components of the figure, but
also their "face" and "wrong side". There is no need for us
to conceal from the reader that this very fact played a basic
role in our treatment of symmetry.

The Operation of 180° Antirotation

The operation of *180° antirotation*, which may also be called
antirevolution, represents a 180° rotation about a given axis

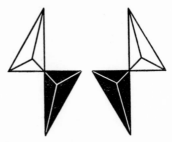

FIG. 73. Enantiomorphic figures with one two-fold antiaxis
placed perpendicularly to the plane of the diagram.

accompanied by a change of sign of the figure. If antirotation
is performed about axis X_1, the corresponding matrix takes
the form

$$\begin{pmatrix} 1 & 0 & 0 & 0 \\ 0 & -1 & 0 & 0 \\ 0 & 0 & -1 & 0 \\ 0 & 0 & 0 & -1 \end{pmatrix} \quad (23)$$

If anti-rotation is performed about axis X_3, the matrix takes
the form

$$\begin{pmatrix} -1 & 0 & 0 & 0 \\ 0 & -1 & 0 & 0 \\ 0 & 0 & 1 & 0 \\ 0 & 0 & 0 & -1 \end{pmatrix} \quad (24)$$

Figures for which the forementioned operation is an operation of symmetry are shown in Fig. 73. It is easy to see from

the diagram that each of the figures depicted in it coincides with itself after a 180° rotation about an axis normal to the plane of the diagram, and a subsequent change of sign of the figure. Figures which, like those under consideration, have one two-fold antiaxis, exist in two enantiomorphic forms and are transformed into one another by simple reflection in a plane. Another variant of figures with one two-fold antiaxis is given in Fig. 74. The indicated axis in these figures is

FIG. 74.   Enantiomorphic figures with one two-fold antiaxis located in the plane of the diagram.

located in the plane of the diagram. Let us agree to designate the operation under consideration by the symbol 2 [2'].

The Operation of Anti-inversion

Negative inversion, or *anti-inversion* $\bar{2}$ [$\bar{1}'$], is equivalent in its result to the product of inversion and change of sign of a figure. Anti-inversion is described by the matrix

$$\begin{pmatrix} -1 & 0 & 0 & 0 \\ 0 & -1 & 0 & 0 \\ 0 & 0 & -1 & 0 \\ 0 & 0 & 0 & -1 \end{pmatrix} \qquad (25)$$

with four negative *1*'s on the main diagonal of the matrix. In Fig. 75 are shown examples of figures for which anti-inversion is a symmetrical transformation and a *center of antisymmetry* (anti-inversion) is the only element of symmetry, It is evident from the diagram that figures of this kind may be encountered in two enantiomorphic forms.

The General Case of Antirotation

It is necessary to distinguish between two varieties of anti-rotation in its general occurrence: antirotation through angles equal to odd and to even parts of a circle. Let us consider, for example, the operation of antirotation through an angle

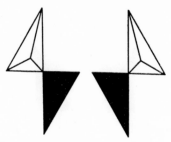

FIG. 75. Enantiomorphic figures with an anticenter of symmetry.

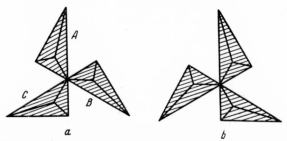

FIG. 76. Neutral enantiomorphic figures with a three-fold antiaxis.

equal to 1/3 of a revolution. This operation $\underline{3}$ [3′] transforms *white* tetrahedron *A* into black tetrahedron *B* (Fig. 76). Having repeated this operation, we transfer this black tetrahedron *B* to the white tetrahedron *C*. Having repeated the operation a third time, we transfer this white tetrahedron *C* to the black tetrahedron *A*. The final result is that tetrahedron *A* must simultaneously be both black and white. This means that all the components *A*, *B*, *C* of the figure may only be neutral, or gray. The result obtained may be generalized to include all figures having one odd-numbered axis of antirotation. It is evident from the diagram that these figures may exist in two enantiomorphic forms.

In case of an even-numbered axis, figures result which consist of an equal number of positive (white) and negative (black) components. An example of figures having one four-fold

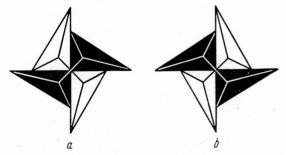

FIG. 77. Enantiomorphic figures with a four-fold antiaxis.

antiaxis $\underline{4}$ [4'] is shown in Fig. 77. All the figures of this kind may exist in two enantiomorphic forms.

The matrix of antirotation about axis X_3 takes the general form

$$\begin{pmatrix} \cos\alpha & -\sin\alpha & 0 & 0 \\ \sin\alpha & \cos\alpha & 0 & 0 \\ 0 & 0 & 1 & 0 \\ 0 & 0 & 0 & -1 \end{pmatrix} \qquad (26)$$

The General Case of Mirror Antirotation

In the given instance, one must again distinguish two variations of this operation: mirror antirotation about even-numbered and about odd-numbered axes. An example of figures having one three-fold mirror antiaxis $\underline{3}$ [6̄'] is shown in Fig. 78. The figure exists in two enantiomorphic modifications a, b. Figure a consists of three white left tetrahedra located on the plane of the diagram, and three black right tetrahedra located behind the white tetrahedra, under the plane of the diagram. We shall designate the white tetrahedra by the letters A, B, C;

the black tetrahedra located beneath them, correspondingly, by the letters A', B', C'. The white tetrahedra have their four apices turned behind the plane of the diagram and therefore appear to the observer in the form of white triangles. The black tetrahedra are completely hidden by the white ones and therefore are not visible. In order to make them visible we shall make openings through the white tetrahedra. These openings are shown in the diagram by small circles.

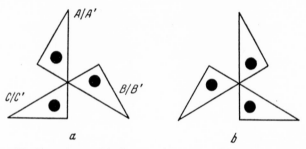

FIG. 78. Enantiomorphic figures with a three-fold mirror antiaxis.

Let us agree to depict these circles in black, if the hidden tetrahedra, as in the given instance, are black, and in white if the hidden tetrahedra are white. Let us agree, moreover, to consider that the tetrahedra hiding one another are *always* (we shall not have to deal with other instances) turned with their four apices on opposite sides.

In order to show that figure a, which we described, actually has a three-fold mirror antiaxis, we shall introduce the following considerations. Let us recall that mirror antirotation may be treated as the product of three operations: rotation, reflection in a plane normal to the axis of rotation, and the operation of a change of sign. Considering this, we easily realize that after the first operation of 120° mirror antirotation, we will derive the right black tetrahedron in position B' from the left white tetrahedron in position A. Upon repeating the operation, we further derive the white left tetrahedron C, and subsequently the black right tetrahedron A', located under A. We further derive B, C', and, finally, A again. We will derive figure a as a whole. Enantiomorphic figure b

is derived in an analogous manner from the white right tetrahedron. It is evident from the above that figures having an uneven-fold mirror antiaxis always have an antiplane of symmetry normal to the axis, which in the example under consideration is located in the plane of the diagram.

In Fig. 79 figures are shown which are enantiomorphic to

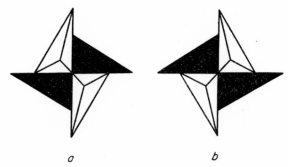

a   b

FIG. 79. Enantiomorphic figures with a four-fold mirror antiaxis.

one another and have one four-fold mirror antiaxis. Figure *a* consists of two left positive and two right negative tetrahedra. The positive tetrahedra are turned with their apices toward the observer; the negative with their apices away from the observer. In contrast to figures with an uneven-numbered antiaxis, the figures under consideration and also all similar figures with an even-numbered antiaxis have no antiplane of symmetry normal to the axis. As a consequence of this, the white tetrahedra located above the plane of the diagram do not hide the black tetrahedra located below the plane of the diagram.

The matrix of the operation of mirror antirotation about axis X generally takes the form

$$\begin{pmatrix} \cos\alpha & -\sin\alpha & 0 & 0 \\ \sin\alpha & \cos\alpha & 0 & 0 \\ 0 & 0 & -1 & 0 \\ 0 & 0 & 0 & -1 \end{pmatrix} \quad (27)$$

GROUPS OF ANTISYMMETRY OF FINITE FIGURES

Three Types of Groups of Antisymmetry

We saw above that every classical point group may be represented by one model figure. This also pertains to the new groups. Inasmuch as we shall describe the new groups by either neutral or polar figures or figures of mixed polarity, it is appropriate to divide these groups into *neutral groups* (gray),

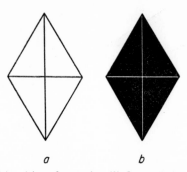

a   *b*

FIG. 80. Positive (*a*) and negative (*b*) figures belonging to group
$2 \cdot m$ [*mm*2].

polar groups (arbitrarily depicted either by white or by black figures), and *groups of mixed polarity* (two colors).

All the previously established categories of classical groups (Table 1) are included in the broader category as polar groups. These groups may be depicted in the same way as we depicted them earlier: by figures made up only of white tetrahedra. They may also be depicted with equal justification by figures made up only of black tetrahedra. This means that any figure belonging to any polar group may exist, according to the enlarged view of symmetry, if it has no enantiomorphic modifications, in two forms (white and black) and if it has an enantiomorphic modification, in four forms. For example the figure shown in Fig. 80, which belongs to group $2 \cdot m$ [*mm*2] and consists of four tetrahedra turned with their apices away from the observer, has one modification in classical symmetry and two modifications in the new symmetry: white *a* and black b. On the other hand, the figure shown in Fig. 81, belonging to group 2 [2] and consisting of two tetrahedra, has two modifications in classical symmetry, right and left, and four modifications in the new symmetry: white left a; white right b; black left c; and black right d.

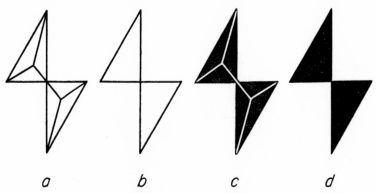

$$a \qquad\qquad b \qquad\qquad c \qquad\qquad d$$

FIG. 81. Four modifications of figures belonging to group 2 [2].

As was already mentioned earlier, polar groups contain only operations of the type

$$\begin{pmatrix} c_{11} & c_{12} & c_{13} & 0 \\ c_{21} & c_{22} & c_{23} & 0 \\ c_{31} & c_{32} & c_{33} & 0 \\ 0 & 0 & 0 & +1 \end{pmatrix}$$

Neutral groups are derived from polar ones by the addition of anti-identification as an independent operation of symmetry. The total number of non-equivalent operations is doubled by this, since all the products of each operation of a given group and the operation of identification must also be taken into account. Thus, one neutral group is obtained from each polar group. In our adopted system of designation, the transition from a polar group to the corresponding neutral one means the replacement of the white tetrahedra by the corresponding gray ones, and the addition of the symbol $\underline{1}$ [1'] to the symbol of the polar group. Thus from white group m [m] we derive gray group $m \cdot \underline{1}$ [$m1'$] (Fig. 82, top), and from white group

4 [4], gray group *4·1* [41′] (Fig. 82, bottom), etc. Let us note in passing that we depicted the previous group *m* [*m*] and group *4* [4] by tetrahedra with vertices turned toward the observer (Fig. 1, Fig. 2*b*), while from now on these and similar groups

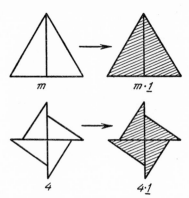

FIG. 82. Examples of transformation of polar groups into neutral ones.

will be depicted by tetrahedra with one of their faces turned toward the observer, in order to simplify the diagrams.

It follows from the above that only the groups of mixed polarity, which we will now consider, are essentially new and not reducible to classical groups.

Groups of Mixed Polarity*

These are groups among which are various anti-operations, with the exception of anti-identification. At the same time when speaking of the composition of a group, we mean as usual operations which are non-equivalent to one another. Consequently if we say that anti-identification is not included in a group, this means that it is absent only as an independent operation, but it does not follow from this that it may not be used for describing other operations. In order to clarify this important observation completely we introduce the

* ["Dichromatic" or "black and white" groups in Belov's notation, see p. 175.]

following example. The figure depicted in Fig. 77, which consists of white and black tetrahedra, by this alone already belongs to figures of mixed polarity. The group of symmetry corresponding to it contains the following four operations: (1) identification, (2) 90° antirotation, (3) 180° rotation, and (4) 270° antirotation. As we see, anti-identification is not included in the group as an independent (non-equivalent) operation. At the same time, however, it is permissible to consider operations of 90° and 270° antirotations as complex operations, consisting of rotation and change of sign (anti-identification) of a figure; similarly it is permissible, if desired, to consider identification as a 360° rotation, or as double reflection in the same plane.

Since symmetrical figures of mixed polarity are externally distinguished from classical symmetrical figures only by the fact that some of the components of the figure are colored black, the complete derivation of all groups of mixed polarity may be reduced to easily accomplished experiments in re-painting a certain component of the white tetrahedra of a figure in black, controlled so that, as a result of this procedure, a figure is actually derived which will satisfy the requirements of antisymmetry. The derivation of groups of mixed polarity itself is given in the following paragraphs.

Groups of Mixed Polarity Determined by One Operation

Let us turn to Table 1, in which all the classical point groups are summarized in order of complexity, and consider consecutively for all the series of this table (beginning with I and ending with XVI) the possibility of transforming the old groups into new ones by replacing the old generating operations by new ones.

Series I

Series I includes groups determined by one rotation through an odd-numbered part of a revolution. As already explained (Fig. 76), replacing a simple rotation through an odd-numbered part of a circle by the corresponding antirotation leads to a series of neutral groups

$$\underline{1}, \underline{3}, \underline{5}, \ldots, \infty \; [1', 3' = 31', 5' = 51', \ldots, \infty 1'].$$

Series II

Series II of the old groups is determined by one rotation through an even-numbered part of a revolution. Having

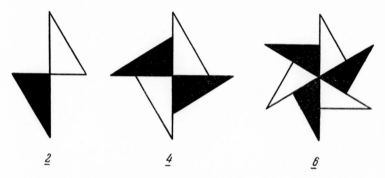

$$\underline{2} \qquad\qquad \underline{4} \qquad\qquad\qquad \underline{6}$$

FIG. 83. Figures belonging to groups of the series $\underline{2}, \underline{4}, \underline{6}, \ldots, \infty$
$[2', 4', 6', \ldots, \infty'].$

replaced a simple rotation by the corresponding antirotation, we arrive at the new series of groups of mixed polarity

$$\underline{2}, \underline{4}, \underline{6} \ldots, \underline{\infty} \quad [2', 4', 6', \ldots, \infty']*$$

Figures corresponding to these groups are shown in Fig. 83. It is evident from the diagram that groups $\underline{2}, \underline{4}, \underline{6} \ldots$ $[2', 4', 6', \ldots]$, are 2nd, 4th, 6th, . . . order groups. Group $\underline{2} \, [2']$ consists of the operation of identification and the operation of a 180° antirotation about a normal to the plane of the diagram. Group $\underline{4} \, [4']$ consists of the following four operations: (1) identification, (2) 90° antirotation, (3) 180° rotation, and (4) 270° antirotation about a normal to the plane of the diagram. The following groups also consist of ordinary rotations, antirotations, and identification.

* [In revising this volume for translation, the author has distinguished this limiting group as $\underline{\infty} \; [\infty']$, a sequence of separated black and white points, from the preceding limiting group $\infty \; [\infty]$, a sequence of coincident black and white points (that is, gray points). See Preface.]

Series III

Series III contains groups determined by one mirror axis of order $(2 + 4n)$. Having replaced it by the corresponding antimirror axis, we arrive at series

$$\underline{\bar{2}},\ \underline{\bar{6}},\ \underline{\overline{10}},\ \ldots,\ \infty:\underline{m} \quad [\bar{1}',\ \bar{3}',\ \bar{5}',\ \ldots,\ \overline{\infty}' = \infty/m']$$

It has been previously explained (Fig. 75, 77) that these groups may be depicted by figures consisting of alternating white and black tetrahedra (Fig. 84). Group $\underline{\bar{2}}$ $[\bar{1}']$ contains,

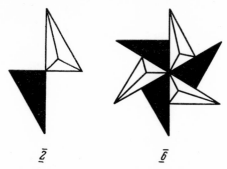

$$\underline{\bar{2}} \qquad\qquad\qquad \underline{\bar{6}}$$

FIG. 84. Figures belonging to groups of series $\underline{\bar{2}},\ \underline{\bar{6}},\ \underline{\overline{10}},\ \ldots,\ \infty:m$
$[\bar{1}',\ \bar{3}',\ \bar{5}',\ \ldots,\ \infty/m']$.

besides identification, only anti-inversion. Group $\underline{\bar{6}}$ $[\bar{3}']$ contains six operations: (1) identification, (2) 60° antirotation, (3) 120° rotation, (4) anti-inversion, (5) 240° rotation, and (6) 300° antirotation. The limiting group of this series will be group $\infty:m[\infty/m']$. With respect to limiting groups in general, see below (p. 141).

Series IV

Series IV is determined by one mirror axis of order $4n$. Replacing this axis by the corresponding antiaxis, we come to the series

$$\underline{\bar{4}},\ \underline{\bar{8}},\ \underline{\overline{12}},\ \ldots,\ \infty:m \quad [\bar{4}',\ \bar{8}',\ \overline{12}',\ \ldots,\ \infty/m'].$$

These groups, like the preceding ones, are depicted by alternating white and black tetrahedra, as shown in Fig. 85.

Series V

Groups of series V are determined by one mirror rotation through an uneven-numbered part of a revolution. Having

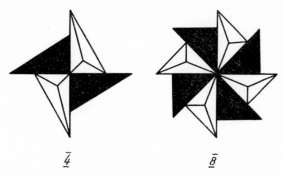

FIG. 85. Figures belonging to groups of the series $\bar{4}$, $\bar{8}$, $\overline{12}$, . . . ,
$\infty:m$ [$\bar{4}'$, $\bar{8}'$, $\overline{12}'$, . . . , ∞/m'].

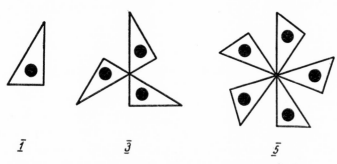

FIG. 86. Figures belonging to groups of the series $\underline{\bar{1}}$, $\underline{\bar{3}}$, $\underline{\bar{5}}$, . . . ,
$\infty:m$ [$2'$, $6'$, $10'$, . . . , ∞/m'].

replaced this rotation by the corresponding mirror antirotation, we arrive at the series

$$\underline{\bar{1}}, \underline{\bar{3}}, \underline{\bar{5}}, . . . , \infty:m \quad [\bar{2}', \bar{6}', \overline{10}', . . . , \infty/m']$$

or in different notation

$$1:\underline{m}, \quad 3:\underline{m}, \quad 5:\underline{m}, . . . , \infty:\underline{m} \quad [1/m', 3/m', 5/m', . . . , \infty/m'].$$

As was explained previously (Fig. 78), these groups may be

depicted by rosettes of white triangles with black circles in the center (Fig. 86).

Groups of Mixed Polarity, Determined by Two Mutually Parallel or Perpendicular Elements of Symmetry

Series VI

Series VI of the old groups is distinguished from the preceding one only by the fact that it contains an even-numbered axis instead of an odd-numbered one. But if the preceding

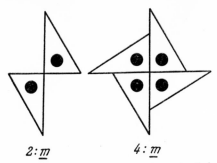

$2:\underline{m}$ $4:\underline{m}$

Fig. 87. Figures belonging to groups of the series $2:\underline{m}$, $4:\underline{m}$, $6:\underline{m}$, . . ., $\infty:m$ [$2/m'$, $4/m'$, $6/m'$, . . ., ∞/m'].

groups may be considered as groups determined by one operation of mirror rotation, then these groups require two operations for their determination: rotation and reflection in a plane normal to the rotation axis. Therefore, during the transition to new groups we must try all the possibilities of replacing old operations by new ones, namely: (1) replacing reflection by antireflection, (2) replacing rotation by antirotation, and (3) replacing both old operations by the corresponding new ones. In the first instance we arrive at the series

$2:\underline{m}$, $4:\underline{m}$, $6:\underline{m}$, . . ., $\infty:\underline{m}$ [$2/m'$, $4/m'$, $6/m'$, . . . ∞/m'].

The figures of this series are reproduced in Fig. 87. In the second instance we obtain the series

$\underline{2}:m$, $\underline{4}:m$, $\underline{6}:m$, . . ., $\underline{\infty}:m$ [$2'/m$, $4'/m$, $6'/m$, . . ., ∞'/m].

In the figures of this series, the white tetrahedra hide the white, and the black tetrahedra hide the black. Let us agree in this and in similar cases to draw white-filled circles on the white tetrahedra and black-filled circles on the black tetrahedra (Fig. 88). As was already stated, these circles represent

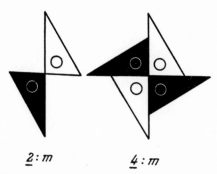

$\underline{2}:m$ $\underline{4}:m$

FIG. 88. Figures belonging to groups of the series $\underline{2}:m$, $\underline{4}:m$, $\underline{6}:m, \ldots, \underline{\infty}:m$ [2′/m, 4′/m, 6′/m, . . ., ∞′/m].

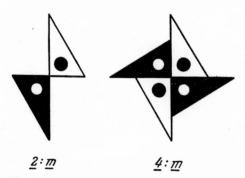

$2:\underline{m}$ $\underline{4}:\underline{m}$

FIG. 89. Figures belonging to groups of the series $\underline{2}:\underline{m}$, $\underline{4}:\underline{m}$, $\underline{6}:\underline{m}, \ldots, \underline{\infty}:\underline{m}$ [2′/m, 4′/m, 6′/m, . . ., ∞′/m].

openings made in the front tetrahedra through which the hidden tetrahedra are partially visible.

In the third instance we obtain the series

$$\underline{2}:\underline{m}, \quad \underline{4}:\underline{m}, \quad \underline{6}:\underline{m}, \ldots, \underline{\infty}:\underline{m} = \underline{\infty}:m$$
$$[2′/m, 4′/m′, 6′/m′, \ldots, ∞′/m′ = ∞′/m].$$

In the figures of this series a black tetrahedron is located under each white tetrahedron and, conversely, a white one under each black one, indicated by circles of the appropriate color (Fig. 89).

Series VII

Groups of series VII are determined by one ordinary axis and a plane of symmetry parallel to it. During the transition to new groups, here again three cases are possible: we may replace only an axis, only a plane, or both elements by the corresponding antielements.

In the first instance we arrive at the series

$$\underline{2} \cdot m, \quad \underline{4} \cdot m, \quad \underline{6} \cdot m, \ldots, \infty \cdot m$$
$$[2'm'm, \ 4'm'm, \ 6'm'm, \ldots, \ \infty'm].$$

Figures of this series are shown in Fig. 90. Comparing these figures with the corresponding figures of series VII, we find

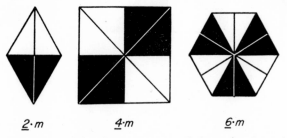

$$\underline{2} \cdot m \qquad \underline{4} \cdot m \qquad \underline{6} \cdot m$$

Fig. 90. Figures belonging to groups of the series $\underline{2} \cdot m$, $\underline{4} \cdot m$, $\underline{6} \cdot m, \ldots, \infty \cdot m$ [$2'm'm$, $4'm'm$, $6'm'm, \ldots, \infty'm$].

that half the planes of symmetry of the old figures are also preserved in the new figures while the other half are transformed into antiplanes. For example, in the first figure of Fig. 90, the vertical plane is a plane of symmetry, while the horizontal is an antiplane of symmetry. In the second figure of the same diagram, the two diagonal planes are planes of symmetry, while the vertical and horizontal planes are antiplanes of symmetry. Hence, it follows that whether we take as the formative elements of a group an antiaxis and a plane of symmetry, or an antiaxis and an antiplane, the result will be the same; that is, groups of type $\underline{N} \cdot m$ [$N'mm'$] are identical to groups of type $\underline{N} \cdot \underline{m}$ [$N'm'm$]. Hence it follows that the third of the indicated possibilities yields nothing new.

The second instance remains to be considered, that is, the groups

$$2 \cdot \underline{m}, \quad 4 \cdot \underline{m}, \quad 6 \cdot \underline{m}, \ldots, \quad \infty \cdot \underline{m}$$
$$[2m'm', 4m'm', 6m'm', \ldots, \infty m'].$$

Figures of this series are shown in Fig. 91.

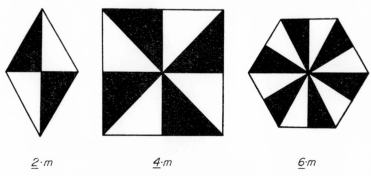

$\underline{2} \cdot m$ $\underline{4} \cdot m$ $\underline{6} \cdot m$

FIG. 91. Figures belonging to groups of the series $2 \cdot \underline{m}$, $4 \cdot \underline{m}$, $6 \cdot \underline{m}, \ldots, \infty \cdot \underline{m}$ [$2m'\underline{m}', 4m'\underline{m}', 6m'\underline{m}', \ldots, \infty m'$].

Series VIII

Having replaced the ordinary odd-numbered axis in the groups derived from groups of Series VIII by the corresponding antiaxes, we arrive at the groups

$$\underline{1} \cdot m, \quad \underline{3} \cdot m, \quad \underline{5} \cdot m, \ldots \quad [1'm, 3'm = 3m1', 5'm = 5m1', \ldots]$$

Earlier (Fig. 76) we saw that replacing an ordinary odd-numbered axis by a corresponding antiaxis leads to neutral figures. The same also takes place in the given case. All groups of the given series are neutral, and, as is easily understandable, indistinguishable from groups of series $\underline{N} \cdot \underline{m}$ [$N'm'$].

Consequently it remains for us to consider only the groups of series

$$1 \cdot \underline{m}, \quad 3 \cdot \underline{m}, \quad 5 \cdot \underline{m}, \ldots, \quad \infty \cdot \underline{m} \quad [1m', 3m', 5m', \ldots, \infty m'].$$

The figures shown in Fig. 92 pertain to these groups. Generally, they very much resemble figures of type $2N \cdot \underline{m}$ $[2Nm']$. It is easy to see that the first of the groups under consideration, group $1 \cdot \underline{m}$ $[1m']$, is identical to the previously described group

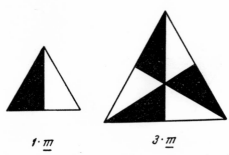

$1 \cdot \underline{m}$ $3 \cdot \underline{m}$

FIG. 92. Figures belonging to groups of the series $1 \cdot \underline{m}$, $3 \cdot \underline{m}$, $5 \cdot \underline{m}, \ldots, \infty \cdot \underline{m}$ $[1m', 3m', 5m', \ldots, \infty m']$.

$\overline{1}$ $[\overline{2}']$ (Fig. 86). The corresponding figures differ from one another only by the position of the antiplane of symmetry: in group $1 \cdot \underline{m}$ $[1m']$ it is perpendicular, while in group $\overline{1}$ $[\overline{2}']$ it is parallel to the plane of the diagram.

Series IX

The groups of series IX are determined by an even-numbered main axis and a two-fold lateral axis. Here again it is necessary to consider three possibilities of transition to new groups.

Having replaced the main axis by the corresponding anti-axis, we arrive at groups of series

$$\underline{2}:2, \quad \underline{4}:2, \quad \underline{6}:2, \ldots, \quad \underline{\infty}:2 \qquad [2'2'2, 4'2'2, 6'2'2, \ldots, \infty'2].$$

Examples of figures characterizing these groups are shown in Fig. 93. Comparing these new figures with the corresponding old figures of series IX, we find that half of the two-fold lateral axes are also preserved in the new figures, while the other half are transformed into two-fold antiaxes. For example, in the second figure of Fig. 93, it is evident that the diagonal axes of the square section of the figure are simple two-fold axes, while the other two axes lying in the same section are two-fold antiaxes. Hence, it follows that the groups under consideration may, with equal justification, be determined either by one

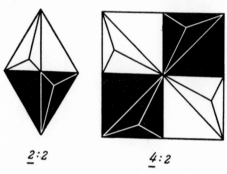

$\underline{2}{:}2$ $\underline{4}{:}2$

FIG. 93. Figures belonging to groups of the series $\underline{2}{:}2$, $\underline{4}{:}2$, $6{:}2, \ldots, \underline{\infty}{:}2$ [2′2′2, 4′2′2, 6′2′2, . . . , ∞′2].

main antiaxis and one two-fold, ordinary transverse axis, or by one main antiaxis and one two-fold transverse antiaxis. In other words, groups of type $\underline{2N}{:}2$ [(2N)′22′] and groups of type $\underline{2N}{:}\underline{2}$ [(2N)′2′2] are identical to one another. Thus we have exhausted two possibilities of transition from the old groups of series IX to the new groups, and therefore there only remain to be analyzed the groups of the series

$2{:}\underline{2}, \quad 4{:}\underline{2}, \quad 6{:}\underline{2}, \ldots, \infty{:}\underline{2}$

[22′2′, 42′2′, 62′2′, . . . , ∞2′].

Having taken the white tetrahedron and subjected it to the operations indicated in the symbol of each of these groups, we arrive at the figures depicted in Fig. 94. In the figures under consideration, in contrast to the figures of the preceding series, all the lateral axes are two-fold antiaxes. Comparing the last two series of groups, it is easy to discover that their first members, that is, groups $\underline{2}{:}2$ [2′2′2] and $2{:}\underline{2}$ [22′2′], are identical to each other, and that the entire difference between them is reduced to the fact that one of the double axes, which in one group is taken as the main axis, is lateral in the other group. This is also immediately evident in the corresponding figures.

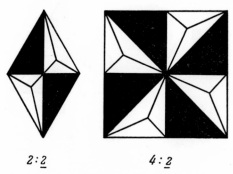

$2:\underline{2}$ $4:\underline{2}$

FIG. 94. Figures belonging to groups of the series $2:\underline{2}$, $4:\underline{2}$, $6:\underline{2}, \ldots, \infty\underline{2}$: [2 2′2′, 4 2′2′, 6 2′2′, . . ., ∞2′].

Series X

Having replaced the main axis of the groups of series X by the corresponding antiaxis, we arrive at series

$\underline{1}:2$, $\underline{3}:2$, $\underline{5}:2$, . . .   [1′2, 3′2 = 321′, 5′2 = 521′, . . .].

We already know (Fig. 76) that odd-numbered antiaxes are possible only in neutral groups. Therefore, groups of series $(2N + 1):2$ [$(2N + 1)′2$] must be equivalent to neutral groups of series $(2N + 1):2$ [$(2N + 1)2$]. It is evident that replacing both ordinary axes by antiaxes also leads only to neutral groups. Therefore, it only remains for us to consider series

$1:\underline{2}$, $3:\underline{2}$, $5:\underline{2}$, . . ., $\infty:\underline{2}$
                    [12′, 32′, 52′, . . ., ∞2′],

Figures of this series (Fig. 95) resemble in character the figures of series $2N:\underline{2}$ [$2N2′$] which were considered earlier (Fig. 94). It is evident that group $1:\underline{2}$ [12′], represented by the first of the figures shown in Fig. 95, is identical to previously considered group $\underline{2}$ [2'] (Fig. 83). The corresponding figures differ from one another only by the position of axis $\underline{2}$ [2'].

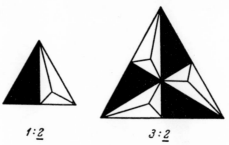

1 :2̲   *3 :2̲*

FIG. 95. Figures belonging to groups of series *1 :2̲, 3 :2̲, 5 :2̲, . . . ,*
∞ :2̲ [12', 32', 52', . . . , ∞ 2'].

Groups of Mixed Polarity Determined by One Axis and Two Planes—Longitudinal and Tranverse

Series XI

These groups are derived from series XI and XII. In series XI are included groups with an even-fold main axis. The general formula of these groups is $m \cdot 2N : m$ [2N/mm]. Each of the elements of symmetry included in this formula may, in principle, be replaced by a corresponding antielement. Thus the following seven combinations of generating elements of symmetry are subject to consideration:

(1) $m \cdot 2N : m$ [2N/mm']   (5) $m \cdot 2N : \underline{m}$ [2N/$m'm'$]

(2) $m \cdot \underline{2N} : m$ [2N'/mm]   (6) $m \cdot \underline{2N} : \underline{m}$ [2N'/$m'm$]

(3) $m \cdot \underline{2N} : \underline{m}$ [2N'/$m'm$]   (7) $\underline{m} \cdot \underline{2N} : m$ [2N'/$m'm'$]

(4) $\underline{m} \cdot \underline{2N} : m$ [2N'/mm']

The first of them leads to series

$\underline{m} \cdot 2 : m$, $\underline{m} \cdot 4 : m$, $\underline{m} \cdot 6 : m$, . . . , $\underline{m} \cdot \infty : m$
          [2/$mm'm'$, 4/$mm'm'$, 6/$mm'm'$, . . . , ∞/mm'].

The corresponding figures are shown in Fig. 96. They contain an ordinary transverse plane of symmetry, an ordinary main axis, and a corresponding number of longitudinal antiplanes of symmetry. These groups do not contain ordinary longitudinal planes of symmetry.

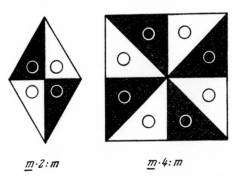

$\underline{m}\cdot 2:m$ $\qquad$ $\underline{m}\cdot 4:m$

Fig. 96. Figures belonging to groups of series $\underline{m}\cdot 2:m$, $\underline{m}\cdot 4:m$, $\underline{m}\cdot 6:m, \ldots, \underline{m}\cdot \infty:m$ [$2/mm'm'$, $4/mm'm'$, $6/mm'm'$, $\ldots$, ∞/mm'].

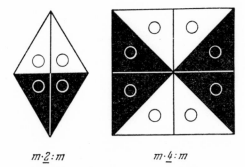

$m\cdot \underline{2}:m$ $\qquad$ $m\cdot \underline{4}:m$

Fig. 97. Figures belonging to groups of series $m\cdot \underline{2}:m$, $m\cdot \underline{4}:m$, $m\cdot \underline{6}:m, \ldots, m\cdot \underline{\infty}:m$ [$2'/mm'm$, $4'/mm'm$, $6'/mm'm$, $\ldots$, ∞'/mm].

The second formula yields series

$$m\cdot \underline{2}:m, \quad m\cdot \underline{4}:m, \quad m\cdot \underline{6}:m, \ldots, m\cdot \underline{\infty}:m$$
$$[2'/mm'm, \ 4'/mm'm, \ 6'/mm'm, \ldots, \ \infty'/mm].$$

The corresponding figures are shown in Fig. 97. It is immediately evident from them that a main antiaxis in conjunction with one ordinary longitudinal plane of symmetry also leads to the appearance of longitudinal antiplanes. This means that the second and fourth of the above formulae are equivalent to each other:

$$m \cdot \underline{2N} : m = \underline{m} \cdot \underline{2N} : m \quad [2N'/mm = 2N'/mm'].$$

The series of groups:

$$m \cdot 2 : \underline{m}, \quad m \cdot 4 : \underline{m}, \quad m \cdot 6 : \underline{m}, \ldots, m \cdot \infty : \underline{m}$$
$$[2/m'mm, \ 4/m'mm, \ 6/m'mm, \ldots, \ \infty/m'm]$$

corresponds to the third formula. The corresponding figures are shown in Fig. 98. It is immediately evident that group

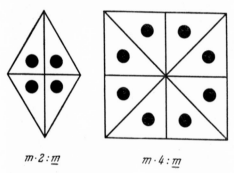

$$m \cdot 2 : \underline{m} \qquad\qquad m \cdot 4 : \underline{m}$$

FIG. 98. Figures belonging to groups of series $m \cdot 2 : \underline{m}$, $m \cdot 4 : \underline{m}$, $m \cdot 6 : \underline{m}, \ldots, m \cdot \infty : \underline{m}$ [2/m'mm, 4/m'mm, 6/m'mm, \ldots, \infty/m'\overline{m}].

$m \cdot 2 : \underline{m}$ [2/m'mm] contains two ordinary planes of symmetry and one antiplane of symmetry, one two-fold ordinary axis and two antiaxes of the same multiplicity, and also an anticenter of symmetry. The above-mentioned group $m \cdot \underline{2} : m$ [2'/mm'm] also has the same elements of symmetry. The figures corresponding to both these groups, depicted in Figs. 97 and 98, differ from one another only by their orientation in space.

The fifth formula leads to the series of groups:

$$\underline{m} \cdot 2 : \underline{m}, \quad \underline{m} \cdot 4 : \underline{m}, \quad \underline{m} \cdot 6 : \underline{m}, \ldots, \underline{m} \cdot \infty : \underline{m}$$
$$[2/m'm'm', \ 4/m'm'm', \ 6/m'm'm', \ldots, \ \infty/m'm'].$$

The main axis in these groups is an ordinary axis of symmetry, while all the longitudinal planes and the transverse plane are antiplanes of symmetry. Examples of figures belonging to these groups are given in Fig. 99.

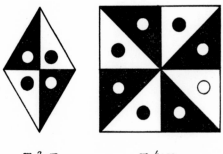

$$\underline{m}\cdot 2:\underline{m} \qquad\qquad \underline{m}\cdot 4:\underline{m}$$

FIG. 99. Figures belonging to groups of series $\underline{m}\cdot 2:\underline{m}$, $\underline{m}\cdot 4:\underline{m}$, $\underline{m}\cdot 6:\underline{m}, \ldots, \underline{m}\cdot\infty:\underline{m}$ [$2/m'm'm'$, $4/m'm'm'$, $6/m'm'm'$, $\ldots$, $\infty/m'm'$].

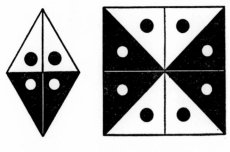

$$m\cdot\underline{2}:m \qquad\qquad m\,\underline{4}:m$$

FIG. 100. Figures belonging to groups of series $m\cdot\underline{2}:\underline{m}$, $m\cdot\underline{4}:\underline{m}$, $m\cdot\underline{6}:\underline{m}, \ldots, m\cdot\underline{\infty}:\underline{m} = m\cdot\underline{\infty}:m$ [$2'/m'm'm$, $4'/m'm'm$, $6'/m'm'm$, $\ldots$, $\infty'/m'm = \infty'/mm$].

The sixth formula leads to the series of groups:

$$m\cdot\underline{2}:\underline{m}, \quad m\cdot\underline{4}:\underline{m}, \quad m\cdot\underline{6}:\underline{m}, \ldots, m\cdot\underline{\infty}:\underline{m} = m\cdot\underline{\infty}:m$$
$$[2'/m'm'm, \; 4'/m'm'm, \; 6'/m'm'm, \ldots, \infty'/m'm = \infty'/mm].$$

Having constructed according to these formulae the figures corresponding to them (Fig. 100), we see that they contain, along with ordinary longitudinal planes of symmetry, also longitudinal antiplanes of symmetry. This means that the sixth and seventh formulae lead to the same groups:

$$m \cdot \underline{2N} : \underline{m} = \underline{m} \cdot \underline{2N} : \underline{m} \quad [2N'/m'm = 2N'/m'm'].$$

It is also easy to be convinced that the first group of this series $m \cdot \underline{2} : \underline{m}$ $[2'/m'm'm]$ is identical to the previously considered group $\underline{m} \cdot 2 : m$ $[2/mm'm']$.

Series XII

Groups of series XII have the general formula $m \cdot (2N+1) : m$ $[\overline{4N + 2m}]$. It has previously been explained that replacing an odd-numbered main axis by an antiaxis of the same multiplicity leads to neutral groups. Thus, only particular cases

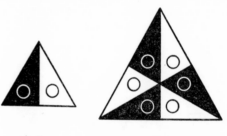

$$\underline{m} \cdot 1 : m \qquad\qquad \underline{m} \cdot 3 : m$$

Fig. 101. Figures belonging to groups of series $\underline{m} \cdot 1 : m$, $\underline{m} \cdot 3 : m$, $\underline{m} \cdot 5 : m, \ldots, \underline{m} \cdot \infty : m$ $[mm'2', \overline{6}m'2', \overline{10}m'2', \ldots, \infty/mm']$.

of the formula under consideration are subject to investigation, in which only the planes of symmetry are replaced by corresponding antielements; that is, the following three formulae:

(1) $\underline{m} \cdot (2N + 1) : m$ $[\overline{4N + 2m}]$,

(2) $m \cdot (2N + 1) : \underline{m}$ $[\overline{4N + 2'm}]$,

(3) $\underline{m} \cdot (2N + 1) : \underline{m}$ $[\overline{4N + 2'm'}]$.

The first of them leads to the series

$$\underline{m} \cdot 1 : m, \ \underline{m} \cdot 3 : m, \ \underline{m} \cdot 5 : m, \ldots, \underline{m} \cdot \infty : m$$
$$[\overline{2}m'2' = mm'2', \ \overline{6}m'2', \ \overline{10}m'2', \ldots, \overline{\infty}m' = \infty/mm'].$$

Figures of this series are shown in Fig. 101. They contain one transverse ordinary plane of symmetry, and longitudinal antiplanes of symmetry. The first group of this series obviously does not differ from the previously considered group $\underline{2} \cdot m$ [$2'm'm$] (Fig. 90).

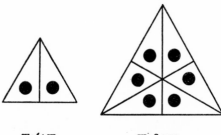

$$m \cdot 1 : \underline{m} \qquad\qquad m \cdot 3 : \underline{m}$$

FIG. 102. Figures belonging to groups of series $m \cdot 1 : \underline{m}$, $m \cdot 3 : \underline{m}$, $m \cdot 5 : \underline{m}, \ldots, m \cdot \infty : \underline{m}$ [$m'm2'$, $\bar{6}'m2'$, $\overline{10}'m'2, \ldots, \bar{\infty}'m = \infty/m'm$].

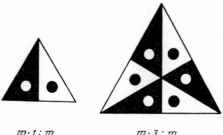

$$\underline{m} \cdot 1 : \underline{m} \qquad\qquad \underline{m} \cdot 3 : \underline{m}$$

FIG. 103. Figures belonging to groups of series $\underline{m} \cdot 1 : \underline{m}$, $\underline{m} \cdot 3 : \underline{m}$, $\underline{m} \cdot 5 : m, \ldots, \underline{m} \cdot \infty : \underline{m}$ [$m'm'2$, $\bar{6}'m'2$, $\overline{10}'m'2, \ldots, \infty/m'm'$].

The second formula forms the series of groups

$$m \cdot 1 : \underline{m}, \quad m \cdot 3 : \underline{m}, \quad m \cdot 5 : \underline{m}, \ldots, m \cdot \infty : \underline{m}$$
$$[\bar{2}'m2' = m'm2', \; \bar{6}'m2', \; \overline{10}'m2', \ldots, \bar{\infty}'m = \infty/m'm].$$

Figures corresponding to these groups are given in Fig. 102. It is easy to see that the first of the groups of this series is equivalent to certain of the previously considered groups, namely

$$m \cdot 1 : m = m \cdot 1 : m = \underline{2} \cdot m \quad [\bar{2}'m2' = \bar{2}m'2' = 2'm'm].$$

The third formula leads to the series

$$\underline{m}\cdot 1{:}\underline{m}, \quad \underline{m}\cdot 3{:}\underline{m}, \quad m\cdot 5{:}m, \ldots, \underline{m}\cdot\infty{:}\ \underline{m}$$
$$[\bar{2}'m'2 = m'm'2,\ \bar{6}m'2,\ \overline{10}'m'2, \ldots,\ \infty/m'm'].$$

Figures of this series are reproduced in Fig. 103. The first of the groups of this series is equivalent to the previously considered group $2\cdot m$ $[2m'm']$.

Groups of Mixed Polarity, Derived from Series XIII and XIV

Series XIII

In groups of series XIII are included groups determined by a main mirror axis of order $4n$ and a longitudinal plane of

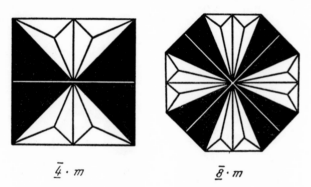

$$\underline{\bar{4}}\cdot m \qquad\qquad \underline{\bar{8}}\cdot m$$

FIG. 104. Figures belonging to groups of series $\underline{\bar{4}}\cdot m$, $\underline{\bar{8}}\cdot m$, $\underline{\overline{12}}\cdot m$, $\ldots$, $m\cdot\infty{:}\underline{m}$ $[\bar{4}'2'm,\ \bar{8}'2'm,\ \overline{12}'2'm, \ldots, \infty/m'm]$.

symmetry. In order to make the transition from groups of this series to new groups, each of these elements of symmetry separately and both together may be replaced by the corresponding antielement. Thus the following three general formulae of new groups are subject to consideration:

(1) $\overline{4N}\cdot m$ $[\overline{4N}'m]$,

(2) $\overline{4N}\cdot\underline{m}$ $[\overline{4N}m']$,

(3) $\overline{4N}\cdot\underline{m}$ $[\overline{4N}'m']$.

The first of these formulae leads to groups

$$\underline{4}\cdot m, \quad \underline{8}\cdot m, \quad \overline{12}\cdot m, \ldots, m\cdot\infty:\underline{m}$$
$$[\overline{4}'2'm, \overline{8}'2'm, \overline{12}'2'm, \ldots, \overline{\infty}'m = \infty/m'm].$$

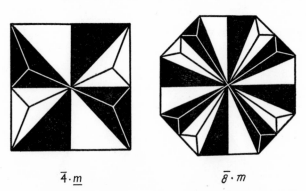

$$\overline{4}\cdot\underline{m} \qquad\qquad \overline{8}\cdot m$$

FIG. 105. Figures belonging to groups of series $\overline{4}\cdot\underline{m}$, $\overline{8}\cdot\underline{m}$, $\overline{12}\cdot\underline{m}$, ..., $m\cdot\infty:m$ [$\overline{4}2'm'$, $\overline{8}2'm'$, $\overline{12}2'm'$, ..., ∞/mm'].

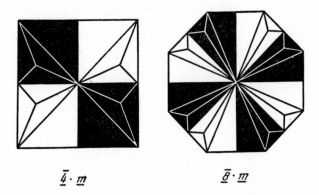

$$\underline{\overline{4}}\cdot\underline{m} \qquad\qquad \overline{\underline{8}}\cdot\underline{m}$$

FIG. 106. Figures belonging to groups of series $\underline{\overline{4}}\cdot m$, $\underline{\overline{8}}\cdot\underline{m}$, $\overline{12}\cdot m$, ..., $m\cdot\infty:m$ [$\overline{4}'2m'$, $\overline{8}'2m'$, $\overline{12}'2m'$, ..., $\infty/m'm'$].

The first two of these groups are represented in Fig. 104. The second formula yields the series

$$\underline{4}\cdot\underline{m}, \quad \underline{8}\cdot\underline{m}, \quad \overline{12}\cdot\underline{m}, \ldots, m\cdot\infty:m$$
$$[\overline{4}2'm', \overline{8}2'm', \overline{12}2'm', \ldots, \overline{\infty}m' = \infty/mm'].$$

The first two groups of this series are shown in Fig. 105.
   The third formula leads to the series of groups

$$\underline{4}\cdot\underline{m}, \quad \underline{8}\cdot\underline{m}, \quad \overline{12}\cdot\underline{m}, \ldots, \underline{m}\cdot\infty:\underline{m}$$
$$[\overline{4}'2m', \ \overline{8}'2m', \ \overline{12}'2m', \ldots, \overline{\infty}'m' = \infty/m'm'].$$

The first two groups of this series are shown in Fig. 106.

Series XIV

Series **XIV** contains groups determined by one mirror axis
of order $(2 + 4n)$ and a longitudinal plane of symmetry.

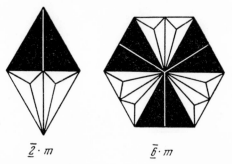

$$\underline{2}\cdot m \qquad\qquad \underline{6}\cdot m$$

FIG. 107. Figures belonging to groups of series $\underline{2}\cdot m$, $\underline{6}\cdot m$, $\overline{1}\cdot m$,
   $\ldots, m\cdot\infty:m$ $[\overline{1}'m, \overline{3}'m, \overline{5}'m, \ldots, \infty/m'm]$.

In order to make the transition from groups of this series to
new groups, each of the indicated elements of symmetry,
separately and together, must be replaced by corresponding
antielements. Thus, we derive three general formulae for
these groups:

(1) $\overline{(2 + 4N)}\cdot m \ [\overline{1 + 2N'}m]$,

(2) $\overline{(2 + 4N)}\cdot\underline{m} \ [\overline{1 + 2N}m']$,

(3) $\overline{(2 + 4N)}\cdot\underline{m} \ [\overline{1 + 2N'}m']$.

The first of these formulae yields the series

$$\underline{2}\cdot m, \quad \underline{6}\cdot m, \quad \overline{10}\cdot m, \ldots, m\cdot\infty:\underline{m}$$
$$[\overline{1}'m, \overline{3}'m, \overline{5}'m, \ldots, \overline{\infty}'m = \infty/m'm'].$$

The first two groups of this series are represented in Fig. 107. It is easy to verify the identity of group $\underline{2} \cdot m$ [$\bar{1}'m$] with the previously considered group $\underline{2} : m$ [$2'/m$].

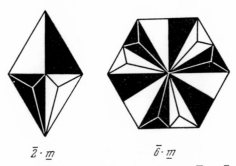

$$\bar{2} \cdot \underline{m} \qquad \bar{6} \cdot \underline{m}$$

Fig. 108. Figures belonging to groups of series $\bar{2} \cdot \underline{m}$, $\bar{6} \cdot \underline{m}$, $\overline{10} \cdot \underline{m}$, . . ., $\underline{m} \cdot \infty : m$ [$\bar{1}'m'$, $\bar{3}m'$, $\bar{5}m'$, . . ., $\infty/m'm'$].

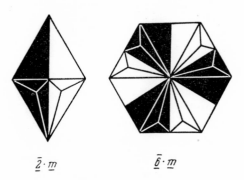

$$\bar{2} \cdot m \qquad \underline{\bar{6}} \cdot \underline{m}$$

Fig. 109. Figures belonging to groups of series $\underline{\bar{2}} \cdot \underline{m}$, $\underline{\bar{6}} \cdot \underline{m}$, $\overline{\underline{10}} \cdot \underline{m}$, . . ., $\underline{m} \cdot \infty : \underline{m}$ [$\bar{1}'m'$, $\bar{3}'m'$, $\bar{5}'m'$, . . ., $\infty/m'm'$].

The second formula leads to groups of series

$$\bar{2} \cdot \underline{m}, \quad \bar{6} \cdot \underline{m}, \quad \overline{10} \cdot \underline{m}, \ldots, \underline{m} \cdot \infty : m$$
$$[\bar{1}m', \bar{3}m', \bar{5}m', \ldots, \overline{\infty}m' = \infty/mm'].$$

The first two groups of this series are represented in Fig. 108. Group $\bar{2} \cdot \underline{m}$ [$\bar{1}m'$] is identical to the previously considered group $\underline{2} : \underline{m}$ [$2'/\underline{m}$].

The third formula yields groups

$$\underline{2}\cdot\underline{m}, \quad \underline{\bar{6}}\cdot\underline{m}, \quad \overline{\underline{10}}\cdot\underline{m}, \ldots, \underline{m}\cdot\infty:\underline{m}$$
$$[\bar{1}'m', \, \bar{3}'m', \, \bar{5}'m', \ldots, \overline{\infty}'m' = \infty/m'm'].$$

The first two of these are represented in Fig. 109. Group $\underline{2}\cdot\underline{m}$ $[\bar{1}'m']$ is identical to the previously considered group $2:m$ $[2/m']$.

Groups of Mixed Polarity, Derived from Series XV and XVI

Series XV

Only the three groups $3/2$, $3/4$, $3/5$ [23, 43, 53] belong to series XV, not counting the limiting group ∞/∞ [$\infty\infty$]. Let us begin with group $3/2$ [23]. Each of its formative elements of symmetry or both together may, in principle, be replaced by corresponding antielements of symmetry. Thus the existence of the following three new groups of symmetry may be predicted:

$$\underline{3}/2, \quad 3/\underline{2}, \quad \underline{3}/\underline{2} \quad [23', \, 2'3, \, 2'3'].$$

The first and third of these groups, as groups containing an odd-numbered antiaxis, are neutral groups and therefore are not subject to consideration. The second group is also neutral for the following reasons: this group contains four three-fold ordinary axes of symmetry passing along the diagonals of a cube. The existence of these axes also stipulates the existence of six two-fold ordinary axes, passing through the center of each pair of opposite edges of the cube; according to agreement, however, these axes must also simultaneously be antiaxes of the same multiplicity and this is possible only for neutral groups.

Let us proceed to group $3/4$ [43]. Three new groups may be derived from it:

$$\underline{3}/4, \quad 3/\underline{4}, \quad \underline{3}/\underline{4} \quad [43', \, 4'3, \, 4'3'].$$

The first and third groups, as groups with odd-numbered antiaxes, are neutral. The second group is a new group of mixed polarity. It may be represented by Fig. 110. This is a cardboard pentagonal trisoctahedron [pentagonal icosite-trahedron] with black and white faces. The black pentagons are colored white on the reverse side, and the white pentagons colored black. The figure contains three antiaxes $\underline{4}$ [4′], four axes 3 [3], and six antiaxes $\underline{2}$ [2′].

FIG. 110. Figure belonging to group $3/\underline{4}$ [4′3].

Let us proceed to group $3/5$ [53]. Three new groups may be derived from it:

$$\underline{3}/5,\ 3/\underline{5},\ \underline{3}/\underline{5} \quad [5\,3',\ 5'3,\ 5'3'].$$

All three groups, as groups with odd-numbered antiaxes, are neutral.

Series XVI

Four groups,

$$\overline{6}/2,\ 3/\overline{4},\ \overline{6}/4,\ 3/\overline{10} \quad [2/m\overline{3},\ \overline{4}3m,\ 4/m\overline{3}2/m,\ \overline{5}3m],$$

belong to series XVI, not counting the limiting group $\infty/\infty \cdot m$ [$\infty\infty m$]. We derive three new groups from group $\overline{6}/2$ [$2/m\overline{3}$]:

$$\underline{\overline{6}}/2,\ \overline{6}/\underline{2},\ \underline{\overline{6}}/\underline{2}$$
$$[2/m'\overline{3}' = m'3,\ 2'/m\overline{3} = m31',\ 2'/m\overline{3}' = m31'].$$

The first of them contains four six-fold mirror antiaxes, three two-fold ordinary axes, and three antiplanes of symmetry. This group of mixed polarity may be represented by a didodecahedron [diploid] with twelve black and twelve white faces (Fig. 111).

The second group $\bar{6}/2$ [$2/m\bar{3}1'$] is neutral. This is already evident from the fact that due to the existence of four six-fold mirror axes, there exist three two-fold ordinary axes. Thus,

Fig. 111. Figure belonging to group $\underline{\bar{6}}/2$ [$m'3$].

Fig. 112. Figure belonging to group $3/\bar{\underline{4}}$ [$\bar{4}'3m'$].

axes $\underline{2}$ [$2'$] are also simultaneously axes 2 [2], and this also means that the group under consideration is neutral.

The third group $\underline{\bar{6}}/2$ [$2/m\bar{3}1'$] is also neutral, since along with the existence of four axes $\underline{\bar{6}}$ [$\bar{3}'$], axes $\underline{2}$ [$2'$] will simultaneously be axes 2 [2].

From group $3/\bar{4}$ [$\bar{4}3m$] we derive the three new groups:

$$\underline{3}/\bar{4},\ 3/\underline{\bar{4}},\ \underline{3}/\underline{\bar{4}}\ [\bar{4}3'm = \bar{4}3m1',\ \bar{4}'3m' = \bar{4}'3'm = \bar{4}3m1'].$$

The first and third of them are neutral, as groups containing odd-fold antiaxes. The construction of group $3/\underline{\overline{4}}$ [$\overline{4}'3m'$], according to the formative elements indicated in it, leads to Fig. 112.

FIG. 113. Figure belonging to group $\overline{\underline{6}}/4$ [$m'3m'$].

FIG. 114. Figure belonging to group $\overline{\underline{6}}/\underline{4}$ [$m3m'$].

From group $\overline{6}/4$ we derive the three new groups:

$\overline{\underline{6}}/4$, $\overline{6}/\underline{4}$, $\overline{\underline{6}}/\underline{4}$

$[4/m'\overline{3}'2/m' = m'3m', \quad 4'/m\overline{3}'2'/m' = m3m', \quad 4'/m'\overline{3}'2'/m = m'3m']$.

All three groups are groups of order 48 and of mixed polarity. Group $\overline{\underline{6}}/4$ [$m'3m'$] may be represented by a 48-hedron with 24 white and an equal number of black faces, alternating in checkerboard fashion (Fig. 113).

As always, it is understood that each face, black on the

outside, is white on the inside and vice versa. Group $\underline{\bar{6}}/4$ [*m'3m'*] contains three axes *4* [4], four axes $\bar{6}$ [$\bar{3}'$], six axes *2* [2], nine antiplane *m* [*m'*], and an anticenter $\underline{\bar{2}}$ [$\bar{1}'$].

Group $\bar{6}/\underline{4}$ [*m3m'*] is represented in Fig. 114. It contains four axes $\bar{6}$ [$\bar{3}$], three antiaxes $\underline{4}$ [4'], six antiaxes $\underline{2}$ [2'], three

FIG. 115. Figure belonging to group $\underline{\bar{6}}/\underline{4}$ [*m'3m*].

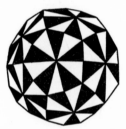

FIG. 116. Figure belonging to group $3/\underline{\overline{10}}$ [5'3m'].

planes of symmetry, six antiplanes of symmetry and a center of symmetry. The figure represents a 48-hedron with black and white faces, but arranged differently from the preceding case.

Group $\underline{\bar{6}}/\underline{4}$ [*m'3m*] is represented by the special 48-hedron shown in Fig. 115. The group contains four antiaxes $\underline{\bar{6}}$ [$\bar{3}'$], three antiaxes $\underline{4}$ [4'], six antiaxes $\underline{2}$ [2'], three antiplanes of symmetry, six planes of symmetry, and an anticenter $\underline{\bar{2}}$ [$\bar{1}'$].

Only group $3/\overline{10}$ of series XVI remains for us to consider. We derive three new groups from it:

$$\underline{3}/\overline{10},\ 3/\underline{\overline{10}},\ \underline{3}/\underline{\overline{10}} \quad [\bar{5}'3'm = \bar{5}\,3m1',\ \bar{5}'3m',\ \bar{5}'3'm = \bar{5}\,3m1'].$$

The first and third of them, as groups with odd-numbered antiaxes, are neutral. Group $3/\overline{10}$ [$\overline{5}'3m'$] of mixed polarity remains, shown in Fig. 116 by a 120-hedron with black and white faces, arranged relative to one another in checkerboard fashion.

Limiting Groups of Mixed Polarity

In order to complete the entire derivation of all point groups of mixed polarity, it is necessary to dwell separately upon the limiting groups which we temporarily left out of consideration. A detailed description of limiting groups will be given below (p. 161).

Survey of Point Groups of Mixed Polarity

For convenience of review, all the groups of mixed polarity we derived are listed in series in Table 6. Each series is entered in the corresponding horizontal line of the table and is represented by its first three members and its corresponding limiting group. Certain of the first members of series are enclosed in a square, namely those first members of groups which have already been written in another form in the lines above. Thus, group $1 \cdot m$ [$1m'$], which is equivalent to group $\underline{1}$ [m'] is enclosed in a square, group $2 : \underline{2}$ [$2\,2'2'$], which is equivalent to group $\underline{2} : 2$ [$2'2'2$]. The following equations exhaust all those instances:

$$1 \cdot m = \underline{1} \qquad\qquad [1m' = \overline{2}']$$
$$2 : \underline{2} = \underline{2} : 2 \qquad\qquad [2\,2'2' = 2'2'2]$$
$$1 : \underline{2} = \underline{2} \qquad\qquad [1\,2' = 2']$$
$$m \cdot \underline{2} : \underline{m} = \underline{m} \cdot 2 : m \qquad [2'/m'm'm = 2/mm'm]$$
$$\underline{m} \cdot 1 : m = m \cdot 1 : \underline{m} = \underline{2} \cdot m \quad [\overline{2}m'2' = \overline{2}'m2' = 2'm'm]$$
$$\underline{m} \cdot 1 : \underline{m} = \underline{2} \cdot \underline{m} \qquad [\overline{2}'m'2 = 2m'm']$$
$$\overline{2} \cdot \underline{m} = \underline{2} : \underline{m} \qquad [\overline{1}m' = 2'/m']$$
$$\underline{2} \cdot \underline{m} = 2 : \underline{m} \qquad [\overline{1}'m' = 2/m']$$
$$m \cdot 2 : \underline{m} = m \cdot \underline{2} : m \qquad [2/m'mm = 2'/mm'm]$$
$$\underline{2} \cdot m = \underline{2} : m \qquad\qquad [\overline{1}'m = 2'/m]$$

The last series contains six groups.

TABLE 6
GROUPS OF MIXED POLARITY

Shubnikov notation		International notation	
2, 4, 6, . . .	∞̄	2', 4', 6', . . .	∞'
2̄, 6̄, 10̄, . . .		1̄', 3̄', 5̄', . . .	
4̄, 8̄, 12̄, . . .	∞:m	4̄', 8̄', 12̄', . . .	∞/m'
1̄, 3̄, 5̄, . . .		5̄', 6̄', 10̄', . . .	
2:m, 4·m, 6:m, . . .		2/m', 4/m', 6/m', . . .	
2:m, 4:m, 6:m, . . .	∞̄:m	2'/m, 4'/m, 6'/m, . . .	∞'/m
2:m, 4:m, 6:m, . . .		2'/m', 4'/m', 6'/m', . . .	
2·m, 4·m, 6·m, . . .	∞·m	2'm'm, 4'm'm, 6'm̃'m, . . .	∞'m
2·m, 4·m, 6·m, . . .	∞·m̄	2m'm', 4m'm', 6m'm', . . .	∞m'
1·m, 3·m, 5·m, . . .		1m', 3m', 5m', . . .	
2:2, 4:2, 6:2, . . .	∞̄:2	2'2'2, 4'2'2, 6'2'2, . . .	∞'2
2:2, 4:2, 6:2, . . .	∞:2̄	22'2', 42'2', 62'2', . . .	∞2'
1·2, 3·2, 5·2		12', 32', 52'	

| ∞/mm' | | ∞'/mm | | ∞/m'm' | | ∞'/m'm | |

$\boxed{\bar{5}\,m'2}$, $6m'2$, $\overline{10}m'2$, . . .

$\bar{4}2'm'$, $\bar{8}2'm'$, $\overline{12}2'm'$, . . .

$\boxed{1m'}$, $3m'$, $\bar{5}m'$, . . .

$2'|mm'm$, $4'|mm'm$, $6'|mm'm$, . . .

$\boxed{2'|m'm'm}$, $4'|m'm'm$, $6'|m'm'm$, . . .

$2|m'm'm'$, $4|m'm'm'$, $6|m'm'm'$, . . .

$\boxed{\bar{5}m'2}$, $\bar{6}'m'2$, $\overline{10}'m'2$, . . .

$\bar{4}2'm$, $\bar{8}2'm$, $\overline{12}2'm'$, . . .

$\boxed{\bar{1}m'}$, $3'm'$, $\bar{5}'m'$, . . .

$2|m'mm$, $4|m'mm$, $6|m'mm$, . . .

$\boxed{\bar{5}'m2'}$, $\bar{6}'m2'$, $\overline{10}'m2'$, . . .

$\bar{4}2'm$, $\bar{8}2'm$, $\overline{12}2'm$, . . .

$\boxed{\bar{1}'m}$, $3'm$, $\bar{5}'m$, . . .

$4'32'$, $\bar{4}'3m'$, $m'3$, $\bar{4}'3m'$, $m3m'$, $m'3m$, $\bar{5}'3m'$,

$\infty'\infty$, $\infty'\infty m$, $\infty\infty'm'$

| $\underline{m}\cdot\infty:m$ | | $m\cdot\underline{\infty}:m$ | | $\underline{m}\cdot\infty:\underline{m}$ | | $m\cdot\infty:\underline{m}$ | |

$\boxed{\underline{m}\cdot1:m}$, $\underline{m}\cdot3\cdot m$, $\underline{m}\cdot5\cdot m$, . . .

$\bar{4}m$, $\bar{8}m$, $\overline{12}m$, . . .

$\boxed{\bar{2}\cdot\underline{m}}$, $6\cdot\underline{m}$, $\overline{10}\cdot\underline{m}$, . . .

$m\cdot2:m$, $m\cdot4:m$, $m\cdot\underline{6}:m$, . . .

$\boxed{m\cdot\underline{2}:\underline{m}}$, $m\cdot\underline{4}:\underline{m}$, $m\cdot6:\underline{m}$, . . .

$m\cdot2:\underline{m}$, $m\cdot4:\underline{m}$, $m\cdot6:\underline{m}$, . . .

$\boxed{\underline{m}\cdot1:\underline{m}}$, $m\cdot3:\underline{m}$, $\underline{m}\cdot5\cdot\underline{m}$, . . .

$\bar{4}\cdot m$, $\bar{8}\cdot m$, $\overline{12}\cdot m$, . . .

$\boxed{\bar{2}\cdot\underline{m}}$, $\bar{6}\cdot\underline{m}$, $\overline{10}\cdot\underline{m}$, . . .

$m\cdot2:\underline{m}$, $m\cdot4:\underline{m}$, $m\cdot6\cdot\underline{m}$, . . .

$\boxed{m\cdot1:\underline{m}}$, $m\cdot3:\underline{m}$, $m\cdot5:\underline{m}$, . . .

$\bar{4}\cdot m$, $\bar{8}\cdot m$, $\overline{12}\cdot m$, . . .

$\boxed{\bar{2}\cdot m}$, $\bar{6}\cdot m$, $\overline{10}\cdot m$, . . .

$3/\bar{4}$, $3/\bar{4}$, $\bar{6}/2$, $\bar{6}/4$, $\bar{6}/\underline{4}$, $3/\overline{10}$,

∞/∞, $\infty/\infty\cdot m$, $\infty/\infty\cdot m$

It is easy to verify by the table that the total number of *crystallographic* groups of mixed polarity, that is, groups which do not contain other than 1-, 2-, 3-, 4-, 6-fold axes, is equal to 58. If limiting groups are also added to the category of crystallographic groups of mixed polarity, which is expedient for a number of reasons, then the total number of crystallographic groups of mixed polarity will be equal to 72.

Simple Forms of Groups of Mixed Polarity

In crystallography, a polyhedron, all of whose faces are *equal among themselves*, is called a *simple form* [closed form]. This means that the polyhedron contains only faces which are transformed into one another and into themselves by the operations of symmetry of a given group. A polyhedron made up of two or more simple forms is called a *combination*. The concepts of the simple form and the combination may be carried over from symmetrical forms to antisymmetrical ones.

In order to construct all the possible simple forms for each group of symmetry, the crystallographer proceeds in the following manner. First of all, the given group of symmetry is represented in the form of a rosette of elements of symmetry. Next, a plane in one or another position relative to the elements of symmetry is taken, and is repeated by all the operations of symmetry of the group. As a result of such repetition, a polyhedron is produced, which will also be a simple form. From the plane occupying a *general* position relative to the elements of symmetry, a *general form* is derived. From the plane occupying a *special* position relative to the elements of symmetry, a *special form*, is derived. This method of construction of simple forms may also be applied as a whole to groups of antisymmetry.

Let us take one of the simplest groups of symmetry—group *m* [*m*] with one plane of symmetry. In this group, as is known from crystallography, simple forms of only three kinds are possible: *monohedra*—forms consisting of one face, *dihedra*—forms consisting of two non-parallel faces, and the *pinacoid*—a form consisting of a pair of parallel faces. In Fig. 117 is shown one of the examples of combinations of the indicated forms.

Face *a* is a monohedron, the pair of faces *b*, *b'* and the pair of faces *c*, *c'* are dihedra, the pair of lateral faces *d*, *d'* form a

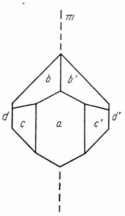

FIG. 117. Example of a combination of simple forms in group *m* [*m*].

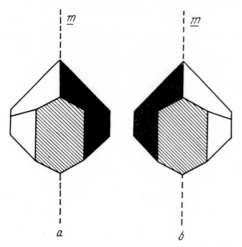

a   *b*

FIG. 118. Example of a combination of simple forms in group *m̲* [*m'*].

pinacoid. The left faces *b*, *c*, *d* are enantiomorphic to the right faces *b'*, *c'*, *d'*. Face *a* has no enantiomorph. It is, if such an expression is permissible, *neutral with respect to right-handedness and left-handedness,* or enantiomorphic to itself, since it contains both right and left components.

If we replace plane *m* [*m*] by antiplane <u>*m*</u> [*m'*], according to the given faces *a, b, c, d,* we construct the combination shown in Fig. 118*a.* Face *a,* normal to plane <u>*m*</u> [*m'*], must at the same time be neutral, since only under this condition may it be transformed into itself after the complex operation of reflection in a plane *m* [*m*] and the subsequent change of sign. It is

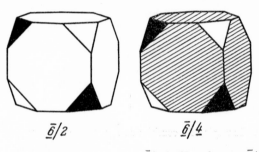

$$\bar{\underline{6}}/2 \qquad\qquad \bar{\underline{6}}/4$$

FIG. 119. Cubo-octahedron in group $\bar{\underline{6}}/2$ [*m'*3] and group $\bar{\underline{6}}/4$ [*m'*3*m*].

easy to see that the described combination may also exist in the enantiomorphic modifications shown in Fig. 118*b.* It may be seen from this example that simple forms whose faces are normal to antiplanes of symmetry are always neutral. In the instance under consideration, face *a* is neutral, not only with respect to right-handedness and left-handedness, but also in our adopted sense, that is, in relation to *sign,* so it is depicted in gray in Fig. 118.

It is easy to demonstrate, moreover, that those simple forms whose faces are normal to simple antiaxes must also always be neutral. Let us assume the opposite: let a certain face of a simple form have a plus sign, and at the same time be oriented perpendicularly to an antiaxis of one or another multiplicity. Then this face must be transformed into itself as the result of an operation consisting of rotation and change of sign. But this means that our face simultaneously has a plus sign and a minus sign, that is, it is neutral.

In groups of mixed polarity, simple forms may be polar forms of one sign, or neutral, or, of course, forms of mixed polarity.

Let us illustrate this by examples. In the cubo-octahedron of group $\underline{6}/2$ [$m'3$], all the faces of the cube are polar and have one sign, while the faces of an octahedron have mixed polarity. In the cubo-octahedron of group $\underline{6}/\underline{4}$ [$m'3m$], the faces of the cube are neutral, while the faces of an octahedron have mixed polarity (Fig. 119).

In classical symmetry the simple form may exist in two enantiomorphic modifications only when it consists solely of right or left components. An antisymmetrical simple form has two enantiomorphic modifications even when it consists simultaneously of right and left components. For this it is necessary only that the right components differ from the left by sign. For example the figure in Fig. 112, composed of right black and left white triangular faces, may have an enantiomorphic modification composed of left black and right white triangles.

The detailed consideration of the properties of simple antisymmetrical forms might serve as the theme of a special investigation.

Appendix

THE DIVISION OF SYMMETRICAL FIGURES INTO EQUAL DOMAINS

ANY symmetrical figure may be geometrically divided into equal asymmetrical domains by an infinite number of methods. The maximum number of these domains is equal to the order of the group. Let us show this by examples of plane figures.

In Fig. 120 is shown a polar plane figure belonging to group

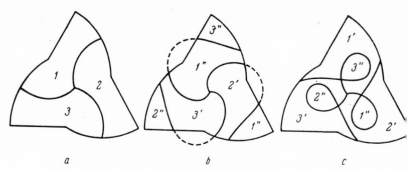

FIG. 120. Examples of division of a figure into equal domains.

3 [3]. In order to divide it into the maximum number of equal asymmetrical domains, it is sufficient to pass an arbitrary line from the center of the figure to the periphery of the figure, and repeat this line by operations of symmetry of the figure. The lines drawn may or may not intersect one another, and also may or may not intersect the boundaries of the figure. Nevertheless, in case of the intersection of a line, each of the equal asymmetrical domains of the figure will, in its turn, consist of a certain number of unequal subdomains. In the adjoining diagrams, each of the equal asymmetrical domains of the figure is labelled with its own number. The unequal subdomains of each domain have the same number with a different number of primes.

If the figure has a plane of symmetry, the surface of division must pass along these planes. Otherwise, the domains of the figure will contain a plane of symmetry, and therefore cannot be asymmetrical. Let us take as an example a figure possessing symmetry $4 \cdot m$ [4mm]. As is shown in Fig. 121a it may be divided along planes of symmetry into eight asymmetrical domains. It may seem at first glance that such a division into the maximum number of equal domains is unique. Actually

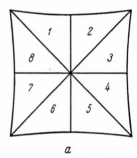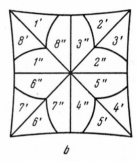

a   *b*

FIG. 121. Example of division of a figure, having plane symmetry, into equal domains.

this is not so, inasmuch as each domain may be arbitrarily divided into subdomains, and these same subdomains may be ascribed to various domains by no one method. For example, part 1″ of the first domain in Fig. 121b, might have been ascribed to any of the eight domains of the figure, let us say to the fifth. In this case this part would have received the designation 5″, and all the other equal parts would also have correspondingly changed their designations. Thus the assertion that every symmetrical figure may be divided into a maximum number of asymmetrical domains by an infinite number of methods, is still true for figures with planes of symmetry.

To complete the picture, it is necessary to consider one more example, from which it will be evident that if a figure is divided into a number of domains equal to the order of the corresponding group, then these components are asymmetrical and therefore not divisible into smaller equal parts. Let us take a polar square. Like the figure just considered, it possesses symmetry

4·m [4mm], and therefore may be divided into eight domains with planes of symmetry. Each domain is an isosceles right triangle. *Taken separately,* such a triangle is symmetrical, since it contains a plane of symmetry passing along its height, dropped from the apex of the right angle to the hypotenuse. But this plane of symmetry is not the same for every square, as a consequence of which the legs of the triangle (occupying a *different* position in a square) cannot be considered equal. We may therefore, in the example under consideration, consider the domains of the figure asymmetrical, and therefore, not divisible into equal domains. If we, nevertheless, divide them along their heights into smaller triangles (such a division may be carried out to infinity), then the parts derived from each triangle will differ from one another by their position inside the square, they will not change places by the symmetrical operations of the square, and therefore will be *unequal* in our adopted sense.

EXAMPLES OF ANTISYMMETRICAL FIGURES FROM THE FIELD OF PHYSICAL CRYSTALLOGRAPHY

If a sphere made of pyroelectric crystal, tourmaline for example, is heated, one half of the sphere's surface will be charged with positive electricity, the other half negatively. The density of the charges will be at a maximum in the poles of these hemispheres, and equal to zero along the equator. It is easy to show that the density of charges δ_ρ must diminish with the increase of the angular distance ρ between the positive pole and the point at which the density is measured, according to the law

$$\delta_\rho = \delta_0 \cos \rho.$$

If we lay off segments proportional to the corresponding densities of the charges along the radii of the sphere, and mark them with the appropriate sign, we shall obtain a *density indicatrix*, in the form of two adjoining spheres. One of them will be positive, that is, made up of positive segments, the other negative (Fig. 122). From the classical point of view, the derived figure has symmetry $\infty \cdot m$ [∞m], while from the point of view of antisymmetry this figure must have a higher symmetry

$m \cdot \infty : m \ [\infty/m'm]$, inasmuch as the positive sphere in this figure is joined with the negative sphere, anti-equal to it, by a transverse antiplane of symmetry.

We will take the second example from the field of piezoelectricity. If a sphere is made of a crystal of quartz and one

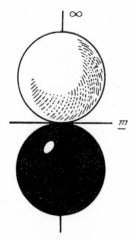

Fig. 122. Indicatrices of components of a polar vector in different directions. An example of an antisymmetrical figure in physical crystallography.

measures the density of the charges obtained during its compression along the ends of its various diameters, and an indicatrix is constructed according to the derived data by plotting in the corresponding directions the segments proportional to the densities of the charges with their sign, then we shall derive Fig. 123. It consists of six egg-shaped nodules: three positive and three negative. From the classical point of view, this surface has symmetry $m \cdot 3 : m \ [\bar{6}m2]$, while from the point of view of antisymmetry, it has the higher symmetry $m \cdot \underline{6} : m$ $[6'/mm'm]$, inasmuch as the main axis of the figure is a six-fold antiaxis.

Let us introduce one more example of antisymmetrical surfaces from the realm of rotation of a plane of polarization. Proceeding from theoretical considerations, it may be assumed that certain crystals belonging to groups m, $2 \cdot m$, $\bar{4}$, $\underline{4} \cdot m$

[*m*, 2*mm*, $\bar{4}$, $\bar{4}2m$], may be optically active. For them the relationship of specific rotation to direction is expressed by the surface shown in Fig. 124*a*. It consists of four nodules. The

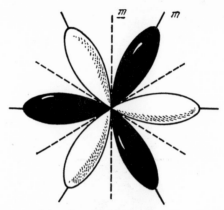

FIG. 123. One of the piezoelectrical surfaces as an example of an antisymmetrical figure.

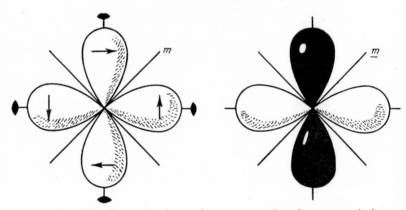

FIG. 124. Some gyrating surfaces as examples of a symmetrical and an antisymmetrical surface.

radii-vectors of two of them are proportional to right specific rotations; the radii-vectors of the other two nodules correspond to left rotations. Right rotation of a plane of polarization may be described as the turning of a linearly polarized ray on a left-hand screw; left rotation as the turning of a polarized ray on a right-hand screw. With such an interpretation of the phenomenon, the surface under consideration will consist of two right and two left nodules arranged relative to one another according to the requirements of the symmetry of the group $\bar{4} \cdot m$ [$\bar{4}2m$]. This means that the main axis of the surface is a four-fold mirror axis. Along it pass two mutually perpendicular planes of symmetry whose bisectors serve as two-fold axes. In crystal physics, left rotation is considered positive, right negative. If this point of view is adopted, the surface under consideration may be treated as antisymmetrical, belonging to group $m \cdot \underline{4} : m$ [$4'/mm'm$]. The remaining elements of symmetry are easily determined from the diagram (Fig. 124b). Without going into details, we shall point out that the first interpretation of the symmetry of the surface under consideration, in our opinion, reflects reality better than the second, since the second, which is accepted by no one, corresponds better to the standard tradition of distinguishing the nature of rotation *by sign*.

THE SYMMETRY OF VECTORS AND TENSORS*

It was previously explained (p. 88) that the symmetry of finite figures may be defined as the property of a figure to be transformed into itself by operations of the form

$$\begin{pmatrix} c_{11} & c_{12} & c_{13} \\ c_{21} & c_{22} & c_{23} \\ c_{31} & c_{32} & c_{33} \end{pmatrix}$$

It is easy to show that the concept of symmetry may be carried over from figures to mathematical expressions and quantities, to vectors and tensors in particular.

It is well known that any vector may be given by its three components p_1, p_2, p_3, relative to a certain system of coordinates X_1, X_2, X_3. During the transition to another system $X_1', X_2', X_3',$

* For a more detailed account of this question, see refs. 72 and 73.

with the same origin, the old components of the *polar vector* are transformed into the new p_1', p_2', p_3' according to the formulae

$$p_1' = c_{11}p_1 + c_{21}p_2 + c_{31}p_3,$$
$$p_2' = c_{12}p_1 + c_{22}p_2 + c_{32}p_3,$$
$$p_3' = c_{13}p_1 + c_{23}p_2 + c_{33}p_3.$$

The reverse operation is carried out according to the formulae

$$p_1 = c_{11}p_1' + c_{12}p_2' + c_{13}p_3',$$
$$p_2 = c_{21}p_1' + c_{22}p_2' + c_{23}p_3', \qquad (A)$$
$$p_3 = c_{31}p_1' + c_{32}p_2' + c_{33}p_3'.$$

As we see, these reverse operations are not different in form from operations of symmetry. In order that they might actually be such for a vector, it is necessary that each of its components be transformed into itself by them, that is, that the equations

$$p_1 = p_1',$$
$$p_2 = p_2',$$
$$p_3 = p_3'$$

hold good.

After these observations it is easy to demonstrate that the polar vector possesses symmetry $\infty \cdot m$ [∞m], where axis ∞ [∞] coincides in direction with the vector itself.

Let us assume for the sake of simplicity that the vector under consideration is directed along the axis X_3'. Then $p_1' = p_2' = 0$, and the vector is equal to its component p_3'. If, as we maintain, the vector possesses an infinite-fold axis of symmetry, then, turning it along axis X_3' through the arbitrary angle α, we should obtain $p_1 = p_2 = 0$ and $p_3 = p_3'$. A rotation through the angle α about axis X_3' brings about the operation (p. 92):

$$\begin{pmatrix} \cos\alpha & -\sin\alpha & 0 \\ \sin\alpha & \cos\alpha & 0 \\ 0 & 0 & 0 \end{pmatrix}$$

Substituting these values of c_{ik} in the formula (A), we actually obtain

$$p_1 = 0$$
$$p_2 = 0$$
$$p_3 = 0$$

We shall now demonstrate that the coordinate plane X_1', X_3' is the plane of symmetry of the vector. If this is correct, then, after reflection in this plane we must again arrive at the same equations. Reflection in plane X_1', X_3' is described by the following scheme of cosines:

$$\begin{array}{rrr} 1 & 0 & 0 \\ 0 & -1 & 0 \\ 0 & 0 & 1 \end{array}$$

Substituting these values of cosines in equations (A), we again obtain

$$p_1 = 0,$$
$$p_2 = 0,$$
$$p_3 = p_3'.$$

This means that plane X_1', X_3' is actually a plane of symmetry of the vector. It passes along axis ∞ [∞] and is one of the longitudinal planes of symmetry. Along with the existence of axis ∞ [∞], an infinite number of such planes must exist. Hence it follows that the vector has all the elements of symmetry of group $\infty \cdot m$ [∞m]. It remains to be shown that the vector has *only* these elements of symmetry.

We shall show that the vector does not have a transverse plane of symmetry, or, to put it differently, that plane X_1', X_2' is not a plane of symmetry of the vector. Reflection in plane X_1', X_2' is described by the scheme

$$\begin{array}{rrr} 1 & 0 & 0 \\ 0 & 1 & 0 \\ 0 & 0 & -1 \end{array}$$

Substituting these values of the cosines in equations (A), we derive

$$p_1 = 0,$$
$$p_2 = 0,$$
$$p_3 = -p_3'.$$

As we see in the given instance, component p_3, changing its sign after reflection in plane X_1', X_2', is not transformed into itself. Hence it follows that the plane under consideration is not a plane of symmetry of the vector. It is easy to see that along with the absence of a transverse plane of symmetry, no other elements of symmetry may exist. Thus, the polar vector actually possesses symmetry $\infty \cdot m$ $[\infty m]$, which justifies the fact that it is generally depicted as a rectilinear arrow.

An *axial vector* possesses different symmetry. It may be demonstrated that its symmetry corresponds to group $\infty \cdot m$ $[\infty/m]$. During the transition from the system X_1', X_2', X_3' to system X_1, X_2, X_3, the components of the axial vector are transformed according to the formula

$$p_i = \pm \sum_{k=1}^{3} c_{ik} p_k', \qquad (B)$$

which differs from formulae (A) only by the fact that the right components take either a positive or a negative sign, depending upon whether both systems of axes are coincident (both right or both left) or mirror (one right, the other left).

Considering this, and repeating the same considerations which related to the polar vector, we arrive at the following conclusions.

The axial vector has an infinite-fold axis, directed along the vector, inasmuch as formula (B) is employed in this instance, just as for the polar vector, with the "plus" sign.

The axial vector has no longitudinal planes of symmetry, since, in this instance, formula (B) must be employed with the "minus" sign, inasmuch as reflection in a plane transfers a right system to a left one, and vice versa. It is evident that the considerations previously applying to the polar vector must now lead to the opposite result.

It is analogously demonstrated that a transverse plane is a plane of symmetry for an axial vector.

Thus polar and axial vectors have different symmetry, while both vectors are depicted by a rectilinear arrow. In most cases this does not lead to any misunderstandings, although in questions linked in some way or another with symmetry, such identification of both vectors may lead to serious errors. To avoid this, it is expedient to depict axial vectors by a straight segment circled with an arrow.

Let us proceed to tensors. It is known that any two-fold tensor has nine components, generally written in table form

$$\begin{matrix} a_{11} & a_{12} & a_{13} \\ a_{21} & a_{22} & a_{23} \\ a_{31} & a_{32} & a_{33} \end{matrix}$$

Tensor a_{ik}, that is, both the nine fixed values and their use, is distinguished from the matrix of cosines c_{ik} with which we are already familiar only by the fact that relationships (2) and (3) (p. 89) are not mandatory for the former.

In tensor computation it is demonstrated (see the book of N. E. Kochin cited on p. 89), that *polar tensor* a_{ik}, during the transition from system X_1', X_2', X_3' to system X_1', X_2', X_3', is transformed according to the formula

$$a_{ik} = \sum_{l=1}^{3} \sum_{m=1}^{3} c_{il} c_{km} a_{lm}' \tag{C}$$

The possibility is not excluded that for certain determinate values of cosines c_{ik}, all the components of the tensor prove to be transformed into themselves, that is, the equation

$$a_{ik} = a_{ik}'$$

may prove to be correct. The corresponding transformation will then be a symmetrical operation for the tensor, and the tensor itself will possess the corresponding given operation of symmetry.

It is easy to demonstrate that any polar tensor with real components a_{ik} possesses a center of symmetry. The operation of inversion, corresponding to the existence of a center of symmetry, is carried out with the aid of the scheme of cosines

$$\begin{matrix} -1 & 0 & 0 \\ 0 & -1 & 0 \\ 0 & 0 & -1 \end{matrix}$$

Having substituted these values of cosines in formula (C), it is easy to see that condition $a_{ik} = a_{ik}'$ is fulfilled, and this also means that tensor a_{ik} has a center of symmetry.

By direct substitution in formula (C), of the concrete values of the cosines corresponding to definite symmetrical operations, one may be convinced that for special forms of polar tensors, specific groups of symmetry are derived, for example the polar tensor

$$\begin{matrix} a_{11} & 0 & 0 \\ 0 & a_{11} & 0 \\ 0 & 0 & a_{33} \end{matrix}$$

has symmetry $m \cdot \infty : m$ [∞/mm], whereupon axis ∞ [∞] coincides with axis X_3. Table 7 collects all the conceivable groups of symmetry of two-fold polar tensors.

In crystal physics, along with two-fold tensors, *two-fold axial tensors* are employed. They differ from polar tensors by

TABLE 7

SYMMETRY AND FORM OF TWO-FOLD POLAR TENSORS

Symmetry of tensor	Form of tensor			Arrangement of axes
$\bar{2}$ [$\bar{1}$]	a_{11} a_{12} a_{13}	a_{21} a_{22} a_{23}	a_{31} a_{32} a_{33}	Arbitrary
$2 : m$ [$2/m$]	a_{11} a_{12} 0	C_{21} C_{22} 0	0 0 a_{33}	Axis 2 [2] coincides with X_3
$m \cdot 2 : m$ [mmm]	a_{11} 0 0	0 a_{22} 0	0 0 a_{33}	Axis 2 [2] coincides with X_1, X_2, X_3
$\infty : m$ [∞m]	a_{11} $-a_{21}$ 0	a_{21} a_{11} 0	0 0 a_{33}	Axis ∞ [∞] coincides with X_3
$m \cdot \infty : m$ [∞/mm]	a_{11} 0 0	0 a_{11} 0	0 0 a_{33}	Axis ∞ [∞] coincides with X_3
$\infty/\infty \cdot m$ [$\infty \infty m$]	a_{11} 0 0	0 a_{11} 0	0 0 a_{11}	Arbitrary

the fact that in the formula of transformation (C), the right side takes both signs:

$$a_{ik} = \pm \sum_{l=1}^{3} \sum_{m=1}^{3} c_{il} c_{km} a'_{lm}. \tag{D}$$

The plus sign is used in those cases where both systems of coordinates are coincident; the minus sign is used when both systems are enantiomorphic to each other. In contrast to polar tensors, axial tensors have no center of symmetry. In Table 8 are gathered all the conceivable groups of symmetry of two-fold axial tensors.

The indicated method of determining symmetry of two-fold tensors, may obviously be extended also to three-fold tensors and to tensors of any desired higher multiplicity. In order to solve this problem for three-fold tensors, it is sufficient to establish by which operations of symmetry the components

$$a_{ikl} = \sum_{m=1}^{3} \sum_{n=1}^{3} \sum_{o=1}^{3} c_{im} c_{kn} c_{lo} a'_{mno} \tag{D}$$

are transformed into themselves. We cannot insert this solution here, inasmuch as it still does not exist for the general case. It does exist for a particular case limited by the condition $a_{ikl} = a_{ilk}$ (piezo-electric tensor)*. The solution exists for the particular case of a four-fold tensor limited by the conditions

$$a_{iklm} = a_{ikml},$$
$$a_{iklm} = a_{kilm},$$
$$a_{iklm} = a_{kiml}.$$

We conclude the consideration of the question of symmetry of tensors—a question having cardinal importance for physical crystallography—with the following observation. From the above it is evident that for the determination of the symmetry of vectors and tensors it is necessary to use the schemes of cosines c_{ik}, which fulfill the role of symmetrical operations. On the other hand these very schemes represent tensors and

---

* A. V. Shubnikov, E. E. Flint, G. B. Bokii. Fundamentals of crystallography. Publisher AN USSR, 1940.

TABLE 8

SYMMETRY AND FORM OF TWO-FOLD AXIAL TENSORS

Symmetry of tensor	Form of tensor			Arrangement of axes
1 [1]	a_{11} a_{21} a_{31}	a_{12} a_{22} a_{32}	a_{13} a_{23} a_{33}	Arbitrary
2 [2]	a_{11} a_{21} 0	a_{12} a_{22} 0	0 0 a_{33}	Axis 2 [2] coincides with X_3
$2:2$ [222]	a_{11} 0 0	0 a_{22} 0	0 0 a_{33}	Axis 2 [2] coincides with X_1, X_2, X_3
∞ [∞]	a_{11} $-a_{12}$ 0	a_{12} a_{11} 0	0 0 a_{33}	Axis ∞ [∞] coincides with X_3
$\infty:2$ [$\infty 2$]	a_{11} 0 0	0 a_{11} 0	0 0 a_{33}	Axis ∞ [∞] coincides with X_3
∞/∞ [$\infty\infty$]	a_{11} 0 0	0 a_{11} 0	0 0 a_{11}	Arbitrary
m [m]	0 0 a_{31}	0 0 a_{32}	a_{13} a_{23} 0	Plane m [m] perpendicular to X_3
$2 \cdot m$ [2/m]	0 a_{21} 0	a_{12} 0 0	0 0 0	Axis 2 [2] coincides with X_3; plane m [m] perpendicular to X_1, X_2
$\bar{4} \cdot m$ [$\bar{4}2m$]	a_{11} 0 0	0 $-a_{11}$ 0	0 0 0	Axis $\bar{4}$ [4] coincides with Axis X_3; Axis 2 [2] coincides with axes X_1, X_2

therefore must in turn possess the property of symmetry. At first glance something quite strange results: symmetry itself may possess symmetry. From a formal point of view, there is nothing surprising here, as there is nothing surprising in the fact that there may be a sum of sums, a product of products, a degree of degrees, etc. To apply practically, however, the concept of symmetry to operations of symmetry, may hardly make sense, since for this there would in turn be necessary completely separate operations having nothing in common with the operations under investigation—operations expressed by schemes of cosines of angles between particular axes Y_1, Y_2, Y_3 and Y_1', Y_2', Y_3', having nothing in common with axes X_1, X_2, X_3 and X_1', X_2', X_3', by which a scheme of cosines is assigned.

ANTISYMMETRY OF TEXTURES (LIMITING GROUPS)*

By texture we mean any homogeneous body with nonlattice structure consisting of a multitude of elementary particles of any physical nature which are oriented in space in a definite way (according to the laws of symmetry). Examples of textures are: crystalline structures consisting of acicular or platy crystals, fibrous materials like wood, layered (smectic) and nonlayered (nematic) liquid crystals consisting of molecules oriented with their lengths parallel to each other, electrets consisting of dipoles oriented in the same direction, and magnets with like orientation of electron spins.

Among an infinite number of textures belonging to a great variety of symmetry groups, of especial interest are the textures belonging to the *limiting* symmetry groups, i.e. to the groups containing infinity-fold axes. It is assumed that the particles constituting a texture, and the distances between them along three mutually perpendicular directions, are so small that according to its macroscopic properties the texture may be

* This section was first published in *Kristallografiia*, **3**, 263–268 (1958) and is reprinted from *Sov. Phys. Crystall.*, **3**, 269–273 by courtesy of the American Institute of Physics.

regarded as a continuum extending in all directions. There are seven limiting point groups of symmetry:

$$\infty, \quad \infty \cdot m, \quad \infty : m, \quad \infty : 2, \quad m \cdot \infty : m, \quad \infty / \infty, \quad \infty / \infty \cdot m$$
$$[\infty, \quad \infty m, \quad \infty / m, \quad \infty 2, \quad \infty / mm, \quad \infty \infty, \quad \infty \infty m]$$

The textures belonging to these groups were described in other works of the author[85, 102]. In the present paper this

TABLE 9
LIMITING ANTISYMMETRY GROUPS

∞ [∞]	∞·m [∞m]	∞:m [∞/m]	∞:2 [∞2]	m·∞:m [∞/mm]	∞/∞ [∞∞]	∞/∞·m [∞∞m]
∞̲ [∞′]	∞·m̲ [∞m′]	∞:m̲ [∞/m′]	∞̲:2 [∞′2]	m·∞:m̲ [∞/m′m]	∞̲/∞ [∞∞]	∞/∞·m [∞∞m′]
	∞̲·m [∞′m]	∞̲:m [∞′/m]	∞:2 [∞2′]	m̲·∞:m [∞/mm′]		∞̲/∞·m [∞′∞m′]
	∞̲·m̲ [∞′m′]	∞̲:m̲ [∞′/m′]	∞̲:2̲ [∞′∞′]	m̲·∞:m̲ [∞/m′m′]		∞̲/∞·m [∞′∞m]
				m·∞̲:m [∞′/mm]		
				m̲·∞̲:m [∞′/mm′]		
				m·∞̲:m̲ [∞′/m′m]		
				m̲·∞̲:m̲ [∞′/m′m′]		

description will be extended to *antisymmetric* textures composed of *antiequal,* in the general case asymmetric, particles with *opposite signs,* there being an equal number of particles of each sign. The question of the real existence of such textures in nature is not discussed here. In any case, such textures can be produced artificially (or drawn on paper).

The limiting groups of antisymmetry may be formally derived from the limiting groups of classical symmetry by the same method which is used for the derivation of all other groups of antisymmetry. It is necessary only to replace in the formulae of the limiting symmetry groups given above the symbols of the symmetry elements, successively, by the corresponding antisymmetry symbols and, after an analysis, to exclude repeated groups from the new groups so obtained.

Thus we form first the groups listed in Table 9.

The analysis for repetition of groups and for their existence is made by direct construction of textures from asymmetric

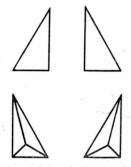

FIG. 125. On the left, a left-handed tetrahedron in two positions; on the right, a right-handed tetrahedron in two positions.

figures of like sign. We have used for this purpose four asymmetric tetrahedra: white right-handed, black right-handed, white left-handed and black left-handed. One face of each tetrahedron is a right triangle. In our diagrams, all tetrahedra have this face in the plane of the paper. The vertex of the tetrahedron opposite this face may be turned towards the observer or away from him. Thus in our diagrams the four tetrahedra will appear in eight different positions. Fig. 125 shows which of the tetrahedra are considered right-handed and which left-handed. It should be noted also that our diagrams (Figs. 126–128) illustrate only the nonspherical point antisymmetry, i.e., those textures which have a single infinity-fold axis or antiaxis (axes parallel to it are not considered). This axis is normal to the plane of the paper in all diagrams.

The upper part of Fig. 126 shows two textures of group $\underline{\infty}\ [\infty']$. On the left is shown a left-handed texture consisting of white left-handed and black left-handed tetrahedra only. On the right is shown the right-handed enantiomorphous texture. In both textures the vertex of each tetrahedron not

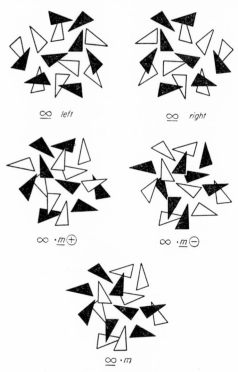

$\underline{\infty}$ *left* $\underline{\infty}$ *right*

$\infty \cdot \underline{m} \oplus$ $\infty \cdot \underline{m} \ominus$

$\underline{\infty} \cdot m$

Fig. 126. Textures of groups $\underline{\infty}$, $\infty \cdot \underline{m}$, and $\underline{\infty} \cdot m\ [\infty',\ \infty m',\ \infty'm]$.

lying on the tetrahedral face parallel to the plane of the drawing (we shall call it the *fourth vertex*) is turned away from the observer. That both these textures belong to group $\underline{\infty}\ [\infty']$ is indicated by the fact that antirotation through any angle about a normal to the plane of the drawing brings each texture (provided that the tetrahedra are small and numerous) into a position practically indistinguishable from the initial position. By antirotation we mean, as in the previously published works, a rotation about the $\underline{\infty}$ [∞'] axis accompanied by a change of sign in the figures, change of all white tetrahedra into black and all black ones into white. The left-handed texture is transformed into right-handed and the right-handed into left-handed by reflection through the plane normal to the plane of the drawing. This reflecting plane is not, of course, a symmetry plane for each separately taken texture. The only symmetry element of the texture is the axis $\underline{\infty}$ [∞'] which is at the same time a simple infinity-fold axis or ∞ [∞] axis.

The textures shown in the middle of Fig. 126 belong to the group $\infty \cdot \underline{m}$ [$\infty m'$] (the period in this symbol indicates parallelism). On the left is a texture consisting of black right-handed and white left-handed tetrahedra, while on the right is a texture composed of black right-handed and white left-handed tetrahedra. The fourth vertex of each tetrahedron in both textures is pointing away from the observer. That these textures belong to the group $\infty \cdot \underline{m}$ [$\infty m'$] is indicated by the fact that each texture is in practice transformed into itself by simple rotation through any angle about the normal to the plane of the drawing (∞ [∞] axis) and by antireflection through any plane normal to the plane of the drawing. By antireflection is meant reflection accompanied by change of sign of the figures. It is evident that each of these textures may also be transformed into itself by complex operations of combined rotations and antireflections. The drawings show that every texture belonging to group $\infty \cdot \underline{m}$ [$\infty m'$] may exist theoretically in two modifications, *positive* and *negative*. It is transformed from one to the other by the change of sign, an operation which is not an antisymmetry operation for each figure taken separately. The first texture can also be transformed into the second by a reflection through a plane parallel or normal to the plane of the drawing, but this is not a symmetry operation either, for either texture taken separately.

The lowermost diagram of Fig. 126 shows a texture belonging to group $\underline{\infty} \cdot m$ [$\infty'm$]. This texture consists of equal numbers of tetrahedra of all four kinds: white left-handed, white right-handed, black left-handed and black right-handed. It is easy to see that this texture transforms into itself both by antirotation about axis $\underline{\infty}$ [∞'] and by simple reflection through the m [m] planes normal to the plane of the drawing. Every texture belonging to this group may exist in only one modification. This texture has one important relation to the textures previously discussed; as the drawing shows, the fourth vertices of all of its tetrahedra point away from the observer. It is

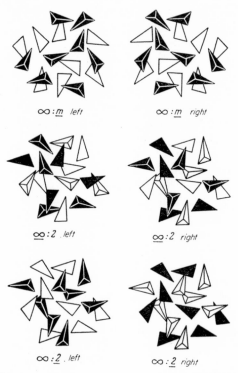

$\infty:\underline{m}$ *left* $\infty:\underline{m}$ *right*

$\underline{\infty}:2$ *left* $\underline{\infty}:2$ *right*

$\infty:\underline{2}$ *left* $\infty:\underline{2}$ *right*

FIG. 127. Textures of groups $\infty:\underline{m}$, $\underline{\infty}:2$ and $\infty:\underline{2}$ [∞/m', $\infty'2$, $\infty\,2'$].

obvious that this texture could also be represented with the fourth vertices of all of its tetrahedra pointing towards the observer. This property of all these textures, belonging to the groups listed above, refers them to the *geometrically polar* or *hemimorphic* type.

In accordance with the table given above the next group to be discussed should be group $\underline{\infty}\cdot\underline{m}$ [$\infty'm'$]. It is easily seen, however, that this group is not distinct from the group $\underline{\infty}\cdot m$ [$\infty'm$] which has already been described.

$$\underline{\infty}\cdot\underline{m} = \underline{\infty}m \quad [\infty'm' = \infty'm]$$

This follows from the fact that among the operations contained in $\underline{\infty}$ [∞'] there is an operation of simple sign change ($\underline{1}$ [$1'$]) which in combination with reflection m gives $\underline{m}$ [m'].

Next in the table is group $\infty:\underline{m}$ [∞/m']. It is defined by the simple ∞ [∞] axis and the transverse antisymmetry plane (the colon in the symbol $\infty:m$ [$\infty m'$] indicates perpendicularity). The textures corresponding to this group are shown in the upper part of Fig. 127. On the left is the texture developed from a single given white left-handed tetrahedron (with its fourth vertex away from the observer) by *reproducing* it through the operations contained in groups ∞ [∞] and $\infty:\underline{m}$ [∞/m'] (and various translation operations contained in the groups). At the right is a texture formed from the one on the left by simple mirror reflection in the plane normal to the plane of the drawing. This means that these textures are enantiomorphous in relation to each other in spite of the fact that each contains both right-handed and left-handed tetrahedra.

The next group is $\underline{\infty}:m$ [∞'/m]. For technical reasons the texture corresponding to it is shown in the lower left corner of Fig. 128 and not in Fig. 127. The method of construction of this texture, as of the preceding ones, is indicated by an appropriate symbol. Starting with any tetrahedron, say a white right-handed one, with its fourth vertex towards the observer, we repeat it by the operations of the axis $\underline{\infty}$ [∞']. We obtain, then, an infinite aggregate of white right-handed and black right-handed tetrahedra with the fourth vertices pointing in the same direction. From this aggregate, by a simple reflection $1:m$, [$1/m$], we obtain a second aggregate of white left-handed and black left-handed tetrahedra with the fourth vertices pointing in the other direction. When superimposed, these two textures form the texture of the group $\underline{\infty}:m$ [∞'/m]. This texture has neither an enantiomorphous nor an opposite sign modification.

Next in the table is group $\underline{\infty}:\underline{m}$ [∞'/m']. It is easy to see by a direct construction of the corresponding texture that this group is identical with group $\underline{\infty}:m$, which has already been discussed

$$\underline{\infty}:\underline{m} = \underline{\infty}:m \quad [\infty'/m' = \infty'm]$$

Let us go on to group $\underline{\infty}:2\ [\infty'2]$. The corresponding textures are given in the middle of Fig. 127. The method of their construction is clear from the preceding. The texture on the

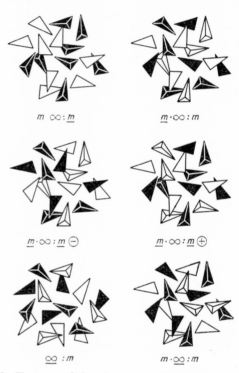

$m\ \infty:\underline{m}$ $\underline{m}\cdot\infty:m$

$\underline{m}\cdot\infty:\underline{m}\ \ominus$ $\underline{m}\cdot\infty:\underline{m}\ \oplus$

$\underline{\infty}\ :m$ $m\cdot\underline{\infty}:m$

FIG. 128. Textures of the groups $m\cdot\infty:\underline{m}$; $\underline{m}\cdot\infty:m$; $\underline{m}\cdot\infty:\underline{m}$; $m\cdot\underline{\infty}:m$ $[\infty/m'm,\ \infty/mm',\ \infty/m'm',\ \infty'/mm]$.

left consists entirely of white left-handed tetrahedra and black left-handed tetrahedra, but half of each type have their fourth vertices towards, and half away from the observer. The texture on the right consists of right-handed tetrahedra only. Apart from that, it is like the texture on the left.

Group $\underline{\infty}:2\ [\infty'2]$ is followed by group $\infty:\underline{2}\ [\infty2']$. The textures corresponding to this group are shown at the bottom of Fig. 127. Like the preceding textures, they consist of right-handed and left-handed tetrahedra. In each of these textures, all white tetrahedra have their fourth vertices pointing in one direction and all black tetrahedra, in the opposite direction.

Next in order is group $\underline{\infty} : \underline{2}$ [$\infty'2'$]. By constructing a corresponding texture, we become convinced that it is identical with group $\underline{\infty} : 2$ [$\infty'2$].

$$\underline{\infty} : \underline{2} = \underline{\infty} : 2 \quad [\infty'2' = \infty'2]$$

We have discussed all groups defined by two symmetry elements (with the necessary participation of ∞ [∞] and $\underline{\infty}$ [∞']). Let us pass now to the groups defined by three symmetry elements. First, the group $m \cdot \infty : \underline{m}$ [$\infty/m'm$]. This group is represented by the texture shown in the left upper corner of Fig. 128. It is obtained by a simple reflection of either the right or left texture of group $\infty : m$ [∞/m'] in the plane parallel to the ∞ [∞] axis or, what is the same, by combining the right and left textures of group $\infty : \underline{m}$ [∞/m']. This texture consists of white (right- and left-handed) tetrahedra pointing with their fourth vertices in one direction and as many black (right- and left-handed) tetrahedra pointing with their fourth vertices in the other direction.

The next group is $\underline{m} \cdot \infty : m$ [∞/mm']. It is represented by the texture in the upper right corner of Fig. 128. The symbol of this group indicates that the corresponding texture may be derived from the texture belonging to the group $\infty \cdot \underline{m}$ ($\infty m'$) by reflection in a plane normal to ∞ [∞] or, what is the same thing, by the combination of positive and negative textures of group $\infty \cdot \underline{m}$ [$\infty m'$]. This texture consists of white left-handed and black right-handed tetrahedra with their fourth vertices pointing in one direction and white right-handed and black left-handed tetrahedra whose fourth vertices point in the other direction.

Let us review group $\underline{m} \cdot \infty : \underline{m}$ [$\infty/m'm'$]. Its textures are given on the right and left in the middle of Fig. 128. They may be obtained from the textures of group $\infty \cdot \underline{m}$ [$\infty m'$] by antireflection in the plane normal to ∞ [∞]. Inasmuch as the texture belonging to group $\infty \cdot \underline{m}$ [$\infty m'$] may be either positive or negative modifications. The negative modification consists of white right-handed tetrahedra in two positions and of black left-handed tetrahedra, also in two positions. The positive modification consists of white left-handed tetrahedra in two positions and of black right-handed tetrahedra, also in two positions.

Let us pass to group $m \cdot \underline{\infty} : m$ $[\infty'/mm]$. The symbol of this group indicates that the corresponding texture may be constructed by doubling the texture belonging to group $\underline{\infty} : m$ $[\infty'/m]$ by reflection in the plane of symmetry parallel to the $\underline{\infty}$ $[\infty']$ axis. The texture is composed of all four types of tetrahedra, and each type enters into the texture in two orientations (Fig. 128, right lower corner).

It remains to review groups $\underline{m} : \underline{\infty} : m$, $m \cdot \underline{\infty} : \underline{m}$ and $\underline{m} \cdot \underline{\infty} : \underline{m}$ $[\infty'/mm', \infty'/m'm, \infty'/m'm']$. It is not difficult to see that these groups repeat the group just described,

$$\underline{m} \cdot \underline{\infty} : m = m \cdot \underline{\infty} : \underline{m} = \underline{m} \cdot \underline{\infty} : \underline{m} = m \cdot \underline{\infty} : m$$
$$[\infty'/mm' = \infty'/m'm = \infty'/m'm' = \infty'/mm].$$

We have derived all the antisymmetry groups of the *anisotropic textures*, i.e., of textures in the proper sense. To these groups we must add the groups of the *isotropic media* or of isotropic textures in the broad sense. These groups are derived from the spherical groups ∞/∞ $[\infty\infty]$ and $\infty/\infty \cdot m$ $[\infty\infty m]$ containing an infinite number of infinity-fold axes, by the same method which was used to derive all of the preceding groups. We shall review groups $\underline{\infty}/\infty$, $\underline{\infty}/\infty \cdot m$, $\underline{\infty}/\infty \cdot \underline{m}$, and $\infty/\infty \cdot \underline{m}$ $[\infty'\infty, \infty'\infty m, \infty'\infty m', \text{ and } \infty\infty m']$.

The textures of group $\underline{\infty}/\infty$ $[\infty'\infty]$ consist either of right-handed (white and black) tetrahedra only, or of left-handed (white and black) tetrahedra only, uniformly and randomly distributed in space (without definite orientation). The number of white and black tetrahedra is the same in every texture.

The textures of group $\underline{\infty}/\infty \cdot m$ $[\infty'\infty m]$ are composed of tetrahedra of all four kinds in equal quantities. As in the preceding group the tetrahedra are uniformly and randomly distributed in space.

It is easy to see that the third group, $\underline{\infty}/\infty \cdot \underline{m}$ $[\infty'\infty m']$, is identical with the preceding one.

Textures of group $\infty/\infty \cdot \underline{m}$ [$\infty \infty m'$] consist of tetrahedra of two sorts: right white and left black or, inversely, left white and right black.

Conclusion

The antisymmetry of textures with infinity-fold symmetry axes can be described in terms of fourteen limiting groups. Five of these groups admit enantiomorphism, that is, the existence of right-handed and left-handed textures derived from each other by a simple reflection in a plane. Two groups admit a special "sign" enantiomorphism, that is, the existence of texture modifications which can be transformed one into another by sign change in all particles of the texture.

ON THE TERMS: "DISSYMMETRY", "ASYMMETRY", AND "ANTISYMMETRY"

"Asymmetry" and "dissymmetry" are often confused in the literature. We propose, in complete conformity with the grammar of these words, that asymmetry means the absence of symmetry, while dissymmetry means the derangement of symmetry. An asymmetrical figure is a figure deprived of all elements of symmetry with the exclusion of the ever-present element of identification. The term "dissymmetry" was first used by Pasteur for designating the absence of elements of symmetry of the second kind in a figure. According to Pasteur, elements of symmetry of the first kind are not excluded in a dissymmetrical figure. Pierre Curie applied the term "dissymmetry" in a broader sense; in the sense of the absence of those elements of symmetry in a crystal upon which depends the existence in it of one or another physical property. We propose, in developing the ideas of Pasteur and Curie, to call dissymmetry the *falling out* of one or another element of symmetry from a *given* group, since to speak of the absence of elements of symmetry makes sense only when they are present somewhere else.

The term "antisymmetry" has been selected by us to signify *reverse symmetry*. The prefix "anti" signifies exactly this oppositeness, and not at all the absence or derangement of symmetry.

It is evident from the text that antisymmetry may be *formally* considered as the *symmetry* of three-dimensional figures in four-dimensional space. We ourselves do not believe in the reality of four-dimensional space. What we mean by it is space with four mutually perpendicular and physically equivalent axes of coordinates. Operations of symmetry in four-dimensional space are, for us, only a *means* of describing what we may observe, without having recourse to the image of four-dimensional space. This explains the fact that we prefer the worldly, materialistic term "*antisymmetry*" to the obscure, idealistic term "symmetry in four-dimensional space".

PART II

Infinite Groups of Colored Symmetry

by N. V. BELOV and others

The 1651 Shubnikov Groups
(Dichromatic Space Groups)*

N. V. BELOV, N. N. NERONOVA and T. S. SMIRNOVA

INTRODUCTION

IN 1951, A. V. Shubnikov[93] introduced into crystallography the concept of antisymmetry—the opposition of faces, points and other crystallographic objects which have been assigned a positive sign, to objects which are analogous but are characterized by a negative sign. In practice it proved convenient to designate positive objects by a white color and negative objects by black, so that the term "black-white" or generally, dichromatic symmetry, is used instead of the term "antisymmetry". The term "dichromatic symmetry" is most convenient since it permits, by developing A. V. Shubnikov's ideas, the construction of groups of multicolored symmetry also[107].

The theoretical constructions of A. V. Shubnikov found unexpected application in the theory and practice of interpreting crystallographic structures by harmonic analysis. The corresponding new methods were developed in the U.S.S.R. by by B. K. Vainshtein[103] and in England by Cochran[95]. Moreover, it is the infinite groups in A. V. Shubnikov's works rather than the black-white point groups which play an important role. Forty-six two-dimensional open black-white groups were derived by Cochran[94], in which he proceeded from the 80 groups of symmetry of plane layers† established by Alexander and Herrmann[81,39] and by Weber[38]. It should be mentioned that concepts of black-white symmetry were fully utilized in the illustrations to the latter work. In reproducing these diagrams in his well-known book, *Symmetry*[59], A. V. Shubnikov introduced the essentially new concept of "gray" crystallographic objects.

* Published in *Trudy Akad. Nauk SSSR., Inst. Kristall.*, **11**, 33–67 (1955).

† He excluded from them 17 Fedorov groups and an equal number of "gray" groups (see below).

In the above works it was demonstrated that plane groups, both black-white and multicolored, are particular cases of the 230 Fedorov groups. This is not the case in the derivation of black-white space groups of symmetry and we must create anew an original system of concepts and theorems.

The total number of black-white space groups was first calculated by A. M. Zamorzaev[98] and it was he who introduced the term "Shubnikov groups". In his derivation, A. M. Zamorzaev proceeded from three basic works: A. V. Shubnikov's book, and in addition, *The Derivation of Regular Systems by the Fedorov Method* by S. A. Bogomolov[49] and *Mathematical Fundamentals of the Structural Analysis of Crystals* by B. N. Delone, N. N. Padurov and A. D. Aleksandrov[83].

The two latter books are little known to contemporary specialists in microcrystallography (crystal chemistry)—the chief users of space groups. The authors of the present work have derived all of the black-white groups, proceeding from the system of Fedorov groups which is to be found in the charts of E. S. Fedorov himself[86] and which now is in the basic manual of the specialist in crystallographic structure, *International Tables for Determination of Crystalline Structures*[84], *Structural Crystallography*[91] and *Class Method*[90] serve as the corresponding training manuals in the U.S.S.R. and all of the concepts which we shall use later are only an extension of "monochromatic" concepts and theorems from the two latter manuals, in cases where dichromatic (or as we abbreviate them, "colored") elements of symmetry are taken into consideration as well as ordinary elements.

Our derivation of all the black-white groups was carried out independently of A. M. Zamorzaev and his methods; we became acquainted with his book only at the last minute, read it quickly and noted in particular the author's desire for the possibility of an independent proof of his results.

BRAVAIS LATTICES FOR SHUBNIKOV GROUPS

The derivation of Bravais lattices for Shubnikov groups is based upon a fundamental property of color translation:

two consecutive color translations in one direction are equivalent to one uncolored translation in the same direction. Consequently, the length of any given shortest color translation is equal to half the length of the shortest uncolored translation in the same direction.

Thus if nodes of "opposite signs" exist in a space lattice, each node is located at half the distance between any given two nodes of opposite sign. It is easy to show that additional

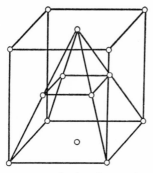

FIG. 129. An important case of colored centering in a Bravais lattice.

nodes of opposite sign may be found only in the center of an edge, face or cell of each of the 14 Bravais lattices, but additional nodes of opposite sign *cannot be located* at $\frac{1}{4}$ of a plane diagonal when there is uncolored centering of a face, or at $\frac{1}{4}$ of a space diagonal when there is uncolored body centering.

If the face of a cell is centered, the existence of additional nodes of an opposite sign at $\frac{1}{4}$ of both plane diagonals of this face will lead to a twofold reduction of the shortest translations along those edges which have already been selected as the shortest (see ref. 91). The existence of such nodes on one diagonal is also impossible. Actually, if there is a centered face in the lattice, it is always rectangular and parallel even if a two-fold axis or a normal to the plane of symmetry passes along one of its edges. In the first case the *digyre* reverses the oblique translation and directs it along a second diagonal, by which the "shortest" uncolored translations again prove to be halved. In the second case, a mirror plane reflects the colored translation and directs it along the second diagonal. In reference 91

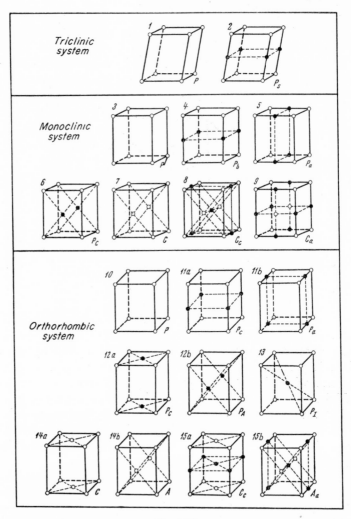

F<small>IG.</small> 130.

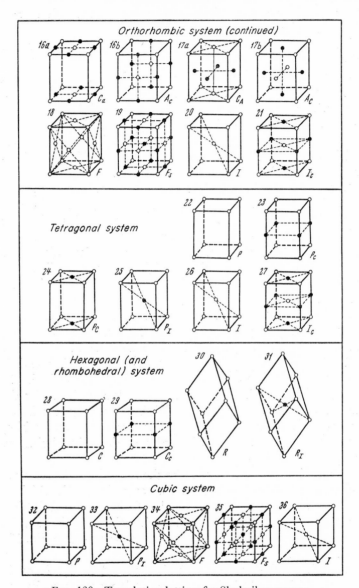

FIG. 130. Translation lattices for Shubnikov groups.

it is demonstrated that the same effect is obtained with a screw axis and a glide plane.

The demonstration is analogous for volumetrically centered cells.

Let us examine one more case. We have a base-centered cell. Let there exist a colored translation $t'(|t'| = \frac{1}{2}|t|)$ in the direction of translation t. But in monoclinic, rhombic and cubic syngony where such a lattice is possible, a second color translation t'_1 inevitably arises due to axes or planes of symmetry, which leads to a two-fold decrease in edges of the cell which are parallel to the centered face (Fig. 129).

In order to obtain Bravais lattices for Shubnikov groups, we proceed from Bravais lattices for Fedorov groups and add color translations only along the edges, diagonals of the faces or spatial diagonals of the cell. Thus from cell P we obtain colored cells P_s*, P_C, and P_I. Color translations along two non-parallel edges determine a C-lattice, not a P-lattice; color translations along the diagonals of two faces yield an I-lattice, etc.

Lattice P and lattices P_s, P_C and P_I obtained from it constitute a family of primitive lattices; lattices C, C_c, C_a and C_A are a family of base-centered and end-centered lattices; I and I_c are a family of body-centered lattices and F and F_s are a family of face-centered lattices. Together with the 14 uncolored ones we have 36 translational lattices in all for the Shubnikov groups (Fig. 130). Joining these lattices in all the possible combinations of simple and colored (black-white) elements of symmetry, we will arrive at the 1651 Shubnikov groups.

1. The rhombic system includes the most diversified Bravais lattices and therefore it is the most convenient with which to start[90]. By color centering of the four uncolored lattices P, C, F and I we will arrive at the eight colored lattices P_s, P_C, P_I, C_a, C_A, C_c, F_s and I_c. All twelve are represented in Fig. 130 (Nos. 10–21).

In each particular case, P_s is interpreted as P_a, P_b or P_c depending along which axis (x, y, z) it is more convenient to

* s (sceles)—edge.

direct the sole colored translation. Cell P, centered (by color) on one face, may also be taken in any given "aspect" P_C, P_A, P_B.

Similarly, for lattices C_c, $C_a(C_b)$ and C_A, aspects A_a, $A_c(A_b)$ and A_C, or B_b, $B_c(B_a)$ and B_C are possible.

From Fig. 130 (No. 21) the identity $I_c \equiv I_C$, and (in other

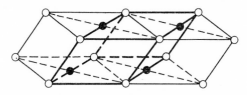

FIG. 131. Identity of triclinic lattices P_C and P_s.

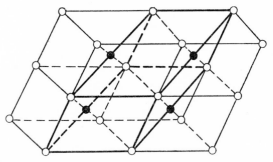

FIG. 132. Identity of triclinic lattices P_I and P_s.

aspects) $I_a \equiv I_A$, $I_b \equiv I_B$ follow, (all within the limits of the orthorhombic system).

2. In the triclinic system there are two lattices: (1) P and (2) P_s. Lattices P_C and P_I, however, both reduce to P_s, as follows from Figs. 131 and 132. It seems more correct for P_C and P_s both to lead to P_I rather than to a simpler one.

3. In the monoclinic system, from monochromatic lattice P (No. 3) we obtain the three colored lattices P_c, (No. 4) P_b (No. 5) and P_C (No. 6); from C (No. 7) we obtain C_c (No. 8) and C_a (No. 9).

Again, P_a and P_A are only other aspects of lattices P_c and

P_C. Lattice P_B reduces to P_c and P_I reduces to P_C (Figs. 133 and 134).

Upon centering face C, the following become identical: on one hand, $C_b \equiv C_a$, and on the other, $C_A \equiv C_B$, whereupon the latter lattice may be reduced to C_c (Fig. 135).

4. In the tetragonal system, from uncolored lattice P (No. 22)

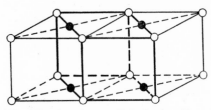

Fig. 133. Identity of monoclinic lattices P_B and P_c.

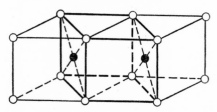

Fig. 134. Identity of monoclinic lattices P_I and P_C.

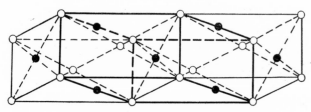

Fig. 135. Identity of monoclinic lattices C_B and C_c.

three more colored lattices are obtained: P_c (No. 23) P_C (No. 24) and P_I (No. 25), and from uncolored I (No. 26) only one colored one, I_c (No. 27).

Figures 136 and 137 show that the possible lattices P_a and

P_A reduce, respectively, to P_C and P_I. Analogously, lattice I_a reduces to P_C.

If, in conformity to accepted mineralogical practice, lattices C and F are used in the tetragonal system (instead of the simpler lattices P and I, see Belov[90,91]), then the corresponding colored groups will look somewhat different, namely, group P_c

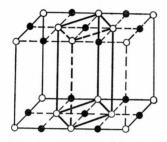

FIG. 136. Identity of tetragonal lattices P_a and P_C.

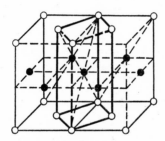

FIG. 137. Identity of tetragonal lattices P_A and P_I.

will be presented as C_c, but group P_C as C_a and group P_I as C_A and group I_c as F_s.

5. In the hexagonal (including the trigonal) system, from uncolored lattice C (No. 28) we obtain colored C_c (No. 29) (or in another mineralogical aspect, H and H_c). From the hexagonal doubly-centered (see Belov[90]) lattice R (No. 30), the colored lattice R_I (No. 31) is obtained.

Figure 138 demonstrates how easily a simpler lattice R_I is derived from a theoretical lattice R_s.

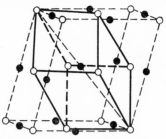

FIG. 138. Identity of rhombohedric lattices R_s and R_I.

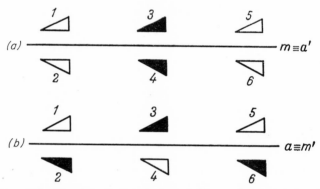

FIG. 139. Identity of colored planes with particular uncolored ones during the parallelism of the colored translation to these planes.

In both diagrams, the solid line is axis x (the trace of the plane $x0y$). In figure 139a, the pair of triangles 1–2 are related by the uncolored mirror plane m; the pair 3–4 are related in the same manner. Pair 1–3 are related by color translation; pair 2–4 are related in the same manner. As a result, pair 1–4 are related by a colored glide plane, and the same applies to pair 2–3; i.e., plane $m \equiv a'$. In figure 139b, the triangles 1–4 are related by an uncolored glide plane; figures 2–3 are related in the same manner. The pair of triangles 1–3 are related by color translation; pair 2–4 are related in the same manner. As a result, both pair 1–2 and pair 3–4 prove to be related by mirror, colored plane $a \equiv m'$.

If the center triangles in both diagrams are raised by half a translation, perpendicular to the plane of the drawing, then the color translation will become oblique and we will obtain $m \equiv n'$ in figure 139a and $n \equiv m'$ in figure 139b.

6. To three uncolored lattices are added only two colored ones: P (No. 32), P_I (No. 33), F (No. 34), F_s (No. 35), I (No. 36).

SYMBOLISM. GENERAL THEOREMS

In the list of Shubnikov groups given at the end of the chapter (Table 10) their symbols are constructed according to the "International" method, the fundamentals of which are given in detail in reference[90]. Each of the elements of symmetry* designated in symbols may be uncolored (not changing the color or "sign" of the objects it relates) or colored. The latter is designated by a "prime".†

In A. V. Shubnikov's basic work[93] and also in reference[59], there is a detailed analysis of the concept of neutral or "gray" groups. Any one of the 230 Fedorov groups may be transformed into the corresponding gray group by the addition of the operation of "anti-identification"; we designate the corresponding element of symmetry (antisymmetry) by a $1'$ (placed at the end of the symbol). This approach made it unnecessary to consider separately the gray Bravais lattices, which would have increased their total number to 50.

THEOREM 1. Reflection in a given plane and subsequent translation in a direction perpendicular to the indicated plane are equivalent to reflection (of the same character, i.e., to mirror or glide reflection) in a "derived" plane which is parallel to the original one but lags behind it by half the translation. The reflection will be non-colored if the first reflection and translation are both non-colored or both colored, and it will

---

* In the derivations of the theorems, the element "symmetry step" (which is absent in the list of groups) plays an important role. It is a translation which may be uncolored (t) or colored (t').

† In the detailed listing of the 1651 groups, which follows later, it did not seem possible to use A. V. Shubnikov's original method of designating colored elements by a line underneath the symbol, because of the possibility of confusing these marks with interlinear marks of the line beneath (mirror or inversion axes). M. A. Porai-Koshits has proposed that colored elements (of antisymmetry) be designated by inverted letters: $m' = \text{ɯ}$ and so on.

be colored if one of the constituent operations is colored and the other is non-colored. In the simplified formulation (which we shall use in the future[70],[90]) the "product" of a plane of symmetry and a perpendicular translation is a parallel plane with the same character of reflection, located in the middle of the two original planes that are related by (the shortest) translation. The derived plane is non-colored if the generating elements of symmetry are of similar color, and it is colored if they are colored differently.

THEOREM 2. If the color translation is parallel to the plane of symmetry (m, n, c, g), then the latter will simultaneously be colored. If this plane coincides with face $x0y$ of the cell, then when the colored translation is parallel to axis x, we will have: $m \equiv a'$, $n \equiv b'$, $a \equiv m'$, and $b \equiv n'$; with $t' \| y$, we will obtain: $m \equiv b'$, $n \equiv a'$, $a \equiv n'$, $b \equiv m'$. If the colored translation is directed along the diagonal of the face, then $m \equiv n'$, $n \equiv m'$, $a \equiv b'$ and $b \equiv a'$ (Fig. 139).

If there are colored translations parallel to both axes, then $m \equiv n \equiv a' \equiv b'$ and $b \equiv a \equiv m' \equiv n'$.

THEOREM 3. If the translation is located obliquely in relation to the plane of symmetry, then we divide the translation into components perpendicular and parallel to the plane. The first component determines the derived plane (by transferring it, preserving the plane's parallelism to itself, a distance of one half the component), and the second component is "injected" into the derived plane as an additional glide component. The derived plane is colored if the generating plane and the translation are of different coloration, and it is non-colored if they are of like coloration.

THEOREM 4. An n-fold axis and a perpendicular translation generate a parallel axis of the same multiplicity and nature (rotation, screw, mirror, glide). The derived axis passes through the apex of an isosceles triangle with an angle of $360°/n$, constructed in the plane of rotation with the generative (shortest) translation as a base. The coloration of the axis is determined by the coloration of the generating elements, as previously.

THEOREM 5. If we have a rotation or screw axis and a colored translation parallel to it, then this axis is simultaneously a colored axis, rotation or screw. The following show such cases:

$$2 \times t'_{\parallel} = 2(2'_1), \qquad 6 \times t'_{\parallel} = 6(6''_3),$$
$$2_1 \times t'_{\parallel} = 2_1(2'), \qquad 6_3 \times t'_{\parallel} = 6_3(6'),$$
$$3 \times t'_{\parallel} = 3(6\uparrow)*, \qquad 6_1 \times t'_{\parallel} = 6_1(6'_4),$$
$$4 \times t'_{\parallel} = 4(4'_2), \qquad 6_3 \times t'_{\parallel} = 6_5(6'_2),$$
$$4_1 \times t'_{\parallel} = 4_1(4'_3), \qquad 6_2 \times t'_{\parallel} = 6_2(6'_5),$$
$$4_2 \times t'_{\parallel} = 4_2(4'), \qquad 6_4 \times t'_{\parallel} = 6_4(6'_1).$$
$$4_3 \times t'_{\parallel} = 4_3(4'_1),$$

THEOREM 6. If the translation is located obliquely in relation to the axis, we separate the translation into a component perpendicular to the axis and a component parallel to the axis. The first component transfers the axis to the apex of an isosceles triangle that lies in the plane of rotation and that has a side equal to the first component, where a rotation is generated with an angle of $360°/n$. The second component combines with the derived axis [as a screw translation component].

Comments. (1) Axes of odd-numbered multiplicity cannot be black-white; (2) 3-fold or 6-fold axes, which are related by color translations, can only be gray.

THEOREM 7. Two planes (mirror or glide) intersecting at angles of 30°, 45°, 60° or 90° generate 6-fold, 4-fold, 3-fold, or 2-fold rotation or screw axes on the line of their intersection or at a specific distance from it and parallel to it; the derived axis is uncolored if both generating planes are the same color, and it is colored if they are of different colors.

THEOREM 8. If two 2-fold rotation axes intersect at angles of 30°, 45°, 60°, or 90°, a 6-fold, 4-fold, 3-fold, 2-fold derived axis will arise, perpendicular to the plane in which the generating axes lie and passing through the point of intersection of the generating axes. The derived axis is uncolored if both generating axes are the same color, and is colored if they are of different colors. If one or both generating axes are screw

---

* A new element of symmetry. The basic operation—a 120° rotation with subsequent elevation and a change of color—is of the 6th order. If the third step of an ordinary rotation about a 6-fold axis is a rotation about a 2-fold axis, of a 6-fold mirror rotation is inversion, and of a 6-fold rotatory inversion is mirror reflection, then we have here as a third step a (colored) translation ($L_6^3 = L_2$; $\bar{L}_6^3 = C$; $\overset{\circ}{L}_6^3 = P$; $\overset{\uparrow}{L}_6'^3 = t'$; see ref. 70).

axes, then the derived axis will be displaced [from the intersect on] by $\frac{1}{4}$ of a translation along each screw axis.

Comment. Since a six-fold axis may be considered as a mechanical combination of a three-fold and a two-fold axis, then as with uncolored axes[90], the following also occurs for colored axes:

$$6' = 3 + 2', \qquad 6'_3 = 3 + 2'_1,$$
$$6'_1 = 3_1 + 2'_1, \qquad 6'_5 = 3_2 + 2'_1,$$
$$6'_2 = 3_2 + 2', \qquad 6'_4 = 3_2 + 2'.$$

THEOREM 9. As a result of the intersection of three mutually perpendicular planes of symmetry, or of the intersection of a 2-fold axis with a perpendicular plane, a derived center of symmetry emerges. If there is an even number of intersecting elements with semi-translations parallel to a given coordinate axis, then along this axis the center is not displaced at all; if this number is uneven, the center is displaced along the axis a quarter of its length. The center is colored if there is an uneven number of colored generating elements, and is uncolored if there is an even number. When three intersecting planes (or an axis and a plane) are not at right angles, they generate a mirror axis, colored or uncolored depending on the number of colored generating elements.

THEOREM 10. The product of a center of symmetry and a translation yields a derived center in the middle, between the two centers related by the translation. The derived center of symmetry is uncolored if the original center and translation are the same color, and is colored if they are of different colors.

THE DERIVATION OF SHUBNIKOV GROUPS

We derive the Shubnikov groups by combining the 36 Bravais lattices with all the possible combinations of colored and uncolored elements of symmetry.

Shubnikov groups with lattices *P, C, F* and *I* include 230 Fedorov groups, 230 gray groups and 674 black-white groups. Lattices P_s, P_c, P_I, C_c, C_a, C_A, F_s and I_c are characteristic only of the black-white groups. The number of such groups is 517.

Let us derive the Shubnikov groups for rhombic hemi-morphy—$C_{2v} = mm$ (horseshoe class[90]). Formally, the matter is reduced to the selection of combinations of two (with repetitions) from the ten different planes of symmetry m, m', c, c', g, g', d, d', the filling in of the twelve different Bravais lattices by these pairs, and discarding the repeated ones. The latter process is simplified by the aid of general con-siderations given below.

In the given class there are ten primitive Fedorov groups

Pmm,			
Pmn,	Pnn,		
Pmc,	Pnc,	Pcc,	
Pmg,	Png,	Pcg,	Pgg,

and ten primitive gray groups

Pmm 1',			
Pmn 1',	Pnn 1',		
Pmc 1',	Pnc 1',	Pcc 1',	
Pmg 1',	Png 1',	Pcg 1',	Pgg 1'.

In the black-white primitive groups, either one or both planes may be colored. The former possibility yields the ten groups

Pm'm',			
Pm'n',	Pn'n',		
Pm'c',	Pn'c',	Pc'c',	
Pm'g',	Pn'g',	Pc'g',	Pg'g'.

If there are two identical letters in the symbol of a group (planes with an identical character of reflection), but one plane is colored while the other is not, then it is of no difference topologically in class C_{2v} on which of the letters the stroke is placed, i.e., we have four such groups

$$Pmm', \qquad Pnn', \qquad Pcc', \qquad Pgg'.$$

There are twelve groups with different letters but with one colored and one uncolored plane $[(10 \times 4) + 2 = 6 \times 2 = 12]$

$$Pmn', \qquad Pm'n, \qquad Pnc', \qquad Pn'c,$$
$$Pmc', \qquad Pm'c, \qquad Png', \qquad Pn'g,$$
$$Pmg', \qquad Pm'g, \qquad Pcg', \qquad Pc'g.$$

Thus there are 46 groups with lattice P in class C_{2v}.

Let us now consider groups with lattice P_s, i.e., with one (color) centered edge. In class C_{2v}, edges c and g are topologically different. For the sake of definiteness, for g we select a. First we write out the ten groups P_c corresponding to the Fedorov groups P,

$$P_c mm,$$
$$P_c mn, \qquad P_c nn,$$
$$P_c mc, \qquad P_c nc, \qquad P_c cc,$$
$$P_c mg, \qquad P_c ng, \qquad P_c cg, \qquad P_c gg.$$

As a result of colored centering of edge c (according to theorem 2), plane m is at the same time plane c' and, in exactly the same way,

$$n \equiv g', \quad c \equiv m', \quad g \equiv n'.$$

Therefore these groups may be written out in greater detail, thus[90]:

$$P_c mm \equiv P_c m(c')m(c') \equiv P_c mc' \equiv P_c c'm \equiv P_c c'c',$$
$$P_c nn \equiv P_c n(g')n(g') \equiv P_c ng' \equiv P_c g'n \equiv P_c g'g',$$
$$P_c cc \equiv P_c c(m')c(m') \equiv P_c cm' \equiv P_c m'c \equiv P_c m'm',$$
$$P_c gg \equiv P_c g(n')g(n') \equiv P_c gn' \equiv P_c n'g \equiv P_c n'n',$$
$$P_c mn \equiv P_c m(c')n(g') \equiv P_c mg' \equiv P_c c'n \equiv P_c c'g',$$
$$P_c mc \equiv P_c m(c')c(m') \equiv P_c mm' \equiv P_c c'c \equiv P_c c'm',$$
$$P_c mg \equiv P_c m(c')g(n') \equiv P_c mn' \equiv P_c c'g \equiv P_c c'n',$$
$$P_c nc \equiv P_c n(g')c(m') \equiv P_c nm' \equiv P_c g'c \equiv P_c g'm',$$
$$P_c ng \equiv P_c n(g')g(n') \equiv P_c nn' \equiv P_c g'g \equiv P_c g'n',$$
$$P_c cg \equiv P_c c(m')g(n') \equiv P_c cn' \equiv P_c m'g \equiv P_c m'n'.$$

We see that any given group P_c with one or both colored planes reduces to (is identical to) one of the ten groups which are similar to the Fedorov groups, i.e., which contain only uncolored planes in the symbol.

Upon color centering of edge a, the places standing in the first and second position of the symbol become topologically different. A plane (uncolored) in the first position, according to Theorem 1, alternates with an analogous colored one and vice versa $(m - m', n - n', c - c', g - g'$, etc.$)$. The uncolored planes in the second position, according to Theorem 2, are simultaneously colored and vice versa: $m \equiv a'$, $n \equiv c'$, $c \equiv n'$, $a(g) \equiv m'$.

Thus with lattice P_a we shall have four groups with identical letters in the symbol, if only uncolored planes are used in the latter:

$$P_a mm \equiv P_a m, \ m'; \ m(\equiv a'),$$
$$P_a nn \equiv P_a n, \ n'; \ n(\equiv c'),$$
$$P_a cc \equiv P_a c, \ c'; \ c(\equiv n'),$$
$$P_a gg \equiv P_a g, \ g'; \ g(\equiv m'),$$

but twelve groups with different uncolored letters in the symbol are

$$P_a mn = P_a m, \ m'; \ n(c'), \quad P_a nm = P_a n, \ n'; \ m(g'),$$
$$P_a mc = P_a m, \ m'; \ c(n'), \quad P_a cm = P_a c, \ c'; \ m(g'),$$
$$P_a mg = P_a m, \ m'; \ g(m'), \quad P_a gm = P_a g, \ g'; \ m(g'),$$
$$P_a nc = P_a n, \ n'; \ c(n'), \quad P_a cn = P_a c, \ c'; \ n(c'),$$
$$P_a ng = P_a n, \ n'; \ g(m'), \quad P_a gn = P_a g, \ g'; \ n(c'),$$
$$P_a cg = P_a c, \ c'; \ g(m'), \quad P_a gc = P_a g, \ g'; \ c(n').$$

In all, we will obtain 26 groups with a (color) centered edge. There are just as many groups with one centered face (in particular, the number of groups with lattice P_C, in which the order of the letters is topologically unimportant, equals $4 + 6 = 10$, whereas the number of groups P_A, for which this order is important, equals $4 + 2 \times 6 = 16$):

	$P_C mm,$	$P_A mm,$		
	$P_C nn,$	$P_A nn,$		
	$P_C cc,$	$P_A cc,$		
	$P_C gg,$	$P_A gg,$		
$P_C mn,$	$P_A mn,$	$P_A nm$	(or	$P_B mn),$
$P_C mc,$	$P_A mc,$	$P_A cm$	(or	$P_B mc),$
$P_C mg,$	$P_A mg,$	$P_A gm$	(or	$P_B mg),$
$P_C nc,$	$P_A nc,$	$P_A cn$	(or	$P_B nc),$
$P_C ng,$	$P_A ng,$	$P_A gn$	(or	$P_B ng),$
$P_C cg,$	$P_A cg,$	$P_A gc$	(or	$P_B cg).$

In the groups of the latter lattice of primitive family P_I, planes m alternate with n', planes n with m', planes c with g',

planes g with c', independently of the position of the letter
in the group symbol. Therefore, there are also ten Shubnikov
groups with lattice P_I, that is, just as many as there are
Fedorov primitive groups.

$$P_Imn = P_Im, n';\ m, n',$$
$$P_Imn = P_Im, n';\ n, m',\qquad P_Inn,$$
$$P_Imc = P_Im, n';\ c, g',\qquad P_Inc,\qquad P_Icc,$$
$$P_Img = P_Im, n';\ g, c',\qquad P_Ing,\qquad P_Icg,\qquad P_Igg.$$

Let us proceed to the series of lattices corresponding to the
Fedorov Bravais lattice with one centered face. In class C_{2v}
we must distinguish[90] base-centered and laterally-centered
lattices (see 14a and 14b in Fig. 130; also 15a and 15b, 16a
and 16b, 18a and 18b), therefore there will be seven $(3 + 4)$
corresponding Fedorov groups

$$\begin{array}{ll} Cmm, & Amm, \\ Cmc, & Amg, \\ Ccc, & Agm, \\ & Agg. \end{array}$$

Seven gray groups correspond to them. The number of black-
white groups equals: with a C-lattice (both positions topologically identical) $2 + 2 + 3 = 7$, and with an A-lattice (positions
topologically different) $3 \times 4 = 12$ (see the list of groups).

Upon the addition of colored translations along the edges
perpendicular to the centered faces, in lattices C and A, the
topological identity of the positions of the two planes in lattice
C_c and their non-identity in lattice A_a are obviously preserved.
According to Theorems 1 and 2, only letters without primes
may be placed in the symbols of the corresponding Shubnikov
groups; thus, we arrive at the same number seven for the
number of groups C_c and A_a:

$$\begin{array}{ll} C_cmm, & A_amm, \\ C_cmc, & A_amg, \\ C_ccc, & A_agm, \\ & A_agg. \end{array}$$

In the first three groups, independently of the position of
the letter in the symbol, $m \equiv c'$ and alternating with it[90] is
$g \equiv n'$, whereas $c \equiv m'$ and alternating with it is $n \equiv g'$.

In the last four groups we have (see ref. 90 and Theorem 2)

$$A_amm = A_am\{(n),\ m'(n')\}; \quad m\{(a'),\ c(n')\},$$
$$A_amg = A_am\{(n),\ m'(n')\}; \quad g\{(m'),\ n(c')\},$$
$$A_agm = A_ag\{(c),\ g'(c')\}; \quad m\{(a'),\ c(n')\},$$
$$A_agg = A_ag\{(c),\ g'(c')\}; \quad g\{(m'),\ n(c')\}.$$

The very same number seven $(3 + 4)$ is retained for groups C_a and A_c, in which the color-centered edge is centered along the Bravais face, and in the same way both edges of this face prove to be centered (see $16a$ and $16b$ in Fig. 130), i.e., $C_a \equiv C_b$ and $A_c \equiv A_b$:

$$C_amm = C_am\{(b'),\ b(m')\}; \quad m\{(a'),\ a(m')\},$$
$$C_amc = C_am\{(b'),\ b(m')\}; \quad c\{(n'),\ n(c')\},$$
$$C_acc = C_ac\{(n'),\ n(c')\}; \quad c\{(n'),\ n(c')\},$$
$$A_cmm = A_cm(\equiv n \equiv c' \equiv g'); \quad m(\equiv c'),\ c(\equiv m'),$$
$$A_cmg = A_cm(\equiv n \equiv c' \equiv g'); \quad g(\equiv n'),\ n(\equiv g'),$$
$$A_cgm = A_cg\ (\equiv c \equiv n' \equiv m'); \quad m(\equiv c'),\ c(\equiv m'),$$
$$A_cgg = A_cg\ (\equiv c \equiv n' \equiv m'); \quad g(\equiv n'),\ n(\equiv g').$$

Let us dwell in more detail on group C_amc. The colored translation perpendicular to m creates a colored m' at a distance of $a/4$ from m, whereas the oblique uncolored translation at the same place generates plane $g = b$, from which the colored translation gives plane $g' = b'$, which coincides with m.

Analogously, we will obtain seven $(3 + 4)$ Shubnikov groups for base-centered and laterally-centered lattices C_A and A_C, with uncolored centering of one face and colored centering of the other (both of the others):

$$C_Amm = C_Am\{(n'),\ g(c')\}; \quad m\{(n'),\ g(c')\},$$
$$C_Amc = C_Am\{(n'),\ g(c')\}; \quad c\{(g'),\ n(m')\},$$
$$C_Acc = C_Ac\{(g'),\ n(m')\}; \quad c\{(g'),\ n(m')\},$$
$$A_Cmm = A_Cm\{(n),\ g'(c')\}; \quad m\{(n'),\ g'(c)\},$$
$$A_Cmg = A_Cm\{(n),\ g'(c')\}; \quad g\{(c'),\ m'(n)\},$$
$$A_Cgm = A_Cg\{(c),\ m'(n')\}; \quad m\{(n'),\ g'(c)\},$$
$$A_Cgg = A_Cg\{(c),\ m'(n')\}; \quad g\{(c'),\ m'(n)\}.$$

There are two Fedorov groups F: Fmm and Fdd; moreover, there are two similar gray groups. According to Belov[90], plane m will simultaneously also be plane $n(m \equiv n)$; in exactly the same way, $c \equiv g$. The colored planes in lattice F_s behave in a similar fashion, namely $m' \equiv n'$ and $c'' \equiv g'$. According to Theorem 2, in the same lattice $m(n)$ coincides with $c'(g')$ and $c(g)$ coincides with $m'(n')$, i.e., only the one group $F_s mm$ is possible. We will not introduce evidence for the similar uniqueness of diamond group $F_s dd$.

The derivation of black-white groups F and I is analogous to the derivation of such groups with lattices P and C, and we refer to the list of these groups.

In class C_{2v}, the three groups I_c are quite similar to the three groups C_c, and just as similar (adding these three to the seven base-centered and laterally-centered groups) to the four groups I_a and A_a.

Planes $m(\equiv c')$ and $c(\equiv n')$ are characteristic (in both positions of the symbol) for the first parallel group of three, and they alternate in C_c correspondingly with $g(\equiv n')$ and $n(\equiv g')$, and in I_c, on the other hand, with $n(\equiv g')$ and $g(\equiv n')$.

In the parallel group of four, A_a and I_a (with topologically different positions in the symbol), face A, perpendicular to colored translation a is color centered by $I_a = I_A$ in one case, and is uncolored in another, which determines the correspondence of the letters with primes to the identical letters without primes in parallel groups

$$I_a mm \equiv I_a m\{(n'), \, m'(n)\}; \quad m\{(a'), \, c'(n)\},$$
$$I_a mg \equiv I_a m\{(n'), \, m'(n)\}; \quad g\{(m'), \, n'(c)\},$$
$$I_a gm \equiv I_a g\{(c'), \, g'(c)\}; \quad m\{(a'), \, c'(n)\},$$
$$I_a gg \equiv I_a g\{(c'), \, g'(c)\}; \quad g\{(m'), \, n'(c)\}.$$

It is not necessary to derive groups I_c and I_A since

$$I_C = I_c, \quad \text{and} \quad I_A = I_a.$$

Certain general considerations have become quite clear in the preceding examples, which will allow the almost mechanical derivation of the remaining Shubnikov groups, and which we repeat here in general form.

It follows from Theorems 1–9 that with the presence of colored translation in a Bravais lattice, any given colored element of symmetry generates a derived uncolored one (and vice-versa), independently of whether the colored translation (or its component) is perpendicular to the generating element of symmetry or parallel to it. The derived uncolored element in the first case is spatially separated from the generating element, and alternates with it, and in the second case the uncolored and colored elements merge in a single geometric image.

Thus, in the symbol of any given group with a colored lattice, *it is sufficient to indicate only the uncolored elements of symmetry*, whereupon their possible combinations will be the same combinations as in the Fedorov groups with the uncolored lattice, that heads the series of colored lattices. In the same way, to any Fedorov group of a given class there corresponds, in each of the 36 independent colored lattices (that are subordinate to the basic Fedorov lattice), either one, two or three Shubnikov groups with the same letters (without primes) depending upon whether the colored centering of the basic lattice is possible by one, two or three topologically different (A, B, C; a, b, c) methods, if this difference is not removed by equalities among the letters in the symbol.

As a result, the computation of the number of Shubnikov groups with colored lattices proves to be simpler than that for uncolored lattices, where it is necessary thoroughly to examine the symbol for all combinations of colored elements with uncolored ones, and to eliminate repetitions. In particular:

1. If lattice P_I is possible in a class under consideration, the number of corresponding groups, independently of the crystallographic system, equals the number of Fedorov groups P of the same class, in view of the single possibility of colored centering according to the above law.

2. If there are groups with lattices P_s and P_C in the class under consideration, their number will equal the number of Fedorov groups in those systems in which there exists one main, specific direction (tetragonal and monoclinic systems). The colored translation may be only parallel to this specific direction in groups P_s, and perpendicular to it in groups P_C, i.e., the sole possibility of colored centering is also characteristic in these cases.

In the rhombic system, there are three mutually perpendicular directions and a corresponding number of possibilities of colored centering, which we saw earlier in examples from class C_{2v}; now we will consider, as an example, groups P_s

in class D_{2h}. Of the 16 primitive groups P of this class, only in three of them, groups *Pmmm*, *Pnnn* and *Pbca*, are all the coordinate directions topologically equal, and upon the colored centering of any given edge, we derive topologically identical groups (listed in each line)

$$P_a m,\ m';\ \ m(a');\ \ m(a') \equiv P_b m(b');\ \ m,\ m';\ \ m(b')$$
$$\equiv P_c m(c);\ \ m(c');\ \ m,\ m',$$
$$P_a n,\ n';\ \ n(c');\ \ n(b') \equiv P_b n(c');\ \ n,\ n',\ n(a')$$
$$\equiv P_c n(b');\ \ n(a'),\ n,\ n',$$
$$P_a b,\ b';\ \ c(n');\ \ a(m') \equiv P_b b(m');\ \ c,\ c';\ \ a(n')$$
$$\equiv P_c b(n');\ \ c(m');\ \ a,\ a'.$$

For six primitive groups of the same class

$$\begin{array}{ll} Pnnm, & Pmmn, \\ Pccm, & Pccn, \\ Pggm, & Pggn. \end{array}$$

colored centering along the edges is possible by two topologically different methods, inasmuch as two coordinate directions are equal. Interpreting groups $P_a ccm$ and $P_c ccm$,

$$P_a ccm \equiv P_a c,\ c';\ \ c(n');\ \ m(g') \equiv P_b c(n');\ \ c,\ c';\ \ m(g'),$$
$$P_c ccm \equiv P_c c(m');\ \ c(m');\ \ m,\ m',$$

we see that these are actually two different groups.

In the seven remaining groups P of the same class

$$\begin{array}{lll} Pmma, & Pbam, & Pmna, \\ Pnna, & Pban, & Pnma, \\ Pcca, & & \end{array}$$

the three coordinate directions are unequal, and colored centering of any given edge in the nucleus leads to a new group. Thus, we have three different groups $P_s mma$

$$P_a mma = P_a m,\ m';\ \ m(a');\ \ a(m'),$$
$$P_b mma = P_b m(b');\ \ m,\ m';\ \ a(n'),$$
$$P_c mma = P_c m(c');\ \ m(c');\ \ a,\ a'.$$

P_A, P_B, and P_C differ in exactly the same way.

3. If in the class under consideration there are groups with lattices

$$\begin{array}{llll} C_c, & C_a, & C_A, & I_c, \\ A_a, & A_c, & A_C, & I_a, \end{array}$$

their number, correspondingly, will be equal to the number of groups C, A and I (excluding groups I_c of the tetragonal system), since, if colored translation in these groups is perpendicular to a centered face (C_c, A_a), then this is the sole possibility; if, however, it lies in the centered face, then both edges of the latter are centered.

With various I_c and I_a, in the first an edge is (color) centered and is topologically different from the two (forms of I_a), which are topologically equal. Thus, only one method of centering is possible in both cases.

4. There are as many groups with lattice F_s as there are Fedorov groups F, since lattice F_s is derived from F by a single method. $F_s = F_I$—a lattice of the face-centered series with colored centering of all edges and volume.

The 1651 Shubnikov space groups are listed in Table 10, with nomenclature and arrangement concordant with the Fedorov space groups in the *International Tables for X-ray Crystallography*[96]*.

* Editor's note: The table published by Belov, Neronova and Smirnova in 1957[113] is here substituted for the table originally published in 1955[101] Corrections to the 1954 table pointed out by Donnay and others in 1958[120] had already been made by Belov, without comment, in his 1957 table. In the explanation of these corrections to group D_{2h}, Belov[120] suggests that the 1954 table could be corrected simply by changing the "coloring" subscripts of the lattice designations. He then gives the equivalents between his 1957 list and the added groups suggested by Donnay, as for example

$$P_amaa = P_cccm \text{ (No. 273 of the 1957 list).}$$

This correction is not completely clear unless it is also stated that No. 388 of the 1954 list, which when listed as P_abmb is equivalent to No. 387, P_accm (as pointed out by Donnay), can be corrected to P_bbmb, which is then equivalent to P_cccm, No. 273 of the 1957 list.

The arrangement of the 1957 list is probably a little more useful because the Shubnikov groups are classified according to the isomorphous Fedorov groups. The only other difference in the two lists is that the gray cubic groups are designated with a prime on the three-fold axis, instead of an additional $1'$.

The original list of Shubnikov groups by Zamorzaev[98] was criticized in detail by Belov in a section at the end of the original Russian publication of the paper that we are here translating. Although in a later publication Zamorzaev[116] reasserted his convictions (except with respect to a single group), Belov's criticism (and list) should be allowed to stand in the absence of any detailed reply by Zamorzaev.

TABLE 10

LIST OF SHUBNIKOV SPACE GROUPS

Triclinic system

C_1

(1)
1. $P1$
2. $P1'$
3. P_s1

C_i

(2)
4. $P\bar{1}$
5. $P\bar{1}1'$
6. $P\bar{1}'$
7. $P_s\bar{1}$

Monoclinic system

C_2

(3)
1. $P2$
2. $P21'$
3. $P2'$
4. P_a2
5. P_b2
6. P_c2

(4)
7. $P2_1$
8. $P2_11'$
9. $P2_1'$
10. P_a2_1
11. P_b2_1
12. P_c2_1

(5)
13. $C2$
14. $C21'$
15. $C2'$
16. C_c2
17. C_a2

C_s

(6)
18. Pm
19. $Pm1'$
20. Pm'
21. P_am
22. P_bm
23. P_cm

(7)
24. Pc
25. $Pc1'$
26. Pc'
27. P_ac
28. P_cc
29. P_bc
30. P_cc
31. P_Ac

(8)
32. Cm
33. $Cm1'$
34. Cm'
35. C_cm
36. C_am

(9)
37. Cc
38. $Cc1'$
39. Cc'
40. C_cc
41. C_ac

C_{2h}

(10)
42. $P2/m$
43. $P2/m1'$
44. $P2'/m$
45. $P2/m'$
46. $P2'/m'$
47. P_a2/m
48. P_b2/m
49. P_c2/m

(11)
50. $P2_1/m$
51. $P2_1/m1'$
52. $P2_1'/m$
53. $P2_1/m'$
54. $P2_1'/m'$
55. P_a2_1/m
56. P_b2_1/m
57. P_c2_1/m

(12)
58. $C2/m$
59. $C2/m1'$
60. $C2'/m$
61. $C2/m'$
62. $C2'/m'$
63. C_c2/m
64. C_a2/m

(13)
65. $P2/c$
66. $P2/c1'$
67. $P2'/c$
68. $P2/c'$
69. $P2'/c'$
70. P_a2/c
71. P_b2/c
72. P_c2/c
73. P_A2/c
74. P_c2/c

(14)
75. $P2_1/c$
76. $P2_1/c1'$
77. $P2_1'/c$
78. $P2_1/c'$
79. $P2_1'/c'$
80. P_a2_1/c
81. P_b2_1/c
82. P_c2_1/c
83. P_A2_1/c
84. P_c2_1/c

(15)
85. $C2/c$
86. $C2/c1'$
87. $C2'/c$
88. $C2/c'$
89. $C2'/c'$
90. C_c2/c
91. C_a2/c

Orthorhombic system

D_2

(16)
1. $P222$
2. $P2221'$
3. $P2'2'2$
4. P_a222
5. P_c222
6. P_I222

(17)
7. $P222_1$
8. $P222_11'$
9. $P2'2'2_1$
10. $P22'2_1'$
11. P_a222_1
12. P_c222_1

13. $P_A 222_1$

14. $P_C 222_1$

15. $P_I 222_1$

(18) 16. $P2_1 2_1 2$

17. $P2_1 2_1 21'$

18. $P2_1' 2_1' 2$

19. $P2_1 2_1' 2'$

20. $P_a 2_1 2_1 2$

21. $P_c 2_1 2_1 2$

22. $P_A 2_1 2_1 2$

23. $P_C 2_1 2_1 2$

24. $P_I 2_1 2_1 2$

(19) 25. $P2_1 2_1 2_1$

26. $P2_1 2_1 2_1 1'$

27. $P2_1' 2_1' 2_1$

28. $P_a 2_1 2_1 2_1$

29. $P_c 2_1 2_1 2_1$

30. $P_I 2_1 2_1 2_1$

(20) 31. $C222_1$

32. $C222_1 1'$

33. $C2' 2' 2_1$

34. $C22' 2_1'$

35. $C_c 222_1$

36. $C_a 222_1$

37. $C_A 222_1$

(21) 38. $C222$

39. $C2221'$

40. $C2' 2' 2$

41. $C22' 2'$

42. $C_c 222$

43. $C_a 222$

44. $C_A 222$

(22) 45. $F222$

46. $F2221'$

47. $F2' 2' 2$

48. $F_s 222$

(23) 49. $I222$

50. $I2221'$

51. $I2' 2' 2$

52. $I_c 222$

(24) 53. $I2_1 2_1 2_1$

54. $I2_1 2_1 2_1 1'$

55. $I2_1' 2_1' 2_1$

56. $I_c 2_1 2_1 2_1$

C_{2v}

(25) 57. $Pmm2$

58. $Pmm21'$

59. $Pm'm2'$

60. $Pm'm'2$

61. $P_c mm2$

62. $P_a mm2$

63. $P_C mm2$

64. $P_A mm2$

65. $P_I mm2$

(26) 66. $Pmc2_1$

67. $Pmc2_1 1'$

68. $Pm'c2_1'$

69. $Pmc'2_1'$

70. $Pm'c'2_1$

71. $P_a mc2_1$

72. $P_b mc2_1$

73. $P_c mc2_1$

74. $P_A mc2_1$

75. $P_B mc2_1$

76. $P_C mc2_1$

77. $P_I mc2_1$

(27) 78. $Pcc2$

79. $Pcc21'$

80. $Pc'c2$

81. $Pc'c'2$

82. $P_c cc2$

83. $P_a cc2$

84. $P_C cc2$

85. $P_A cc2$

86. $P_I cc2$

(28) 87. $Pma2$

88. $Pma21'$

89. $Pm'a2'$

90. $Pma'2'$

91. $Pm'a'2$

92. $P_a ma2$

93. $P_b ma2$

94. $P_c ma2$

95. $P_A ma2$

96. $P_B ma2$

97. $P_C ma2$

98. $P_I ma2$

(29) 99. $Pca2_1$

100. $Pca2_1 1'$

101. $Pc'a2_1'$

102. $Pca'2_1'$

103. $Pc'a'2_1$

104. $P_a ca2_1$

105. $P_b ca2_1$

106. $P_c ca2_1$

107. $P_A ca2_1$

108. $P_B ca2_1$

109. $P_C ca2_1$

110. $P_I ca2_1$

(30) 111. $Pnc2$

112. $Pnc21'$

113. $Pn'c2'$

114. $Pnc'2'$

115. $Pn'c'2$

116. $P_a nc2$

117. $P_b nc2$

118. $P_c nc2$

119. $P_A nc2$

120. $P_B nc2$

121. $P_C nc2$

122. $P_I nc2$

(31) 123. $Pmn2_1$

124. $Pmn2_1 1'$

125. $Pm'n2_1'$

126. $Pmn'2_1'$

127. $Pm'n'2_1$

128. $P_a mn2_1$

129. $P_b mn2_1$

130. $P_c mn2_1$

131. $P_A mn2_1$

132. $P_B mn2_1$

133. $P_C mn2_1$

134. $P_I mn2_1$

(32) 135. $Pba2$

136. $Pba21'$

137. $Pb'a2'$

138. $Pb'a'2$

139. $P_c ba2$

140. $P_a ba2$

141. $P_C ba2$

142. $P_A ba2$

143. $P_I ba2$

(33) 144. $Pna2_1$

145. $Pna2_1 1'$

146. $Pn'a2_1'$

147. $Pna'2_1'$
148. $Pn'a'2_1$
149. $P_a na2_1$
150. $P_b na2_1$
151. $P_c na2_1$
152. $P_A na2_1$
153. $P_B na2_1$
154. $P_C na2_1$
155. $P_I na2_1$

(34) 156. $Pnn2$
157. $Pnn21'$
158. $Pn'n2'$
159. $Pn'n'2$
160. $P_a nn2$
161. $P_c nn2$
162. $P_A nn2$
163. $P_C nn2$
164. $P_I nn2$

(35) 165. $Cmm2$
166. $Cmm21'$
167. $Cm'm2'$
168. $Cm'm'2$
169. $C_c mm2$
170. $C_a mm2$
171. $C_A mm2$

(36) 172. $Cmc2_1$
173. $Cmc2_1 1'$
174. $Cm'c2_1'$
175. $Cmc'2_1'$
176. $Cm'c'2_1$
177. $C_c mc2_1$
178. $C_a mc2_1$
179. $C_A mc2_1$

(37) 180. $Ccc2$
181. $Ccc21'$
182. $Cc'c2'$
183. $Cc'c'2$
184. $C_c cc2$
185. $C_a cc2$
186. $C_A cc2$

(38) 187. $Amm2$
188. $Amm21'$
189. $Am'm2'$
190. $Amm'2'$

191. $Am'm'2$
192. $A_a mm2$
193. $A_c mm2$
194. $A_C mm2$

(39) 195. $Abm2$
196. $Abm21'$
197. $Ab'm2'$
198. $Abm'2'$
199. $Ab'm'2$
200. $A_a bm2$
201. $A_c bm2$
202. $A_C bm2$

(40) 203. $Ama2$
204. $Ama21'$
205. $Am'a2'$
206. $Ama'2'$
207. $Am'a'2$
208. $A_a ma2$
209. $A_c ma2$
210. $A_C ma2$

(41) 211. $Aba2$
212. $Aba21'$
213. $Ab'a2'$
214. $Aba'2'$
215. $Ab'a'2$
216. $A_a ba2$
217. $A_c ba2$
218. $A_C ba2$

(42) 219. $Fmm2$
220. $Fmm21'$
221. $Fm'm2'$
222. $Fm'm'2$
223. $F_s mm2$

(43) 224. $Fdd2$
225. $Fdd21'$
226. $Fd'd2'$
227. $Fd'd'2$
228. $F_s dd2$

(44) 229. $Imm2$
230. $Imm21'$
231. $Im'm2'$
232. $Im'm'2$
233. $I_c mm2$
234. $I_a mm2$

(45) 235. $Iba2$
236. $Iba21'$
237. $Ib'a2'$
238. $Ib'a'2$
239. $I_c ba2$
240. $I_a ba2$

(46) 241. $Ima2$
242. $Ima21'$
243. $Im'a2'$
244. $Ima'2'$
245. $Im'a'2$
246. $I_c ma2$
247. $I_a ma2$
248. $I_b ma2$

$\mathbf{D}_{2h}$

(47) 249. $Pmmm$
250. $Pmmm1'$
251. $Pm'mm$
252. $Pm'm'm$
253. $Pm'm'm'$
254. $P_a mmm$
255. $P_C mmm$
256. $P_I mmm$

48) 257. $Pnnn$
258. $Pnnn1'$
259. $Pn'nn$
260. $Pn'n'n$
261. $Pn'n'n'$
262. $P_a nnn$
263. $P_C nnn$
264. $P_I nnn$

(49) 265. $Pccm$
266. $Pccm1'$
267. $Pc'cm$
268. $Pccm'$
269. $Pc'c'm$
270. $Pc'cm'$
271. $Pc'c'm'$
272. $P_a ccm$
273. $P_c ccm$
274. $P_A ccm$
275. $P_C ccm$
276. $P_I ccm$

(50) 277. $Pban$
278. $Pban1'$

279. $Pb'an$
280. $Pban'$
281. $Pb'a'n$
282. $Pb'an'$
283. $Pb'a'n'$
284. P_aban
285. P_cban
286. P_Aban
287. P_oban
288. P_Iban

(51) 289. $Pmma$
290. $Pmma1'$
291. $Pm'ma$
292. $Pmm'a$
293. $Pmma'$
294. $Pm'm'a$
295. $Pmm'a'$
296. $Pm'ma'$
297. $Pm'm'a'$
298. P_amma
299. P_bmma
300. P_cmma
301. P_Amma
302. P_Bmma
303. P_Cmma
304. P_Imma

(52) 305. $Pnna$
306. $Pnna1'$
307. $Pn'na$
308. $Pnn'a$
309. $Pnna'$
310. $Pn'n'a$
311. $Pnn'a'$
312. $Pn'na'$
313. $Pn'n'a'$
314. P_anna
315. P_bnna
316. P_cnna
317. P_Anna
318. P_Bnna
319. P_Cnna
320. P_Inna

(53) 321. $Pmna$
322. $Pmna1'$
323. $Pm'na$
324. $Pmn'a$

325. $Pmna'$
326. $Pm'n'a$
327. $Pmn'a'$
328. $Pm'na'$
329. $Pm'n'a'$
330. P_amna
331. P_bmna
332. P_cmna
333. P_Amna
334. P_Bmna
335. P_Cmna
336. P_Imna

(54) 337. $Pcca$
338. $Pcca1'$
339. $Pc'ca$
340. $Pcc'a$
341. $Pcca'$
342. $Pc'c'a$
343. $Pcc'a'$
344. $Pc'ca'$
345. $Pc'c'a'$
346. P_acca
347. P_bcca
348. P_ecca
349. P_Acca
350. P_Bcca
351. P_Ccca
352. P_Icca

(55) 353. $Pbam$
354. $Pbam1'$
355. $Pb'am$
356. $Pbam'$
357. $Pb'a'm$
358. $Pb'am'$
359. $Pb'a'm'$
360. P_abam
361. P_cbam
362. P_Abam
363. P_obam
364. P_Ibam

(56) 365. $Pccn$
366. $Pccn1'$
367. $Pc'cn$
368. $Pccn'$
369. $Pc'c'n$
370. $Pc'cn'$

371. $Pc'c'n'$
372. P_accn
373. P_eccn
374. P_Accn
375. P_Cccn
376. P_Iccn

(57) 377. $Pbcm$
378. $Pbcm1'$
379. $Pb'cm$
380. $Pbc'm$
381. $Pbcm'$
382. $Pb'c'm$
383. $Pbc'm'$
384. $Pb'cm'$
385. $Pb'c'm'$
386. P_abcm
387. P_bbcm
388. P_cbcm
389. P_Abcm
390. P_Bbcm
391. P_Cbcm
392. P_Ibcm

(58) 393. $Pnnm$
394. $Pnnm1'$
395. $Pn'nm$
396. $Pnnm'$
397. $Pn'n'm$
398. $Pnn'm'$
399. $Pn'n'm'$
400. P_annm
401. P_cnnm
402. P_Annm
403. P_Cnnm
404. P_Innm

(59) 405. $Pmmn$
406. $Pmmn1'$
407. $Pm'mn$
408. $Pmmn'$
409. $Pm'm'n$
410. $Pmm'n'$
411. $Pm'm'n'$
412. P_ammn
413. P_cmmn
414. P_Ammn
415. P_Cmmn
416. P_Immn

(60) 417. $Pbcn$
418. $Pbcn1'$
419. $Pb'cn$
420. $Pbc'n$
421. $Pbcn'$
422. $Pb'c'n$
423. $Pbc'n'$
424. $Pb'cn'$
425. $Pb'c'n'$
426. P_abcn
427. P_bbcn
428. P_cbcn
429. P_Abcn
430. P_Bbcn
431. P_Cbcn
432. P_Ibcn

(61) 433. $Pbca$
434. $Pbca1'$
435. $Pb'ca$
436. $Pb'c'a$
437. $Pb'c'a'$
438. P_abca
439. P_Cbca
440. P_Ibca

(62) 441. $Pnma$
442. $Pnma1'$
443. $Pn'ma$
444. $Pnm'a$
445. $Pnma'$
446. $Pn'm'a$
447. $Pnm'a'$
448. $Pn'ma'$
449. $Pn'm'a'$
450. P_anma
451. P_bnma
452. P_cnma
453. P_Anma
454. P_Bnma
455. P_Cnma
456. P_Inma

(63) 457. $Cmcm$
458. $Cmcm1'$
459. $Cm'cm$
460. $Cmc'm$
461. $Cmcm'$
462. $Cm'c'm$

463. $Cmc'm'$
464. $Cm'cm'$
465. $Cm'c'm'$
466. C_cmcm
467. C_amcm
468. C_Amcm

(64) 469. $Cmca$
470. $Cmca1'$
471. $Cm'ca$
472. $Cmc'a$
473. $Cmca'$
474. $Cm'c'a$
475. $Cmc'a'$
476. $Cm'ca'$
477. $Cm'c'a'$
478. C_cmca
479. C_amca
480. C_Amca

(65) 481. $Cmmm$
482. $Cmmm1'$
483. $Cm'mm$
484. $Cmmm'$
485. $Cm'm'm$
486. $Cmm'm'$
487. $Cm'm'm'$
488. C_cmmm
489. C_ammm
490. C_Ammm

(66) 491. $Cccm$
492. $Cccm1'$
493. $Cc'cm$
494. $Cccm'$
495. $Cc'c'm$
496. $Ccc'm'$
497. $Cc'c'm'$
498. C_cccm
499. C_accm
500. C_Accm

(67) 501. $Cmma$
502. $Cmma1'$
503. $Cm'ma$
504. $Cmma'$
505. $Cm'm'a$
506. $Cmm'a'$
507. $Cm'm'a'$
508. C_cmma

509. C_amma
510. C_Amma

(68) 511. $Ccca$
512. $Ccca1'$
513. $Cc'ca$
514. $Ccca'$
515. $Cc'c'a$
516. $Ccc'a'$
517. $Cc'c'a'$
518. C_ccca
519. C_acca
520. C_Acca

(69) 521. $Fmmm$
522. $Fmmm1'$
523. $Fm'mm$
524. $Fm'm'm$
525. $Fm'm'm'$
526. F_smmm

(70) 527. $Fddd$
528. $Fddd1'$
529. $Fd'dd$
530. $Fd'd'd$
531. $Fd'd'd'$
532. F_sddd

(71) 533. $Immm$
534. $Immm1$
535. $Im'mm'$
536. $Im'm'm$
537. $Im'm'm'$
538. I_cmmm

(72) 539. $Ibam$
540. $Ibam1'$
541. $Ib'am$
542. $Ibam'$
543. $Ib'a'm$
544. $Iba'm'$
545. $Ib'a'm'$
546. I_cbam
547. I_abam

(73) 548. $Ibca$
549. $Ibca1'$
550. $Ib'ca$
551. $Ib'c'a$
552. $Ib'c'a'$
553. I_cbca

(74) 554. *Imma*
555. *Imma*1′
556. *Im′ma*
557. *Imma′*
558. *Im′m′a*
559. *Imm′a′*
560. *Im′m′a′*
561. $I_c mma$
562. $I_a mma$

**Tetragonal
system**

C_4

(75) 1. *P*4
2. *P*41′
3. *P*4′
4. $P_c 4$
5. $P_C 4$
6. $P_I 4$

(76) 7. $P4_1$
8. $P4_1 1′$
9. $P4_1′$
10. $P_c 4_1$
11. $P_C 4_1$
12. $P_I 4_1$

(77) 13. $P4_2$
14. $P4_2 1′$
15. $P4_2′$
16. $P_c 4_2$
17. $P_C 4_2$
18. $P_I 4_2$

(78) 19. $P4_3$
20. $P4_3 1′$
21. $P4_3′$
22. $P_c 4_3$
23. $P_C 4_3$
24. $P_I 4_3$

(79) 25. *I*4
26. *I*41′
27. *I*4′
28. $I_c 4$

(80) 29. $I4_1$
30. $I4_1 1′$
31. $I4_1′$
32. $I_c 4_1$

S_4

(81) 33. $P\bar{4}$
34. $P\bar{4}1′$
35. $P\bar{4}′$
36. $P_c \bar{4}$
37. $P_C \bar{4}$
38. $P_I \bar{4}$

(82) 39. $I\bar{4}$
40. $I\bar{4}1′$
41. $I\bar{4}′$
42. $I_c \bar{4}$

C_{4h}

(83) 43. *P*4/*m*
44. *P*4/*m*1′
45. *P*4′/*m*
46. *P*4/*m′*
47. *P*4′/*m′*
48. $P_c 4/m$
49. $P_C 4/m$
50. $P_I 4/m$

(84) 51. $P4_2/m$
52. $P4_2/m1′$
53. $P4_2′/m$
54. $P4_2/m′$
55. $P4_2′/m′$
56. $P_c 4_2/m$
57. $P_C 4_2/m$
58. $P_I 4_2/m$

(85) 59. *P*4/*n*
60. *P*4/*n*1′
61. *P*4′/*n*
62. *P*4/*n′*
63. *P*4′/*n′*
64. $P_c 4/n$
65. $P_C 4/n$
66. $P_I 4/n$

(86) 67. $P4_2/n$
68. $P4_2/n1′$
69. $P4_2′/n$
70. $P4_2/n′$
71. $P4_2′/n′$
72. $P_c 4_2/n$
73. $P_C 4_2/n$
74. $P_I 4_2/n$

(87) 75. *I*4/*m*
76. *I*4/*m*1′
77. *I*4′/*m*
78. *I*4/*m′*
79. *I*4′/*m′*
80. $I_c 4/m$

(88) 81. $I4_1/a$
82. $I4_1/a1′$
83. $I4_1′/a$
84. $I4_1/a′$
85. $I4_1′/a′$
86. $I_c 4_1/a$

D_2

(89) 87. *P*422
88. *P*4221′
89. *P*4′22′
90. *P*42′2′
91. *P*4′2′2
92. $P_c 422$
93. $P_C 422$
94. $P_I 422$

(90) 95. $P42_1 2′$
96. $P42_1 21′$
97. $P4′2_1 2′$
98. $P42_1′2′$
99. $P4′2_1′2$
100. $P_c 42_1 2$
101. $P_C 42_1 2$
102. $P_I 42_1 2$

(91) 103. $P4_1 22$
104. $P4_1 221′$
105. $P4_1′22′$
106. $P4_1 2′2′$
107. $P4_1′2′2$
108. $P_c 4_1 22$
109. $P_C 4_1 22$
110. $P_I 4_1 22$

(92) 111. $P4_1 2_1 2$
112. $P4_1 2_1 21′$
113. $P4_1′2_1 2′$
114. $P4_1 2_1′2′$
115. $P4_1′2_1′2$
116. $P_c 4_1 2_1 2$
117. $P_C 4_1 2_1 2$
118. $P_I 4_1 2_1 2$

(93) 119. $P4_222$
120. $P4_2221'$
121. $P4_2'22'$
122. $P4_22'2'$
123. $P4_2'2'2$
124. P_c4_222
125. P_C4_222
126. P_I4_222

(94) 127. $P4_22_12$
128. $P4_22_121'$
129. $P4_2'2_12'$
130. $P4_22_1'2'$
131. $P4_2'2_1'2$
132. $P_c4_22_12$
133. $P_C4_22_12$
134. $P_I4_22_12$

(95) 135. $P4_322$
136. $P4_3221'$
137. $P4_3'22'$
138. $P4_32'2'$
139. $P4_3'2'2$
140. P_c4_322
141. P_C4_322
142. P_I4_322

(96) 143. $P4_32_12$
144. $P4_32_121'$
145. $P4_3'2_12'$
146. $P4_32_1'2'$
147. $P4_3'2_1'2$
148. $P_c4_32_12$
149. $P_C4_32_12$
150. $P_I4_32_12$

(97) 151. $I422$
152. $I4221'$
153. $I4'22'$
154. $I42'2'$
155. $I4'2'2$
156. I_c422

(98) 157. $I4_122$
158. $I4_1221'$
159. $I4_1'22'$
160. $I4_12'2'$
161. $I4_1'2'2$
162. I_c4_122

C_{4v}

(99) 163. $P4mm$
164. $P4mm1'$
165. $P4'm'm$
166. $P4'mm'$
167. $P4m'm'$
168. P_c4mm
169. P_C4mm
170. P_I4mm

(100) 171. $P4bm$
172. $P4bm1'$
173. $P4'b'm$
174. $P4'bm'$
175. $P4b'm'$
176. P_c4bm
177. P_C4bm
178. P_I4bm

(101) 179. $P4_2cm$
180. $P4_2cm1'$
181. $P4_2'c'm$
182. $P4_2'cm'$
183. $P4_2c'm'$
184. P_c4_2cm
185. P_C4_2cm
186. P_I4_2cm

(102) 187. $P4_2nm$
188. $P4_2nm1'$
189. $P4_2'n'm$
190. $P4_2'nm'$
191. $P4_2n'm'$
192. P_c4_2nm
193. P_C4_2nm
194. P_I4_2nm

(103) 195. $P4cc$
196. $P4cc1'$
197. $P4'c'c$
198. $P4'cc'$
199. $P4c'c'$
200. P_c4cc
201. P_C4cc
202. P_I4cc

(104) 203. $P4nc$
204. $P4nc1'$
205. $P4'n'c$
206. $P4'nc'$
207. $P4n'c'$
208. P_c4nc
209. P_C4nc
210. P_I4nc

(105) 211. $P4_2mc$
212. $P4_2mc1'$
213. $P4_2'm'c$
214. $P4_2'mc'$
215. $P4_2m'c'$
216. P_c4_2mc
217. P_C4_2mc
218. P_I4_2mc

(106) 219. $P4_2bc$
220. $P4_2bc1'$
221. $P4_2'b'c$
222. $P4_2'bc'$
223. $P4_2b'c'$
224. P_c4_2bc
225. P_C4_2bc
226. P_I4_2bc

(107) 227. $I4mm$
228. $I4mm1'$
229. $I4'm'm$
230. $I4'mm'$
231. $I4m'm'$
232. I_c4mm

(108) 233. $I4cm$
234. $I4cm1'$
235. $I4'c'm$
236. $I4'cm'$
237. $I4c'm'$
238. I_c4cm

(109) 239. $I4_1md$
240. $I4_1md1'$
241. $I4_1'm'd$
242. $I4_1'md'$
243. $I4_1m'd'$
244. I_cmd

(110) 245. $I4_1cd$
246. $I4_1cd1'$
247. $I4_1'c'd$
248. $I4_1'cd'$
249. $I4_1c'd'$
250. I_c4_1cd

D_{2d}

(111) 251. $P\bar{4}2m$
252. $P\bar{4}2m1'$
253. $P\bar{4}'2'm$
254. $P\bar{4}'2m'$
255. $P\bar{4}2'm'$
256. $P_c\bar{4}2m$
257. $P_C\bar{4}2m$
258. $P_I\bar{4}2m$

(112) 259. $P\bar{4}2c$
260. $P\bar{4}2c1'$
261. $P\bar{4}'2'c$
262. $P\bar{4}'2c'$
263. $P\bar{4}2'c'$
264. $P_c\bar{4}2c$
265. $P_C\bar{4}2c$
266. $P_I\bar{4}2c$

(113) 267. $P\bar{4}2_1m$
268. $P\bar{4}2_1m1'$
269. $P\bar{4}'2_1'm$
270. $P\bar{4}'2_1m'$
271. $P\bar{4}2_1'm'$
272. $P_c\bar{4}2_1m$
273. $P_C\bar{4}2_1m$
274. $P_I\bar{4}2_1m$

(114) 275. $P\bar{4}2_1c$
276. $P\bar{4}2_1c1'$
277. $P\bar{4}'2_1'c$
278. $P\bar{4}'2_1c'$
279. $P\bar{4}2_1'c'$
280. $P_c\bar{4}2_1c$
281. $P_C\bar{4}2_1c$
282. $P_I\bar{4}2_1c$

(115) 283. $P\bar{4}m2$
284. $P\bar{4}m21'$
285. $P\bar{4}'m'2$
286. $P\bar{4}'m2'$
287. $P\bar{4}m'2'$
288. $P_c\bar{4}m2$
289. $P_C\bar{4}m2$
290. $P_I\bar{4}m2$

(116) 291. $P\bar{4}c2$
292. $P\bar{4}c21'$
293. $P\bar{4}'c'2$

294. $P\bar{4}'c2'$
295. $P\bar{4}c'2'$
296. $P_c\bar{4}c2$
297. $P_C\bar{4}c2$
298. $P_I\bar{4}c2$

(117) 299. $P\bar{4}b2$
300. $P\bar{4}b21'$
301. $P\bar{4}'b'2$
302. $P\bar{4}'b2'$
303. $P\bar{4}b'2'$
304. $P_c\bar{4}b2$
305. $P_C\bar{4}b2$
306. $P_I\bar{4}b2$

(118) 307. $P\bar{4}n2$
308. $P\bar{4}n21'$
309. $P\bar{4}'n'2$
310. $P\bar{4}'n2'$
311. $P\bar{4}n'2'$
312. $P_c\bar{4}n2$
313. $P_C\bar{4}n2$
314. $P_I\bar{4}n2$

(119) 315. $I\bar{4}m2$
316. $I\bar{4}m21'$
317. $I\bar{4}'m'2$
318. $I\bar{4}'m2'$
319. $I\bar{4}m'2'$
320. $I_c\bar{4}m2$

(120) 321. $I\bar{4}c2$
322. $I\bar{4}c21'$
323. $I\bar{4}'c'2$
324. $I\bar{4}'c2'$
325. $I\bar{4}c'2'$
326. $I_c\bar{4}c2$

(121) 327. $I\bar{4}2m$
328. $I\bar{4}2m1'$
329. $I\bar{4}'2'm$
330. $I\bar{4}'2m'$
331. $I\bar{4}2'm'$
332. $I_c\bar{4}2m$

(122) 333. $I\bar{4}2d$
334. $I\bar{4}2d1'$
335. $I\bar{4}'2'd$
336. $I\bar{4}'2d'$
337. $I\bar{4}2'd'$
338. $I_c\bar{4}2d$

D_{4h}

(123) 339. $P4/mmm$
340. $P4/mmm1'$
341. $P4/m'mm$
342. $P4'/mm'm$
343. $P4'/mmm'$
344. $P4/m'm'm$
345. $P4/mm'm'$
346. $P4'/m'mm'$
347. $P4/m'm'm'$
348. P_c4/mmm
349. P_C4/mmm
350. P_I4/mmm

(124) 351. $P4/mcc$
352. $P4/mcc1'$
353. $P4/m'cc$
354. $P4'/mc'c$
355. $P4'/mcc'$
356. $P4'/m'c'c$
357. $P4'/mc'c'$
358. $P4'/m'cc'$
359. $P4/m'c'c'$
360. P_c4/mcc
361. P_C4/mcc
362. P_I4/mcc

(125) 363. $P4/nbm$
364. $P4/nbm1'$
365. $P4/n'bm$
366. $P4'/nb'm$
367. $P4'/nbm'$
368. $P4'/n'b'm$
369. $P4'/nb'm'$
370. $P4'/n'bm'$
371. $P4/n'b'm'$
372. P_c4/nbm
373. P_C4/nbm
374. P_I4/nbm

(126) 375. $P4/nnc$
376. $P4/nnc1'$
377. $P4/n'nc$
378. $P4'/nn'c$
379. $P4'/nnc'$
380. $P4'/n'n'c$
381. $P4/nn'c'$
382. $P4'/n'nc'$

383. $P4/n'n'c'$
384. P_c4/nnc
385. P_C4/nnc
386. P_I4/nnc
(127) 387. $P4/mbm$
388. $P4mbm1'$
389. $P4/m'bm$
390. $P4'/mb'm$
391. $P4'/mbm'$
392. $P4'/m'b'm$
393. $P4/mb'm'$
394. $P4'/m'bm'$
395. $P4/m'b'm'$
396. P_c4/mbm
397. P_C4/mbm
398. P_I4/mbm
(128) 399. $P4/mnc$
400. $P4/mnc1'$
401. $P4/m'nc$
402. $P4'/mn'c$
403. $P4'/mnc'$
404. $P4'/m'n'c$
405. $P4/mn'c'$
406. $P4'/m'nc'$
407. $P4/m'n'c'$
408. P_c4/mnc
409. P_C4/mnc
410. P_I4/mnc
(129) 411. $P4nmm$
412. $P4/nmm1'$
413. $P4/n'mm$
414. $P4'/nm'm$
415. $P4'/nmm'$
416. $P4'/n'm'm$
417. $P4/nm'm'$
418. $P4'/n'mm'$
419. $P4/n'm'm'$
420. P_c4/nmm
421. P_C4/nmm
422. P_I4/nmm
(130) 423. $P4/ncc$
424. $P4/ncc1'$
425. $P4/n'cc$
426. $P4'/nc'c$
427. $P4'/ncc'$
428. $P4'/n'cc'$

429. $P4/nc'c'$
430. $P4'/n'cc'$
431. $P4/n'c'c'$
432. P_c4/ncc
433. P_C4/ncc
434. P_I4/ncc
(131) 435. $P4_2/mmc$
436. $P4_2/mmc1'$
437. $P4_2/m'mc$
438. $P4_2'/mm'c$
439. $P4_2'/mmc'$
440. $P4_2'/m'm'c$
441. $P4_2/mm'c'$
442. $P4_2'/m'mc'$
443. $P4_2/m'm'c'$
444. P_c4_2/mmc
445. P_C4_2/mmc
446. P_I4_2/mmc
(132) 447. $P4_2/mcm$
448. $P4_2/mcm1'$
449. $P4_2/m'cm$
450. $P4_2'/mc'm$
451. $P4_2'mcm'$
452. $P4_2'/m'c'm$
453. $P4_2/mc'm'$
454. $P4_2'/m'cm'$
455. $P4_2/m'c'm'$
456. P_c4_2/mcm
457. P_C4_2/mcm
458. P_I4_2/mcm
(133) 459. $P4_2/nbc$
460. $P4_2/nbc1'$
461. $P4_2/n'bc$
462. $P4_2'/nb'c$
463. $P4_2'/nbc'$
464. $P4_2'/n'b'c$
465. $P4_2/nb'c'$
466. $P4_2/n'bc'$
467. $P4_2/n'b'c'$
468. P_c4_2/nbc
469. P_C4_2/nbc
470. P_I4_2/nbc
(134) 471. $P4_2/nnm$
472. $P4_2/nnm1'$
473. $P4_2/n'nm$
474. $P4_2'/nn'm$

475. $P4_2'/nnm'$
476. $P4_2'/n'n'm$
477. $P4_2/nn'm'$
478. $P4_2'/n'nm'$
479. $P4_2/n'n'm'$
480. P_c4_2/nnm
481. P_C4_2/nnm
482. P_I4_2/nnm
(135) 483. $P4_2/mbc$
484. $P4_2/mbc1'$
485. $P4_2/m'bc$
486. $P4_2'/mb'c$
487. $P4_2'/mbc'$
488. $P4_2'/m'b'c$
489. $P4_2/mb'c'$
490. $P4_2'/m'bc'$
491. $P4_2/m'b'c'$
492. P_c4_2/mbc
493. P_C4_2/mbc
494. P_I4_2/mbc
(136) 495. $P4_2/mnm$
496. $P4_2/mnm1'$
497. $P4_2/m'nm$
498. $P4_2'/mn'm$
499. $P4_2'/mnm'$
500. $P4_2'/m'n'm$
501. $P4_2/mn'm'$
502. $P4_2'/m'nm'$
503. $P4_2/m'n'm'$
504. P_c4_2/mnm
505. P_C4_2/mnm
506. P_I4_2/mnm
(137) 507. $P4_2/nmc$
508. $P4_2/nmc1'$
509. $P4_2/n'mc$
510. $P4_2'/nm'c$
511. $P4_2'/nmc'$
512. $P4_2'/n'm'c$
513. $P4_2/nm'c'$
514. $P4_2'/n'mc'$
515. $P4_2/n'm'c'$
516. P_c4_2/nmc
517. P_C4_2/nmc
518. P_I4_2/nmc
(138) 519. $P4_2/ncm$
520. $P4_2/ncm1'$

521. $P4_2/n'cm$

522. $P4_2'/nc'm$

523. $P4_2'/ncm'$

524. $P4_2'/n'c'm$

525. $P4_2/nc'm'$

526. $P4_2'/n'cm'$

527. $P4_2/n'c'm'$

528. P_c4_2/ncm

529. P_O4_2/ncm

530. P_I4_2/ncm

(139) 531. $I4/mmm$

532. $I4/mmm1'$

533. $I4/m'mm$

534. $I4'/mm'm$

535. $I4'/mmm'$

536. $I4'/m'm'm$

537. $I4/mm'm'$

538. $I4'/m'mm'$

539. $I4/m'm'm'$

540. I_c4/mmm

(140) 541. $I4/mcm$

542. $I4/mcm1'$

543. $I4/m'cm$

544. $I4'/mc'm$

545. $I4'/mcm'$

546. $I4'/m'c'm$

547. $I4'/mc'm'$

548. $I4'/m'cm'$

549. $I4/m'c'm'$

550. I_c4/mcm

(141) 551. $I4_1/amd$

552. $I4_1/amd1'$

553. $I4_1/a'md$

554. $I4_1'/am'd$

555. $I4_1'/amd'$

556. $I4_1'/a'm'd$

557. $I4_1/am'd'$

558. $I4_1'/a'md'$

559. $I4_1/a'm'd'$

560. I_c4_1/amd

(142) 561. $I4_1/acd$

562. $I4_1/acd1'$

563. $I4_1/a'cd$

564. $I4_1'/ac'd$

565. $I4_1'/acd'$

566. $I4_1'/a'c'd$

567. $I4_1/ac'd'$

568. $I4_1'/a'cd'$

569. $I4_1/a'c'd'$

570. I_c4_1/acd

Hexagonal system
A. Rhombohedral subsystem

C_3

(143) 1. $P3$

2. $P31'$

3. P_c3

(144) 4. $P3_1$

5. $P3_11'$

6. P_c3_1

(145) 7. $P3_2$

8. $P3_21'$

9. P_c3_2

(146) 10. $R3$

11. $R31'$

12. R_I3

C_{3i}

(147) 13. $P\bar{3}$

14. $P\bar{3}1'$

15. $P\bar{3}'$

16. $P_c\bar{3}$

(148) 17. $R\bar{3}$

18. $R\bar{3}1'$

19. $R\bar{3}'$

20. $R_I\bar{3}$

D_3

(149) 21. $P312$

22. $P31'2$

23. $P312'$

24. P_c312

(150) 25. $P321$

26. $P321'$

27. $P32'1$

28. P_c321

(151) 29. $P3_112$

30. $P3_11'2$

31. $P3_112'$

32. P_c3_112

(152) 33. $P3_121$

34. $P3_121'$

35. $P3_12'1$

36. P_c3_121

(153) 37. $P3_212$

38. $P3_21'2$

39. $P3_212'$

40. P_c3_212

(154) 41. $P3_221$

42. $P3_221'$

43. $P3_22'1$

44. P_c3_221

(155) 45. $R32$

46. $R321'$

47. $R32'$

48. R_I32

C_{3v}

(156) 49. $P3m1$

50. $P3m1'$

51. $P3m'1$

52. P_c3m1

(157) 53. $P31m$

54. $P31'm$

55. $P31m'$

56. P_c31m

(158) 57. $P3c1$

58. $P3c1'$

59. $P3c'1$

60. P_c3c1

(159) 61. $P31c$

62. $P31'c$

63. $P31c'$

64. P_c31c

(160) 65. $R3m$

66. $R3m1'$

67. $R3m'$

68. R_I3m

(161) 69. $R3c$

70. $R3c1'$

71. $R3c'$

72. R_I3c

D_{3d}

(162) 73. $P\bar{3}1m$
74. $P\bar{3}1'm$
75. $P\bar{3}'1m$
76. $P\bar{3}'1m'$
77. $P\bar{3}1m'$
78. $P_c\bar{3}1m$

(163) 79. $P\bar{3}1c$
80. $P\bar{3}1'c$
81. $P\bar{3}'1c$
82. $P\bar{3}'1c'$
83. $P\bar{3}1c'$
84. $P_c\bar{3}1c$

(164) 85. $P\bar{3}m1$
86. $P\bar{3}m1'$
87. $P\bar{3}'m1$
88. $P\bar{3}'m'1$
89. $P\bar{3}m'1$
90. $P_c\bar{3}m1$

(165) 91. $P\bar{3}c1$
92. $P\bar{3}c1'$
93. $P\bar{3}'c1$
94. $P\bar{3}'c'1$
95. $P\bar{3}c'1$
96. $P_c\bar{3}c1$

(166) 97. $R\bar{3}m$
98. $R\bar{3}m1'$
99. $R\bar{3}'m$
100. $R\bar{3}'m'$
101. $R\bar{3}m'$
102. $R_I\bar{3}m$

(167) 103. $R\bar{3}c$
104. $R\bar{3}c1'$
105. $R\bar{3}'c$
106. $R\bar{3}'c'$
107. $R\bar{3}c'$
108. $R_I\bar{3}c$

B. Hexagonal subsystem

C_6

(168) 109. $P6$
110. $P61'$
111. $P6'$
112. P_c6

(169) 113. $P6_1$
114. $P6_11'$
115. $P6_1'$
116. P_c6_1

(170) 117. $P6_5$
118. $P6_51'$
119. $P6_5'$
120. P_c6_5

(171) 121. $P6_2$
122. $P6_21'$
123. $P6_2'$
124. P_c6_2

(172) 125. $P6_4$
126. $P6_41'$
127. $P6_4'$
128. P_c6_4

(173) 129. $P6_3$
130. $P6_31'$
131. $P6_3'$
132. P_c6_3

C_{3h}

(174) 133. $P\bar{6}$
134. $P\bar{6}1'$
135. $P\bar{6}'$
136. $P_c\bar{6}$

C_{6h}

(175) 137. $P6/m$
138. $P6/m1'$
139. $P6'/m$
140. $P6/m'$
141. $P6'/m'$
142. P_c6/m

(176) 143. $P6_3/m$
144. $P6_3/m1'$
145. $P6_3'/m$
146. $P6_3/m'$
147. $P6_3'/m'$
148. P_c6_3/m

D_6

(177) 149. $P622$
150. $P6221'$
151. $P6'2'2$

152. $P6'22'$
153. $P62'2'$
154. P_c622

(178) 155. $P6_122$
156. $P6_1221'$
157. $P6_12'2$
158. $P6_122'$
159. $P6_12'2'$
160. P_c6_122

(179) 161. $P6_522$
162. $P6_5221'$
163. $P6_52'2$
164. $P6_522'$
165. $P6_52'2'$
166. P_c6_522

(180) 167. $P6_222$
168. $P6_2221'$
169. $P6_22'2$
170. $P6_222'$
171. $P6_22'2'$
172. P_c6_222

(181) 173. $P6_422$
174. $P6_4221'$
175. $P6_42'2$
176. $P6_422'$
177. $P6_42'2'$
178. P_c6_422

(182) 179. $P6_322$
180. $P6_3221'$
181. $P6_32'2$
182. $P6_322'$
183. $P6_32'2'$
184. P_c6_322

C_{6v}

(183) 185. $P6mm$
186. $P6mm1'$
187. $P6'm'm$
188. $P6'mm'$
189. $P6m'm'$
190. P_c6mm

(184) 191. $P6cc$
192. $P6cc1'$
193. $P6'c'c$
194. $P6'cc'$

195. $P6c'c'$
196. P_c6cc

(185) 197. $P6_3cm$
198. $P6_3cm1'$
199. $P6_3'c'm$
200. $P6_3'cm'$
201. $P6_3c'm'$
202. P_c6_3cm

(186) 203. $P6_3mc$
204. $P6_3mc1'$
205. $P6_3'm'c$
206. $P6_3'mc'$
207. $P6_3m'c'$
208. P_c6_3mc

D_{3h}

(187) 209. $P\bar{6}m2$
210. $P\bar{6}m21'$
211. $P\bar{6}'m'2$
212. $P\bar{6}'m2'$
213. $P\bar{6}m'2'$
214. $P_c\bar{6}m2$

(188) 215. $P\bar{6}c2$
216. $P\bar{6}c21'$
217. $P\bar{6}'c'2$
218. $P\bar{6}'c2'$
219. $P\bar{6}c'2'$
220. $P_c\bar{6}c2$

(189) 221. $P\bar{6}2m$
222. $P\bar{6}2m1'$
223. $P\bar{6}'2'm$
224. $P\bar{6}'2m'$
225. $P\bar{6}2'm'$
226. $P_c\bar{6}2m$

(190) 227. $P\bar{6}2c$
228. $P\bar{6}2c1'$
229. $P\bar{6}'2'c$
230. $P\bar{6}'2c'$
231. $P\bar{6}2'c'$
232. $P_c\bar{6}2c$

D_{6h}

(191) 233. $P6/mmm$
234. $P/6mmm1'$
235. $P6/m'mm$

236. $P6'/mm'm$
237. $P6'/mmm'$
238. $P6'/m'm'm$
239. $P6'/m'mm'$
240. $P6/mm'm'$
241. $P6/m'm'm'$
242. P_c6/mmm

(192) 243. $P/6mcc$
244. $P6/mcc1'$
245. $P6/m'cc$
246. $P6'/mc'c$
247. $P6'/mcc'$
248. $P6'/m'c'c$
249. $P6'/m'cc'$
250. $P6/mc'c'$
251. $P6/m'c'c'$
252. P_c6/mcc

(193) 253. $P6_3/mcm$
254. $P6_3/mcm1'$
255. $P6_3/m'cm$
256. $P6_3'/mc'm$
257. $P6_3'/mcm'$
258. $P6_3'/m'c'm$
259. $P6_3'/m'cm'$
260. $P6_3/mc'm'$
261. $P6_3/m'c'm'$
262. P_c6_3/mcm

(194) 263. $P6_3mmc$
264. $P6_3/mmc1'$
265. $P6_3/m'mc$
266. $P6_3'/mm'c$
267. $P6_3'/mmc'$
268. $P6_3'/m'm'c$
269. $P6_3'/m'mc'$
270. $P6_3/mm'c'$
271. $P6_3/m'm'c'$
272. P_c6_3/mmc

Cubic system

T

(195) 1. $P23$
2. $P23'$
3. P_I23

(196) 4. $F23$
5. $F23'$
6. F_s23

(197) 7. $I23$
8. $I23'$

(198) 9. $P2_13$
10. $P2_13'$
11. P_I2_13

(199) 12. $I2_13$
13. $I2_13'$

T_h

(200) 14. $Pm3$
15. $Pm3'$
16. $Pm'3$
17. P_Im3

(201) 18. $Pn3$
19. $Pn3'$
20. $Pn'3$
21. P_In3

(202) 22. $Fm3$
23. $Fm3'$
24. $Fm'3$
25. F_sm3

(203) 26. $Fd3$
27. $Fd3'$
28. $Fd'3$
29. F_sd3

(204) 30. $Im3$
31. $Im3'$
32. $Im'3$

(205) 33. $Pa3$
34. $Pa3'$
35. $Pa'3$
36. P_Ia3

(206) 37. $Ia3$
38. $Ia3'$
39. $Ia'3$

O

(207) 40. $P432$
41. $P43'2$
42. $P4'32'$
43. P_I432

(208) 44. $P4_232$
45. $P4_23'2$

46. $P4_2'32'$
47. P_I4_232

(209) 48. $F432$
49. $F43'2$
50. $F4'32'$
51. F_s432

(210) 52. $F4_132$
53. $F4_13'2$
54. $F4_1'32'$
55. F_s4_132

(211) 56. $I432$
57. $I43'2$
58. $I4'32'$

(212) 59. $P4_332$
60. $P4_33'2$
61. $P4_3'32'$
62. P_I4_332

(213) 63. $P4_132$
64. $P4_13'2$
65. $P4_1'32'$
66. P_I4_132

(214) 67. $I4_132$
68. $I4_13'2$
69. $I4_1'32'$

$\boldsymbol{T_d}$

(215) 70. $P\bar{4}3m$
71. $P\bar{4}3'm$
72. $P\bar{4}'3m'$
73. $P_I\bar{4}3m$

(216) 74. $F\bar{4}3m$
75. $F\bar{4}3'm$
76. $F\bar{4}'3m'$
77. $F_s\bar{4}3m$

(217) 78. $I\bar{4}3m$
79. $I\bar{4}3'm$
80. $I\bar{4}'3m'$

(218) 81. $P\bar{4}3n$
82. $P\bar{4}3'n$
83. $P\bar{4}'3n'$
84. $P_I\bar{4}3n$

(219) 85. $F\bar{4}3c$
86. $F\bar{4}3'c$
87. $F\bar{4}'3c'$
88. $F_s\bar{4}3c$

(220) 89. $I\bar{4}3d$
90. $I\bar{4}'3'd$
91. $I\bar{4}3d$

$\boldsymbol{O_h}$

(221) 92. $Pm3m$
93. $Pm3'm$
94. $Pm'3m$
95. $Pm3m'$
96. $Pm'3m'$
97. P_Im3m

(222) 98. $Pn3n$
99. $Pn3'n$
100. $Pn'3n$
101. $Pn3n'$
102. $Pn'3n'$
103. P_In3n

(223) 104. $Pm3n$
105. $Pm3'n$
106. $Pm'3n$
107. $Pm3n'$
108. $Pm'3n'$
109. P_Im3n

(224) 110. $Pn3m$
111. $Pn3'm$
112. $Pn'3m$
113. $Pn3m'$
114. $Pn'3m'$
115. P_In3m

(225) 116. $Fm3m$
117. $Fm3'm$
118. $Fm'3m$
119. $Fm3m'$
120. $Fm'3m'$
121. F_sm3m

(226) 122. $Fm3c$
123. $Fm3'c$
124. $Fm'3c$
125. $Fm3c'$
126. $Fm'3c'$
127. F_sm3c

(227) 128. $Fd3m$
129. $Fd3'm$
130. $Fd'3m$
131. $Fd3m'$
132. $Fd'3m'$
133. F_sd3m

(228) 134. $Fd3c$
135. $Fd3'c$
136. $Fd'3c$
137. $Fd3c'$
138. $Fd'3c'$
139. F_sd3c

(229) 140. $Im3m$
141. $Im3'm$
142. $Im'3m$
143. $Im3m'$
144. $Im'3m'$

(230) 145. $Ia3d$
146. $Ia3'd$
147. $Ia'3d$
148. $Ia3d'$
149. $Ia'3d'$

Dichromatic Plane Groups*

N. V. BELOV and T. N. TARKHOVA

INTRODUCTION

INFINITE two-dimensional groups of antisymmetry[93], or more simply (according to the usual method of depiction) black and white groups, were first derived by selecting from the 230 Fedorov groups those which left a figure in a certain plane lying in the same plane, but in which some of the derived figures might be inverted. This means that if a figure—the simplest being a scalene triangle—turned its "face" toward us (or was white) in its initial position, then it would turn its reverse or "wrong side" (black) toward us in half of the derived positions. There are 80 groups in all[38,59,65,81] which leave the initial figure in one plane. If from these one excludes the 17 one-sided plane symmetry groups which do not invert the original figure, and a similar number of groups in which each figure actually consists of two identical figures superimposed on each other, so that their principal plane is a mirror plane of symmetry ("gray" groups in A. V. Shubnikov's terminology), then 46 plane dichromatic groups in the strict sense of the word will remain.

DERIVATION OF THE GROUPS

These groups may also be derived without recourse to the 230 groups by following the method used by Neronova, Smirnova and Belov[101] for the derivation of 1651 Shubnikov (black and

* A part of the paper "Groups of colored symmetry" published in *Kristallografiia*, **1**, 4–9 (1956).

white) space groups of antisymmetry*. To the generally known five plane Bravais lattices we will add the dichromatic plane Bravais lattices. These include one monoclinic lattice $p'_b(p'_a, p'_C)$ in which any given edge (or diagonal) of an elementary parallelogram is centered in a "colored" manner, (i.e., by a different color); and three rhombic (rectangular) lattices: p'_b (one edge is centered in a "colored" manner),

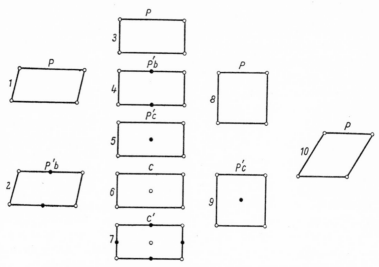

FIG. 140. The plane dichromatic nets (lattices) of Bravais.

p'_C (an elementary rectangle centered arealy by using a different color), and c' (both edges of an ordinary centered rectangular cell centered in a "colored" manner). A square p'_C centered arealy in a colored manner will be the final colored lattice. Thus, in addition to the five ordinary plane Bravais lattices, we must take into account another five colored ones, which makes ten in all (Fig. 140).

We use "International" designations for the 17 ordinary

---

* Editor's note: That paper did in fact contain an abbreviated derivation of the 46 plane dichromatic groups, on pp. 48–49, but it was deleted from the translated edition in this volume to avoid confusion. It used the dichromatic three-dimensional lattices P_a, P_i, and C_a in place of the dichromatic two-dimensional lattices p'_b, p'_C, and c', respectively (described here).

plane groups[96] which contain no more than two basic "generative" elements of symmetry in all. We color the latter alternately (they are distinguished by primes), first one, then the other, and finally both basic elements together.

According to the theorem demonstrated in the above article[101] for dichromatic translation groups in the direction of any given color translation, any element of symmetry either alternates with a (similar) non-colored element or coincides with it. Therefore, a complete enumeration of dichromatic groups can be made by alternately replacing the non-colored symbol of the Bravais lattice in each of the ordinary 17 groups with all the colored ones of the same syngony. If the dichromatic Bravais lattice is non-identically related to the generative elements in the first and second places of the symbol, the number of corresponding groups doubles. In Table 11 all of the 46 dichromatic groups* are arranged according to this order of their derivation. Designations using non-colored and dichromatic Bravais lattices, which we consider the most rational, are given in the first column. Cochran's less rational designations, from his well-known article in *Acta Crystallographica*[94], are shown in the second column. The third column shows (in both Schoenflies and International designations) the Fedorov (space) group that corresponds to the given colored one and which was the initial one in the first derivation of the 80 "bilateral" dichromatic groups. The last column shows another Fedorov space group from the 230, which may also be used to derive the corresponding dichromatic group; we will dwell on this later in more detail.

Diagrams of all 46 dichromatic groups are assembled in Fig. 141. These diagrams have been set forth repeatedly, when first derived by Alexander and Herrmann[81], Weber[38], and later by Shubnikov in his *Atlas*[65] and *Symmetry*[59]. Upon comparison, certain diagrams may not appear to correspond to the diagram in the indicated sources. This is explained, first, by the fact that in the indicated works the rhombic lattice is sometimes centered (by coloring) along edge $a - p'_a$

* Editor's note: I substitute the table published later by Belov[130] because, although otherwise identical, it also lists the "one color" and "gray" groups.

TABLE 11
List of Plane Dichromatic Groups

No.	Rational symbol	Cochrane symbol	Initial Fedorov group with inversion elements of symmetry	Initial Fedorov group arranged on two levels
1	$p2'$	$p2'$	$C_i = P\bar{1}$	$C_2^2 = P112_1$
2	$p_b'1$	pt'	$C_s = P11b$	$C_1^1 = A111$
3	$p_b'2$	$p2t'$	$C_{2h}^4 = P112/b$	$C_2^1 = A112$
4	pm'	pm'	$C_2^1 = P121$	$C_s^2 = Pc11$
5	pg'	pg'	$C_2^2 = P12_11$	$C_s^2 = Pn11$
6	cm'	cm'	$C_2^3 = C121$	$C_s^4 = Cc$
7	$p_b'm$	$pm + t'$	$C_{2v}^2 = Pm2_1b$	$C_s^3 = Am11$
8	$p_b'g$	$pg + t'$	$C_{2v}^3 = Pb2b$	$C_s^4 = Ab11$
9	$p_b'1m$	$pm + m'$	$C_{2v}^4 = P2mb$	$C_s^1 = A1m1$
10	$p_b'1g$	$pg + g'$	$C_{2v}^5 = P2_1ab$	$C_s^2 = A1a1$
11	$p_c'm$	$pm + g'$	$C_{2v}^7 = Pm2_1n$	$C_s^3 = Im11$
12	p_cg	$pg + m'$	$C_{2v}^6 = Pb2n$	$C_s^4 = Ib11$
13	$c'm$	$cm + m'$	$C_{2v}^{15} = Cm2a$	$C_s^3 = Fm11$
14	pmm'	pmm'	$C_{2h}^1 = P2/m$	$C_{2v}^2 = Pmc2_1$
15	$pm'm'$	$pm'm'$	$D_2^1 = P222$	$C_{2v}^3 = Pcc2$
16	$pm'g$	$pm'g$	$C_{2h}^4 = P12/a1$	$C_{2v}^5 = Pca2_1$
17	pmg'	pmg'	$C_{2h}^2 = P2_1/m$	$C_{2v}^7 = Pmn2_1$
18	pgg'	pgg'	$C_{2h}^5 = P2_1/b$	$C_{2v}^9 = Pbn2_1$
19	$pg'g'$	$pg'g'$	$D_2^3 = P2_12_12$	$C_{2v}^{10} = Pnn2$
20	$pm'g'$	$pm'g'$	$D_2^2 = P2_122$	$C_{2v}^6 = Pcn2$
21	cmm'	cmm'	$C_{2h}^3 = C2/m$	$C_{2v}^{12} = Cmc2_1$
22	$cm'm'$	$cm'm'$	$D_2^6 = C222$	$C_{2v}^{13} = Ccc2$
23	$p_b'mm$	$pm, m + m'$	$D_{2h}^5 = Pmmb$	$C_{2v}^{14} = Amm2$
24	$p_b'mg$	$pm, g + g'$	$D_{2h}^1 = Pmab$	$C_{2v}^{16} = Ama2$
25	$p_b'gm$	$pg, m + m'$	$D_{2h}^3 = Pbmb$	$C_{2v}^{15} = Abm2$
26	$p_b'gg$	$pg, g + g'$	$D_{2h}^8 = Pbab$	$C_{2v}^{17} = Aba2$
27	$p_c'mm$	$pm + g', m + g'$	$D_{2h}^{13} = Pmmn$	$C_{2v}^{20} = Imm2$
28	$p_c'mg$	$pm + g', g + m'$	$D_{2h}^7 = Pman$	$C_{2v}^{22} = Ima2$
29	p_cgg	$pg + m', g + m'$	$D_{2h}^4 = Pban$	$C_{2v}^{21} = Iba2$
30	$c'mm$	$cm + m', m + m',$	$D_{2h}^{21} = Cmma$	$C_{2v}^{18} = Fmm2$
31	$p4'$	$p4'$	$S_4^1 = P\bar{4}$	$C_4^3 = P4_2$
32	p_c4	$p4t'$	$C_{4h}^3 = P4/n$	$C_4^5 = I4$
33	$p4'mm'$	$p4'mm'$	$D_{2d}^5 = P\bar{4}m2$	$C_{4v}^7 = P4_2mc$
34	$p4'm'm$	$p4'm'm$	$D_{2d}^3 = P\bar{4}2m$	$C_{4v}^3 = P4_2cm$
35	$p4m'm'$	$p4m'm'$	$D_4^1 = P422$	$C_{4v}^5 = P4cc$

TABLE 11—*(contd.)*

No.	Rational symbol	Cochrane symbol	Initial Fedorov group with inversion elements of symmetry	Initial Fedorov group arranged on two levels
36	$p4'gm'$	$p4'gm'$	$D_{2d}^7 = P\bar{4}b2$	$C_{4v}^8 = P4_2bc$
37	$p4'g'm$	$p4'g'm$	$D_{2d}^3 = P\bar{4}2_1m$	$C_{4v}^4 = P4_2nm$
38	$p4g'm'$	$p4g'm'$	$D_4^2 = P42_12$	$C_{4v}^6 = P4nc$
39	p_c4mm	$p4m + g', m + m'$	$D_{4h}^7 = P4/nmm$	$C_{4v}^9 = I4mm$
40	$p_c'4gm$	$p4g + m', m + m'$	$D_{4h}^3 = P4/nbm$	$C_{4v}^{10} = I4cm$
41	$p3m'$	$p3m'1$	$D_3^1 = P312$	$C_{3v}^3 = P3c$
42	$p31m'$	$p31m'$	$D_3^2 = P321$	$C_{3v}^4 = P31c$
43	$p6'$	$p6'$	$C_{3i}^1 = P\bar{3}$	$C_6^6 = P6_3$
44	$p6'm'm$	$p6'm'm$	$D_{3d}^1 = P\bar{3}12/m$	$C_{6v}^3 = P6_3cm$
45	$p6'mm'$	$p6'mm'$	$D_{3d}^3 = P\bar{3}2/m1$	$C_{6v}^4 = P6_3mc$
46	$p6m'm'$	$p6m'm'$	$D_6^1 = P622$	$C_{6v}^2 = P6cc$

Degenerate Groups

	Monochromatic			Gray	
47	$p1$	$C_1^1 = P1$	64	$p1'$	$C_s^1 = Pm$
48	$p2$	$C_2^1 = P2$	65	$p21'$	$C_{2h}^1 = P2/m$
49	pm	$C_s^1 = Pm$	66	$pm1'$	$C_{2v}^1 = Pm2m$
50	pg	$C_s^2 = Pa$	67	$pg1'$	$C_{2v}^4 = Pg2_1m$
51	cm	$C_s^3 = Cm$	68	$cm1'$	$C_{2v}^{14} = Cm2m$
52	$pmm2$	$C_{2v}^1 = Pmm2$	69	$pmm21'$	$D_{2h}^1 = Pmmm$
53	$pmg2$	$C_{2v}^4 = Pma2$	70	$pmg21'$	$D_{2h}^5 = Pmam$
54	$pgg2$	$C_{2v}^8 = Pba2$	71	$pgg21'$	$D_{2h}^9 = Pbam$
55	$cmm2$	$C_{2v}^{11} = Cmm2$	72	$cmm2'$	$D_{2h}^{19} = Cmmm$
56	$p4$	$C_4^1 = P4$	73	$p41'$	$C_{4h}^1 = P4/m$
57	$p4mm$	$C_{4v}^1 = P4mm$	74	$p4mm1'$	$D_{4h}^1 = P4/mmm$
58	$p4gm$	$C_{4v}^2 = P4bm$	75	$p4gm1'$	$D_{4h}^1 = P4/mbm$
59	$p3$	$C_3^1 = P3$	76	$p3'$	$C_{3h}^1 = P3/m = P\bar{6}$
60	$p3m$	$C_{3v}^1 = P3m$	77	$p3'm$	$D_{3h}^1 = P3/mm2 = P\bar{6}m2$
61	$p31m$	$C_{3v}^2 = P31m$	78	$p3'1m$	$D_{3h}^3 = P3/m2m = P\bar{6}2m$
62	$p6$	$C_6^1 = P6$	79	$p61'$	$D_{6h}^1 = P6/m$
63	$p6mm$	$C_{6v}^1 = P6mm$	80	$p6mm1'$	$D_{6h}^1 = P6/mmm$

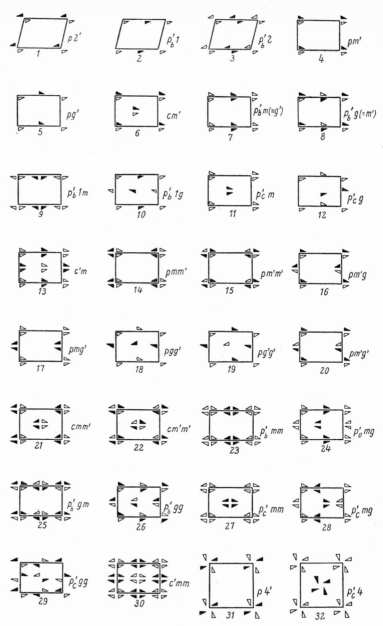

FIG. 141

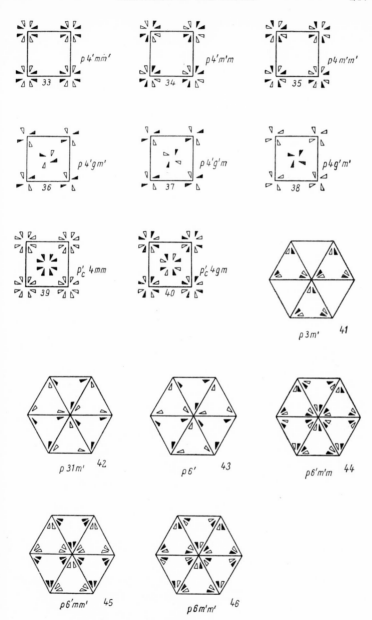

FIG. 141. Forty-six dichromatic plane groups.

usually, and at other times along edge $b - p'_b$; we always select p'_b. Secondly, it is explained by the fact that with alternation of colored elements and uncolored ones (in groups with colored Bravais lattices), preference was sometimes given—in the preceding works—to the colored element of symmetry

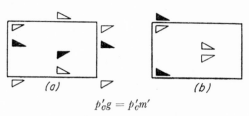

$$p'_0 g = p'_C m'$$

FIG. 142. Different aspects of group $p'_0 g$.

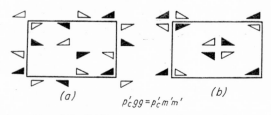

$$p'_C gg = p'_C m'm'$$

FIG. 143. Different aspects of group $p'_0 gg$.

(i.e., the corresponding plane or axis coincided with the coordinates); however, in view of the basic theorem we give preference to uncolored elements. Thus instead of alternating g and m', we give group $p'_0 g$ in the form $p'_C g$ (Fig. 142a) whereas in previous works it has the form $p'_C m'$ (Fig. 142b); group $p'_C gg$ (Fig. 143a) is represented in Fig. 143b as $p'_C m'm'$.

An Alternate Derivation

In the first derivations of dichromatic groups, particularly by A. V. Shubnikov, the concept of antisymmetry was basic—the possibility of a plane figure having dissimilar obverse and reverse sides (a plus side and a minus side)—expressed arbitrarily by coloring the two sides of the figure differently. Dichromatic groups of symmetry may, however, be derived by another method, namely, that of selecting from the 230 Fedorov space symmetry groups those which, originating from one specific figure (the same scalene triangle), dispose all the derived figures on two and only two levels. If the height of a three-dimensional cell is c and the height of the initial figure is z, then half of all the figures of such a group which are related by symmetry remain on level z; the other half, however, will be located on level $z + c/2$. In such groups, however, one may always make z equal to zero. Screw axes 2_1, 4_2, 6_3 and planes of symmetry c and n will obviously be elements of symmetry so disposed. But in addition, Bravais lattices A, B, I and F will act in the same fashion. We will designate figures on level $z(0)$ by one color and figures on level $(z+c/2)c/2$ by another. [This gives the list in column four of Table 11.]

The advantage of the proposed method lies in the fact that it completely avoids monochromatic plane groups as well as gray groups and yields only 46 dichromatic groups.

Mosaics for the
Dichromatic Plane Groups*

N. V. BELOV and E. N. BELOVA

MOSAICS are the clearest representation of the groups corresponding to them, since they do not contain "gray" elements (terminology due to Shubnikov[59]). In the usual schematic representation of plane groups by tetrahedra or triangles of two colors[107] all the "empty" space between triangles is "gray". The symmetry of groups is represented best by mosaics in which all the elementary figures of various colors are geometrically the same and sufficiently simple, particularly if their outlines contain no curves. This condition is relatively easily fulfilled for groups with very high orders of symmetry, and less easily, perhaps even never, for groups with poor symmetry.

In Fig. 144 we present mosaics constructed according to these principles for 46 black-white plane groups† and only in certain special cases have we considered it necessary to give two mosaic diagrams for a single group.

It should be borne in mind[101] that in centered groups and particularly in color-centered groups the symmetry elements entering into the formulae alternate or coincide with similar elements, and these latter may be even more evident than the standard elements entering into the formulas. Thus, in group No. 28 $p'_c mg$ the m plane alternates with the color g' plane,

---

* A part of the paper *Mosaics for 46 plane (Shubnikov) antisymmetry groups and for 15 (Fedorov) color groups* published in *Kristall.*, **2**, 21–22 (1957), and reproduced from the translation in *Sov. Phys. Crystall.*, **2**, 16–18, through the courtesy of the American Institute of Physics.

† Editor's note: The mosaics have been renumbered to correspond to the sequence published both previously[107] and subsequently[130] (see this volume, Table 11) by Belov. Mosaics for $p'_b gm$ (No. 25) and $p4m'm$ (No. 34) have been corrected according to the suggestion of Zamorzaev and Palistrant[183]. Pawley[188] has also suggested another form for the group $p'_c 4$ (No. 32a).

220

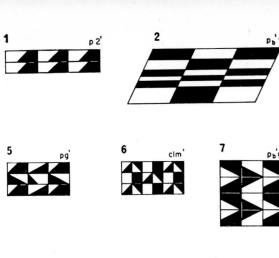
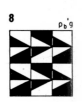

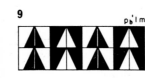
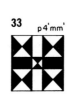
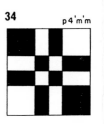
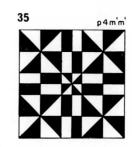
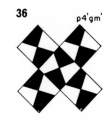

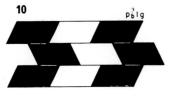
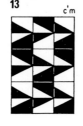
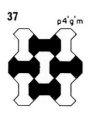
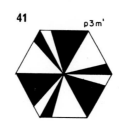
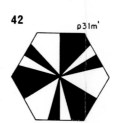
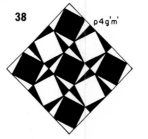

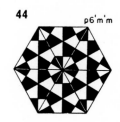
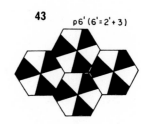

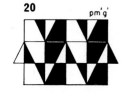

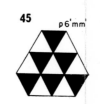

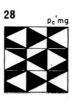
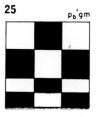
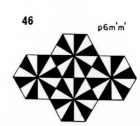

FIG. 144. Mosaics for the dichromatic plane groups.

and the g plane alternates with m', so that the complete formula would be $p'_c m(g')g(m')$. In group No. 23 $p'_b mm$, the first m plane coincides identically with g', and the second m plane alternates with m', so that the total formula would be $p'_b m(\equiv g')m(m')$.

On One-dimensional Infinite Crystallographic Groups*

INTRODUCTION

"INTERNATIONAL" designations of crystallographic groups are quite appropriate for three-dimensional infinite groups such as monochromatic (Fedorov) as well as for dichromatic groups (Shubnikov groups[101]); they are used successfully for two-dimensional infinite groups (and for monochromatic—one-sided—as well as for dichromatic—two-sided—groups[107]) and are equally suitable for the separation and enumeration of one-dimensional infinite groups of various types: one-sided (borders[59]), two-sided (bands[59]) and finally, rods[59, 37]. Employing, as usual, symbols for the three positions and relating the first position to the infinite x-axis of translation (a), the second to axis y, lying in the plane of a border or a band, and the third to axis z, perpendicular to the indicated plane, we can easily determine the limiting conditions which can be placed upon the numbers and letters of each (1, 2, 3) position, and further, rapidly exhaust the possibilities.

LINE GROUPS IN A PLANE

Thus, in the case of one-sided groups (borders), there may be only mirror planes m in the first position, only planes m and a in the second position, and finally, in the third position only the symbol of axis 2 (perpendicular to the plane of the border) is possible. As follows from the elements of crystallography, this axis 2 in the third position must be a necessary product of two elements of symmetry in the first and second position, if

* Published in *Kristallografiia*, **1**, 474–476 (1956).

they are present together; axis 2 may be independent only if they are absent. Thus we arrive at 7 groups of borders: $p111$, $pm11$, $p1m1$, $p1a1$, $pmm2$, $pma2$, $p112$.

The unchanged letter p before the three-membered symbol designates an infinite group of translations ("Bravais lattice") which is compulsory and identical for all one-dimensional

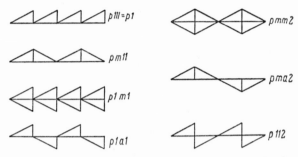

FIG. 145. One-dimensional one-sided infinite groups (borders).

infinite groups. Figure 145 illustrates these seven groups, using scalene triangles in four orientations. The reader will find excellent examples of borders in A. V. Shubnikov's book, "Symmetry."

TWO-SIDED OR DICHROMATIC LINE GROUPS IN A PLANE

In the case of two-sided bands, a second element of symmetry is possible, in each of the three positions normal to the elements of symmetry of the borders. Thus axes 2 and 2_1 are possible in the first position. If one of them is present together with a plane m which is normal to it, then the axis is placed as usual in the "numerator" of the symbol and the plane in the "denominator." In the second position axis 2 is now also possible, and in the third position, both forms of planes, m and a. The presence (designation) of an element of symmetry in the numerator as well as in the denominator of a certain position generates, according to an elementary crystallographic theorem, a derived center of symmetry which is not related to any given coordinate direction and which therefore acts upon elements of symmetry in all three positions. The center of symmetry is not designated if there are both a numerator and a denominator in any given position, but, of course, it must be designated[101] when it remains the sole element of symmetry;   naturally, the three positions then are not designated.

We arrive at 31 groups of (two sided) symmetry of bands:

(1) $p111 = p1$, (2) pi [$p\bar{1}$], (3) $p211$, (4) $p2_111$, (5) $p121$, (6) $p112$, (7) $p222$, (8) $p2_122$, (9) $pm11$, (10) $p2/m11$, (11) $p2_1/m11$, (12) $p1m1$, (13) $p12/m1$, (14) $p1a1$, (15) $p12/a1$, (16) $p11m$, (17) $p11a$, (18) $p112/m$, (19) $p112/a$, (20) $pmm2$, (21) $pma2$, (22) $pm2m$, (23) $pm2a$, (24) $p2mm$, (25) $p2_1am$, (26) $p2_1ma$, (27) $p2aa$, (28) $pmmm$, (29) $pmam$, (30) $pmma$, (31) $pmaa$.

Groups 1, 6, 9, 12, 14, 20, and 21 repeat the above 7 one-sided groups, and groups 16, 18, 22, 24, 25, 28, and 29 are the corresponding gray groups[101,107]. One sided and gray groups are shown alongside each other in Fig. 146. Only the remaining 17 groups are two-sided black-white groups in the strictest sense. Like the 7 groups, the 31 groups may be easily extracted from the corresponding diagrams of 80 plane dichromatic (two-sided) groups[37].

The derivation of the 37 groups is much more easily accomplished if they are considered as being one-sided but dichromatic—black-white[101,107]—and at the same time the possibility of colored translation is taken into account, i.e., of a second "Bravais lattice" p'. Then according to Belov and Tarkhova[107], we start from the 7 monochromatic groups and first write down the "gray" groups (with the dots). Next come the dichromatic groups with uncolored translation (p) which are obtained by replacing in the monochromatic group symbol one or both basic elements of symmetry by colored ones, which we designate[107] by primes. Finally we again write down the 7 symbols of the monochromatic groups and change the sign of the monochromatic lattice to that of a colored one. Such a sequence of $7 + 7 + 10 + 7$ dichromatic groups is shown in Fig. 146. The symbol is given in the form just proposed (on the right in Fig. 146), as well as "three-dimensionally" (on the left). Just as planes m occurred in the space

groups and plane dichromatic groups and were easy to see in
the corresponding diagrams with colored Bravais lattices, so
here (Fig. 146) planes m, perpendicular to the axis of translation, alternate with m', whereas planes m that are parallel

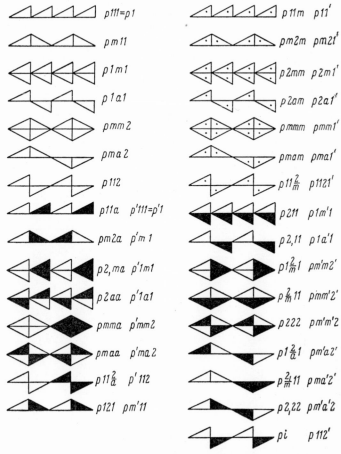

FIG. 146. One-dimensional two-sided infinite (bands).

to the axis of translation are simultaneously colored glide
planes, and vice versa: $m \equiv a'$; $a \equiv m'$; $p'mm2 = p'm(m')$,
$m(\equiv a')$, 2 and so on*.

* The *two-sided* dichromatic bands have been derived by Pabst[187].

ROD GROUPS

In the case of a rod, an axis of any given multiplicity may lie along the first (infinite) axis, whether rotational or a screw axis. The second and third axes cease being topologically different and then their selection is not dictated by the requirement of mutual perpendicularity, but is derived according to the rules of the crystallographic arrangement (crystallographic systems).

Limited only by those rod groups which are sub-groups of the 230, i.e., which are related by the prohibition of 5-, 7-, 8- and higher-fold axes, we arrive at the following groups which are subdivided according to the multiplicity of the main axis:

$n = 3$

$p311$	$p3/m11$	$p\bar{6}11$	$p32$	$p3m$	$p3/mm2 = p\bar{6}m2$
					$p3/ma2 = p\bar{6}a2$
$p3_111$	$p\bar{3}11 = p\overset{\circ}{6}11$		$p3_12$	$p3a$	$p\bar{3}2/m\ \ = p\overset{\circ}{6}2/m$
$p3_211$			$p3_22$		$p\bar{3}2/a\ \ = p\overset{\circ}{6}2/a$

$n = 4$

$p411$	$p4/m11$	$p\bar{4}11$	$p422$		
$p4_111$	$p4_2/m11$		$p4_122$		
$p4_211$			$p4_222$	$p4mm$	$p\bar{4}2m$	$p4/mmm$
$p4_311$			$p4_322$	$p4_2ma$	$p\bar{4}2a$	$p4_2/mma$
				$p4aa$		$p4/maa$

$n = 6$

$p611$	$p6/m11$	$p622$	$p6mm$	$p6/mmm$
$p6_111$	$p6_3/m11$	$p6_122$	$p6_3ma$	$p6_3/mma$
$n6_211$		$p6_222$	$p6aa$	$p6/maa$
$p6_311$		$p6_322$		
$p6_411$		$p6_422$		
$p6_511$		$p6_522$		

With non-crystallographic n, the change in the corresponding number of groups will mainly take place at the expense of an ever-increasing number of possible screw axes; in the absence of "International" designations, we used inversion axes $(\bar{3}, \bar{6})$ as well as mirror axes $(\overset{\circ}{3}, \overset{\circ}{6})$, taking into account the equality $\overset{\circ}{3} = \overset{\circ}{6}$ and $\overset{\circ}{\bar{6}} = \overset{\circ}{3}$. Core groups with limiting (infinite) elements of symmetry are examined in the book, *Symmetry* by A. V. Shubnikov[59]*.

* The dichromatic rod groups were later listed by Neronova and Belov[171].

Polychromatic Plane Groups*

N. V. BELOV, E. N. BELOVA and T. N. TARKHOVA

DERIVATION

EXTENSION of the above method to figures with more than two colors is natural. In order to derive groups of multicolored symmetry, one must separate from the 230 groups those which dispose the figures related by them on three and only three levels, four and only four levels, and six and only six levels, and designate these levels by different colors.

If one proceeds from classical representations of crystallography, five-color, seven-color, etc., symmetries appear to be excluded (see below). Colored elements of symmetry (for more than two colors) will obviously be: axes 3_1, 3_2, 4_1, 4_3, 6_1, 6_5, 6_2, and 6_4, plane d and also Bravais lattice R.

In the tetragonal syngony the colored groups will be $P4_1$ (II, in Plate I), $P4_3$ (I, Ia), $I4_1$ (III, IIIa) and multiples of these groups, namely $I4_1md$ (IV, IVa), $I4_1cd$ (V). In trigonal subsyngony the corresponding groups will be $P3_1$ (VII), $P3_2$ (VIII), $R3$ (IX), $R3m$ (X), $R3c$ (XI) and in hexagonal $P6_1$ (XII), $P6_5$ (XIII), $P6_2$ (XIV), $P6_4$ (XV). The only group of a lower crystallographic class that disposes figures related to it on four levels will be the orthorhombic group Fdd (VI, VIa, VIb).

MOSAICS FOR "CRYSTALLOGRAPHIC" GROUPS

For these 15 groups (one is obtained from two enantiomorphic groups) we do not give triangle diagrams on the color plate

* Editor's note: A part of the paper *Groups of colored symmetry*, published in *Kristallografiia* **1**, 10–13 (1956), with subsequent corrections and emendations in *Kristallografiia* **1**, 615, 619–621 (1956); **2**, 21–22 (1957); and **3**, 618–620 (1958), from all of which an attempt has been made here to edit a consistent whole.

(Plate I)*; these would be analogous to the diagrams of the 46 dichromatic groups (Fig. 141), but we introduce color mosaics with a sufficiently large number of cells so that the mosaic motif is projected in a convex manner. Under each mosaic is designated its symmetry, and the Roman numerals in parenthesis above indicate the illustrated mosaic of the given group. The majority of such mosaics may be found in tiled floors, etc.; in our opinion, however, some appear for the first time and are constructed graphically solely according to the corresponding Fedorov group ($I4_1cd$—V, $R3c$—XI).

We recommend placing a transparent sheet of paper on the mosaic; having traced the elementary cell on it, fill in the corresponding designations of the elements of symmetry according to any reference book[96,100] and follow the chromatic operation of the elements of symmetry.

Screw axis 4_1 disposes figures on four levels, which in our diagrams are designated by the colors yellow–blue–red–green and yellow again. We proceed from yellow to red or from blue to green as the result of operation 4_2 or 2_1, and also as the result of the action of glide plane of symmetry c or n. With the six colors of axis 6_1 we have the corresponding sequence white–red–green–black–yellow–blue–white. The sequence white–black, red–yellow, and green–blue, which are contained in six-fold axis 6_3, and two-fold axis 2_1 will correspond. The latter sequences are present in hexagonal groups also as glide planes c and n.

We originally thought that only the two enantiomorphic groups 6_1 and 6_5 were possible for six-color symmetry. Analysis

---

* Editor's note: Of the several versions of the colored mosaics published by Belov[107,108,112,118], Plate I is essentially that published in 1957[112], with the following corrections: (a) Mosaics I, Ia and II of the original have been relabelled in Plate I, in order to make their color sequences conform with the handedness of their color screw axes, as defined by the sequence yellow–blue–red–green assumed by Belov in this paper. Two other versions[108,118] of I and one other version[118] of Ia and II were correct. (b) Mosaic XI as published[112] was incorrect on several counts; an earlier[107] correct version is substituted in Plate I.

Plate I illustrates the "simplest" mosaics for each color group. More complex versions may be seen, in the original publications, for groups $I4md$[108,118], $I4_1cd$[118], Fdd[108,118], and $R3$[108].

of Fedorov group $R3c$ brought us to mosaic (XI), which up to now has not been found in tiled floors, and showed that in this group the three levels created by a three-fold screw axis are still divided in half by the plane c. The corresponding mosaic (XI) may be broken down either into hexagons of three types, each of which contains two colors with a difference of $c/2$, or into triangles of two types, one of which contains three colors with a difference of $c/3$ and the others contain colors with the same difference but which are "complementary" to the three in the first triangle (differing by $c/2$). There are three-fold rotation axes in the centers of the hexagons and screw axes in the centers of the triangles.

In order to illustrate group $P4_1$ (or $P4_3$) we first conceived[107] two four-color mosaics which were formally correct but not very successful. With two types of axes 4_1 in them being crystallographically equivalent (required by the theory of groups), we found that 8 elementary triangular blocks converged at the exit points of half of the axes, and that 4 blocks converged at the exit points of the other half. This is a natural result of the selection of an elementary figure with only one right angle. A figure with two right angles is desirable. As a solution one may use the corresponding quadrangle of the most general type (for example, group $P4_3$ as No. I in Plate I) or a rectangle (No. Ia in Plate I).

Group $I4_1$, as the more detailed symbol $I4_1(4_3)$ implies, can be built up from sequences of blocks each with $P4_1$ symmetry, but with the blocks related by translations along the diagonals; 4_3 axes occur at the meeting-points of each set of four blocks. The patterns are derived from the symbolic multiplication $4_1 \times I = 4_3$. If the initial mosaics $P4_1$ and $P4_3$ are of the type of mosaic Ia in Plate I (without acute and without obtuse angles), the corresponding $I4_1(4_3)$ mosaics will be of one type only, namely that of mosaic IIIa. If the initial mosaics are of the more general shape of mosaics I and II, the resulting $I4_1(4_3)$ mosaics[118] will be qualitatively different[90], that is will have different geometrical environments. Mosaic IIIa can also be considered as built up from two kinds of large blocks (each composed of four small blocks like mosaic Ia) with 4_1 axes, and of blocks with 4_3 axes. Thereby $4_1 \times 4_3 = I$, that is, the centering in the cell results from our having 4_1 and 4_3 axes alternating along the translation. Alternatively, it can be considered as built up of small square blocks with 2_1 axes. Mosaic III has been built up from square blocks of symmetry 2.

The more elementary motif IV was originally obtained for group $I4_1md$ and it appeared that in IVa we had a new group

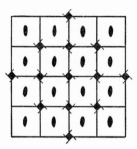

Fig. 147. Symmetry elements in $I4_1md$ (Mosaic IV, Plate I).

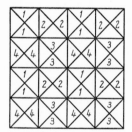

Fig. 148. Relations of two mosaics (IV and IVa) of symmetry $I4_1md$.

of symmetry. However, in spite of the difference in motif, both mosaics are characterized by the same symmetry; but in IV the mirror planes are parallel to the sides of the square blocks whereas in IVa the mirror planes pass along the diagonals of the square blocks. The relation between these two mosaics can also be seen in the following way.

Although mosaic IV consists of strictly square blocks, nevertheless the axes in it (screw or color 4_1 and 4_3 axes) are found only at the junctions of the four blocks, whereas (see Fig. 147) only ordinary two-fold rotation axes pass through the center of each block. If in each monochromatic square of mosaic IV, in conformity with symmetry $mm2$, we leave only two triangles colored out of the four which are formed when the square is broken up by two diagonals, then we can arrange the vacant triangles (see Fig. 148) differently, still preserving, however, the same symmetry $I4_1md = F4_1dm$ in the mosaic. They may be colored the same as triangles in adjacent squares and then we will obtain mosaic IVa with new square blocks, but the area of each block will be half as great and the blocks

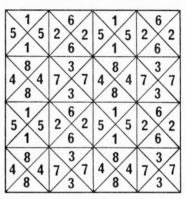

FIG. 149. Two interpenetrating four-color mosaics of symmetry $I4_1md$.

will be oriented so that their sides are at an angle of 45° to the sides of the original squares (lattice of square outline). There are no longer two-fold axes in the centers of these smaller blocks; they now occur only at the junctions of four squares, alternating with axes 4_1 and 4_3 (mosaic IVa in Plate I).

The empty triangles in the second variant (Fig. 148)—there are as many of them as there are colored ones which remained—can also be given four new colors; the latter are related by the same symmetry $I4_1md = F4_1dm$, but they will remain completely independent of the basic triangles. In particular, they will not be related to them by any relationships of ordinary or colored symmetry. The possibility of two analogous inter-penetrating mosaics existing in a lattice of certain symmetry, and the mosaics being independent of each other but each having a symmetry equal to that of the whole lattice, has

often been recorded[99]. In Fig. 149* the four basic colors
(1, 2, 3, 4) are shown in the same manner as in the original
mosaic IV of Plate I, and the four additional colors are
numbered 5, 6, 7, 8.

A square with a different array of colors than either mosaics
IV or IVa gives a mosaic (V) of symmetry $I4_1/cd$. The authors
have so far been unable to construct a more expressive mosaic
of this symmetry.

We obtain rhombic mosaics corresponding to group Fdd

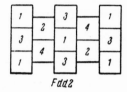

Fdd2

Fig. 150. Mosaic for group $Fdd2$.

Fdd2

Fig. 151. Mosaic for group $Fdd2$.

from tetragonal ones with planes d, by means of a "rhombic
deformation", that is, by the conversion of square blocks
into rectangular or rhombic ones, depending upon whether
the diamond glide planes d pass along the sides of the blocks
(V) or along the diagonals (IV). Elongation and compression
always take place along planes d, and since they are preserved
in rhombic symmetry and determine the coordinate directions,
the original tetragonal cell must be taken in aspect F, and not
in I. We arrive at the unique rhombic group Fdd by proceeding not only from group $I4_1md = F4_1dm$ (mosaic VI from
IV, mosaic VIa from IVa), but also from group $I4_1cd = F4_1dc$
(mosaic VI from V).

* A colored version of this figure was originally published[108].

All these mosaics of *Fdd*2 symmetry are derived from tetragonal ones. Figures 150 and 151 show two examples of *Fdd*2 mosaics which we have so far been unable to relate to tetragonal mosaics.

NON-CRYSTALLOGRAPHIC MOSAICS

It was previously indicated that in the lower syngonies there are no elements of symmetry besides planes *d* (in classical crystallography) which would dispose figures related by them

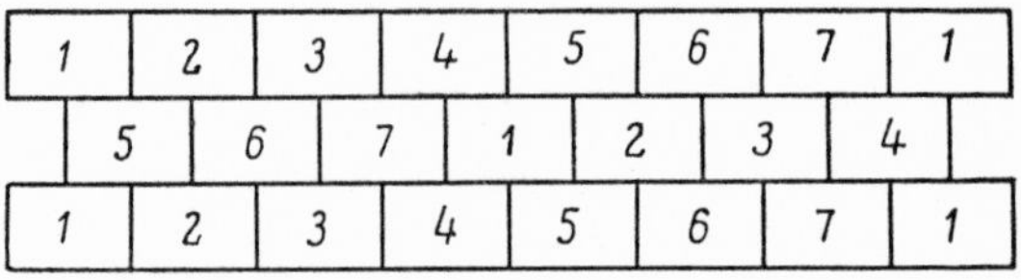

1	2	3	4	5	6	7	1
	5	6	7	1	2	3	4	
1	2	3	4	5	6	7	1

FIG. 152. Seven-color mosaic $A^{VI}PCm$.

on more than two levels, and thus, besides *Fdd*, other multi-colored groups with non-square and non-hexagonal nucleii appear to be impossible. Nevertheless, such multi-colored (non-Fedorov) groups exist and are often encountered in mosaic arrays. Moreover, we can observe 5, 7 and more colors in them, which is forbidden by classical crystallography. We will introduce a number of such mosaics. The first five are executed in colors in Plate II and the subsequent ones are depicted in the text as composed of blocks which should be considered colored, although the colors are only indicated by different numbers (by numbers of corresponding levels in another interpretation).

Mosaics I and II, which are close in motif and are centered, with a plane of symmetry (*Cm*), contain an odd number of colors, 3 and 5; the latter number is forbidden by classical crystallography but the possibility of a similar mosaic with 7, 9 or more colors is quite obvious. Such a seven-color mosaic is shown schematically in Fig. 152. Mosaic III is analogous in symmetry and number of colors to I, but is made up of rectangular blocks instead of rhombuses.

There are an even number of colors (6) in mosaics IV and V. The symmetry of the first is Cm, the second is Im. The numerical diagram of Fig. 153 represents a mosaic analogous to IV but with eight colors. In the diagram in Fig. 154, we see eight colors and no element of symmetry besides (triclinic) lattice F.

1	2	3	4	5	6	7	8	1
5	6	7	8	1	2	3	4	5
1	2	3	4	5	6	7	8	1

FIG. 153. Eight-color mosaic $A^{VIII}BCm$.

1		3		5		7		1
	2		4		6		8	
5		7		1		3		5
	6		8		2		4	
1		3		5		7		1

FIG. 154. Eight-color mosaic $(F)A^{III}BC$.

1	2	3	4	5	6	1
3	4	5	6	1	2	3
5	6	1	2	3	4	5
1	2	3	4	5	6	1

FIG. 155. Six-color mosaic $A^{V}B^{II}C^{II}$.

Finally, the diagram in Fig. 155 shows the cell of a six-color mosaic with a primitive triclinic cell, but with nevertheless a distinct pattern of color alternation.

The emergence of these (non-Fedorov) mosaics is determined by unique reasons. In the monoclinic syngony, the possibility of reducing [hypothetical] lattices I and F to lattices centered only along one rectangular face [C] results from an optional [third] right angle between the third axis and the centered face of the cell. That is, by replacing the color symmetry of the constant third dimension with gradual coloring, we will thereby exclude from consideration the question of various possible angles between the third and the rectangle of the first two axes ($b \times a$). The impossibility of selecting these angles to be different makes the third dimension "perpendicular" or generally fixed in some way relative to the plane ba. If, however, the direction of the third axis is fixed, it is not necessarily the direction of the shortest translation, nor is it necessarily coplanar with the first two axes, and plane ca (or cb) may be centered not only singly, but also doubly, triply, etc.

Let us consider at first an even number of centered points, primarily two. In this case the diagonal of the lateral rectangle is divided into three parts—three levels which allow us to construct a mosaic of three colors (I) which is encountered most frequently in tiled floors. If the lateral "rectangular" face is centered by four nodes, we have five levels and we arrive at a mosaic of five colors (II). In both cases the depicted cell of the mosaic appears to be centered, but the two lateral faces are not centered.

Turning to mosaics with an even number of colors, we see here that an odd number of centered points along face A is possible, and if face C is centered then face B (mosaic III in Plate II; Fig. 153) will also be centered, in agreement with a basic theorem of Bravais lattice theory. In the last two examples there is a plane of symmetry. In Fig. 154 the only element of symmetry is lattice F.

Fourteen Bravais lattices emerge after we select, on the assumption of unique directions in different crystals, six elementary parallelepipeds which correspond to the rules of classical crystallography, that is, which correspond to six systems, and later discover the possibility of the corners of such cells not including all of the nodes of the lattice. In monoclinic cells with one unique direction, after the second direction is fixed in a perpendicular plane, there is no reason for the third direction to be perpendicular to the plane of the first two, and on this basis only two monoclinic cells (to which

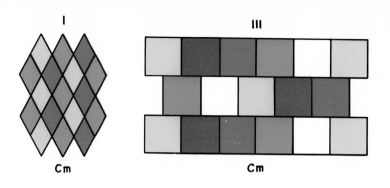

I

Cm

III

Cm

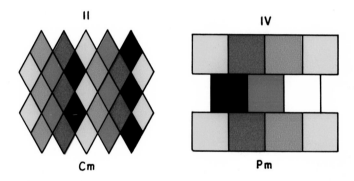

II

Cm

IV

Pm

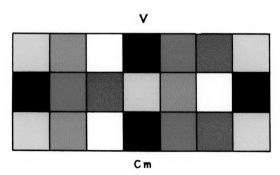

V

Cm

PLATE II. Non-crystallographic plane mosaics.

all the other possible ones reduce) are adopted. Upon the replacement of the third direction by a color this third direction must become "perpendicular", as a result of which arise repeatedly centered cells. Thus in colored mosaics the fifteenth and sixteenth, etc., Bravais lattices are demonstrated, which do not reduce to the fundamental fourteen.

In view of the above, it is not possible to indicate only centered faces by using lattice symbols which refer to the 14 Bravais lattices, that is, centered once and in the center of the face. It is necessary to account for the multiple centering of faces and to write this in the formula. Thus for mosaic I the formula will be $A^{II}PC$, for II and for III $A^{IV}PC$, whereas for IV it will be $A^V BC$. For Fig. 154 the formula is $(F)A^{III}BC$. In both of the latter cases, the designation F is superfluous but on the other hand, in the formula of mosaic V $(I)A^{II}PP$, the designation (I) is appropriate inasmuch as centering by volume does not exclude the possibility (with an even number of nodes) of centering by face. The formula for the triclinic diagram in Fig. 155 will be $A^V B^{II} C^{II}$. In the case of colored lattices, the well-known rule for the 14 Bravais lattices is replaced by a more general one: with an odd number of centered nodes in two faces of a cell, there must also be an odd number of nodes in the third face.

We dealt with analogous considerations above (p. 218), while deriving 46 colored groups by a third method. There (Table 11) we illustrated laterally-centered triclinic cell $A111$; monoclinic cells centered along a face normal to a particular direction $Am11$ and $Ab11$ and even the completely face-centered monoclinic cell $Fm11$. All of these cells are impossible (they reduce to simpler ones) when the third edge is perpendicular to the perpendicular edges of a monoclinic cell; thus we have illustrated more than 14 independent (not reducible to one another) Bravais lattices in the dichromatic groups of symmetry.

Three-Dimensional Mosaics with Colored Symmetry*

N. V. BELOV

INTRODUCTION

THREE-DIMENSIONAL mosaics in two colors are most easily obtained from plane mosaics which correspond to the 46 dichromatic groups[107], by means of superposing identical plane mosaics (of a certain thickness) in the third dimension, but rearranging the colors so that a block of one color lies over a block of another color. This is repeated for each new layer. In other words, we are introducing vertical color translation. The corresponding dichromatic lattices are enumerated by Belov, Neronova and Smirnova[101].

However, color translations may also be slanted from the vertical (the direction of the superposition) and this occurs in several of the simplest mosaics obtained from the Fedorov system of parallelohedra.

CUBIC MOSAICS

If in that group of nine hepta-parallelohedra (Fedorov cubo-octahedra with 14 faces) which usually illustrate a body-centered lattice (its unit cell), we assign to the central cubo-octahedron a different color, we will obtain a simple space mosaic with a cubic dichromatic Bravais lattice (for the 50 lattices see Belov, Neronova and Smirnova[101]) having oblique color translations $P_I m3m$. Its unit cell contains one cubo-octahedron for each (of the two) colors.

By proceeding from the simplest system of triparallelohedra, in particular by using the densest packing of ordinary cubes, but alternating cubes of different colors among them along

* Published in *Kristallografiia*, **1**, 621–625 (1956).

each coordinate direction, we will obtain a three-dimensional checkerboard which we often use to describe the structure of fluorite (CaF_2), saying that populated cubes alternate with unpopulated cubes in it (Fig. 156). Here, however, we prefer to speak of alternation of cubes of two colors (but identical in all other respects). The corresponding Bravais lattice will

FIG. 156. The structure of fluorite as an alternation of populated and unpopulated cubes ($F_s m3m$).

be cubic and face centered with all edges color centered, $F_s m3m^{101}$.

It is easy to see that this packing will be a special case for those mosaics mentioned in the beginning of the article, i.e., it can be broken down into layers of plane identical mosaics, but with a change in color for each plane mosaic along the direction of superposition. In a given three-dimensional mosaic, however, such a breakdown into layers is possible in three mutually perpendicular directions.

By means of Fedorov uniform deformations of original (and consequently dichromatic as well) systems of parallelohedra, we will arrive at the corresponding space mosaics of lower symmetry.

PSEUDO-CUBIC MOSAICS

Starting with the system of hexaparallelohedra for the cubic face-centered lattice (rhombododecahedra), we are unable to derive by this simple method a dichromatic volumetric mosaic with cubic symmetry, inasmuch as there are four rhombododecahedra in the unit cell. Coloring in layers along a four-fold axis lowers the symmetry to tetragonal. The need for a centered base disappears and we make the transition to a primitive tetragonal cell $P_1 4/mmm$, body-color-centered with one rhombododecahedron of each color in the cell.

Coloring rhombododecahedra in levels along a three-fold axis leads to rhombohedral symmetry $R_I \bar{3}m$[101] with two rhombododecahedra of different colors in a unit primitive rhombohedron.

Packing of rhombohedra appears, however, to preserve cubical symmetry if all four rhombododecahedra in the unit cell are colored differently. In this first representative of multicolored—here four-colored—three dimensional mosaics, the Bravais lattice will be primitive and cubic with oblique color translations which center the different faces of the elementary cell, written arbitrarily in the form[101] $P_{A'B'C'}$.

According to the usual method of description, this three-dimensional mosaic with rhombododecahedra of four colors may be characterized as four primitive lattices that are geometrically identical but colored differently, "interpenetrating" one another. All the rhombododecahedra of each of the four lattices are related by a system of translations of the primitive cubic lattice which do not change the color of the rhombododecahedra. We designate this combination of translations $T = 1$. The relation of any given lattice to the three others is accomplished by three-colored diagonal translations (along the faces) of the primitive cube T'_A, T'_B and T'_C (more precisely, by their combinations), i.e., by translations which not only displace the rhombododecahedra on the semi-diagonal of a face, but simultaneously change the color of the rhombododecahedron.

In three-dimensional colored mosaics it is already impossible to juxtapose color upon ascending to a level which corresponds to a certain part of a unit repetition period[107], and the relationships between colors will have a more general character. In our case it is not difficult to establish the incontrovertibility of these relationships by examining Figs. 157*a* and 157*b*, which show the unit cell of our mosaic. If from the zeroth lattice (black) the transition to the first one (yellow) is accomplished by translation T'_A, to the second one (blue) by translation T'_B, and to the third (red) by translation T'_C, then as can easily be seen the transition 1-0 (yellow–black) is accomplished by translation T'_A, the transition 1-2 (yellow–blue) by the translation T'_C, and the transition 1-3 (yellow–red) by translation T'_B.

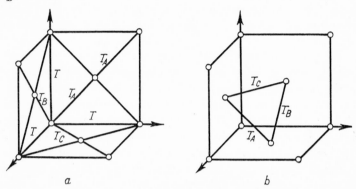

a   b

FIG. 157. Color translations in lattice $P_{A'B'C'}$.

Considering all points (of a rhombododecahedron) of the same (single color) system to be equivalent, we will find

$$T'^2_A = T'^2_B = T'^2_C = T = 1; \quad T'^{-1}_A = T'_A$$

therefore

$$T'_A \cdot T'_B = T'_C; \quad T'_B \cdot T'_C = T'_A; \quad T'_C \cdot T'_A = T'_B.$$

Hence it follows that $T'_A \cdot T'_B \cdot T'_C = 1$ is independent of the order of the factors.

The described relationships unite the four translations T, T'_A, T'_B, T'_C (or to be more precise, their combinations) into a mathematical group. The basic property of the group, that the product of two color translations is equal to a third color translation, shows that in this combination of translations $P_{A'B'C'}$* we have still another representative of a mathematical

* We denote the coloration of corresponding translations and of elements of symmetry in general by primes[101].

four-group (Klein group[89], or a group of equations of the 4th degree) for which only three representatives are as yet known in crystallography[70], namely point groups $V = D_2 = 222$, $C_{2v} = mm2$, and $C_{2h} = 2/m$*.

$$V = D_2 \ C_{2v} \qquad C_{2h} \qquad P_{A'B'C'}$$

	$V=D_2$	C_{2v}	C_{2h}	$P_{A'B'C'}$	
a_0	1	1	1	T	$a_1^2 = a_2^2 = a_3^2 = a_0$
a_1	2_x	m_x	m	T_A'	
a_2	2_y	m_y	$\bar{1} = \overset{\circ}{2}$	T_B'	$a_1 = a_2 a_3; \quad a_2 = a_3 a_1; \quad a_3 = a_1 a_2$
a_3	2_z	2_z	2	T_C'	$a_1 a_2 a_3 = a_0$

It stands to reason that the group of translations $P_{A'B'C'}$ is preserved as such also after uniform deformation of a system of hexaparallelohedra–rhombododecahedra. What is more important is that the system formally loses cubic symmetry even earlier, as a result of being colored in four colors. Although the colored figure in the center of face A, having coincided alternately with the centers of faces B and C, subsequently self-transforms and regains its color, this is achieved by three successive different operations $T_A' \cdot T_B' \cdot T_C' = 1$ and not as a result of the same operation repeated three times, by a left (or right) rotation about a three-fold axis. The latter is absent in the system of colored rhombododecahedra, but four three-fold axes necessarily determine whether a system of figures has cubic symmetry. It is easy to see that the preserved Fedorov symmetry of our packing will only be orthorhombic $P_{A'B'C'}mmm$ with "accidental" equivalence of three parameters of the unit cell. The apparent three-fold axes in the rhombic-deformed cell will obviously not exist, but the centers of the faces will be transformed into one another as before, by color translations, in order to self-coincide on the fourth super-position.

We will arrive at an especially simple pseudo-cubic system of figures with the same symmetry $P_{A'B'C'}mmm$ if we proceed

* Formally this is not quite true, since the corresponding black-white groups[101]: $2'2'2'$, $m'm'2$, $mm'2'$, $2'/m$, $2/m'$ and $2'/m'$ also belong to Klein's four-group. The characteristics of these groups are, however, quite similar to the characteristics of uncolored crystallographic groups and for this reason we only mention these groups.

from the above-mentioned structure of fluorite, represented by Pauling cubes (Fig. 156), and give the "occupied" small cubes which are in the centers of all the faces of the elementary cube three new colors. This will, in fact, be the same mosaic that we have just considered, since a rhombododecahedron is a cube, to each face of which is attached a pyramid equal to one-sixth of the cube, obtained by cleaving the latter with diagonal planes of symmetry (Fig. 158). But if these pyramidal

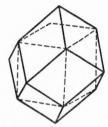

Fig. 158. Relation of rhombododecahedron and cube in group $P_{A'B'C'}$.

extensions are removed, then, as can easily be seen, empty spaces will remain between the small cubes and will appear to be cubes of the same dimensions; and as we have emphasized frequently, the symmetry of this identical system of empty little cubes is equal both to the symmetry of the system of occupied little cubes and to the symmetry of the whole of the two systems of little cubes. The empty little cubes cannot be related by color symmetry—no matter what color they are given—to the original system of little cubes. If given four new colors, the empty cubes will be related only to and among themselves by the same operations of the group $P_{A'B'C'}$.

MOSAICS WITH POLYCHROMATIC TRANSLATIONS

In the groups of symmetry of those mosaics we have constructed, proceeding from systems of parallelohedra, the basic color operations are translations of the second order. In order to obtain groups with color operations of a multiplicity of three or more, it is simplest to resort to those 15 multicolored plane groups and the corresponding mosaics which are given in[107,108]. Considering the latter actually to be plane mosaics of a certain thickness with colored elements, in particular colored axes of symmetry, we extend them upwards by superposing analogous mosaics with colors that have been transformed by color translation of the same order as that by which they alternate about colored axes (or along glide planes, especially planes d). Thus on the four blocks of mosaic II (Plate I) which have the color sequence yellow–blue–red–green* (about a four-fold

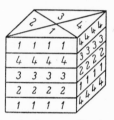

FIG. 159.   Mosaic of group $P_{c'/4}4_{color} = P_{c'/4}4_1$.

color axis) we place four blocks with the sequence blue–red–green–yellow, then four blocks with the sequence red–green–yellow–blue;   then   green–yellow–blue–red,   so   that   the original sequence yellow–blue–red–green is finally repeated. The vertical color translation is of the fourth order. Carried out once, it raises the color 90°, twice—180°, subsequently 270°, and so on;   yellow T_{IV} = blue;   yellow T_{IV}^2 = red;   yellow T_{IV}^3 = yellow T_{IV}^{-1} = green;   yellow T_{IV}^4 = yellow;   blue T_{IV} = red; etc.

If in order to obtain plane mosaics we proceeded from axis 4_1 and denoted each increase along this axis by a change of color, we would then consider that axis 4_{color} exists in our mosaic, and by using color translation to superpose blocks we will reestablish the ordinary monochromatic axis 4_1, which distributes on the four levels of the block four spirals of each of the four colors (Fig. 159).

The symmetry group of the color mosaic thus formed may be designated either as $P_{c'/4}4_{color}$ or $P_{c'/4}4_1$. In the first

* This and subsequent color sequences are corrected to conform to the colors of Plate I.

designation the derived element of symmetry will be $4_1 = 4_{\text{color}} \cdot c'/4$. We will also have $4_1 = 2_1 = 4_{\text{color}} \cdot c'/2$. In the second designation the derived elements of symmetry will be

$$4_{\text{color}} = 4_1 \cdot (c'/4)^{-1}; \quad 4_{\text{color}}^2 = 2_{\text{color}} = 2_1 \cdot (c'/4)^2.$$

In an analogous fashion, by proceeding from mosaics illustrated in Plate I, which belong to other groups of color symmetry, we should recognize in them multicolored elements

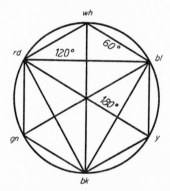

Fig. 160. Alteration of colors in three-dimensional mosaics based on symmetry $R3c$.

of symmetry 6_{color}, $6_{2\,\text{color}} = 3_{\text{color}} \cdot 2$, 3_{color}, d_{color} and the plane three-colored lattice H_{color} which corresponds to lattice R. Upon superposing identical mosaics on each other by using color translations of the same order as that of the old element of symmetry of the plane mosaic, we "reconstruct" the monochromatic elements of symmetry 6_1, 6_2, 3_1, d and R from which we proceeded[107] during the derivation of colored plane groups of symmetry, and which now will be realized in the form of corresponding layers of each color.

We note that the three-dimensional mosaic $R_{c'/3}3m$, obtained from plane mosaic $R3m$ (mosaic X in Plate I) will give us the space motif of ilmenite, $FeTiO_3$, if one considers that in this structure the empty octahedron plays the same crystallographic role as do octahedra for Fe and Ti[69].

Although there are also six colors in mosaic XI (Plate I) with symmetry group $R3c$, the alternation of only three colors corresponds to lattice R (H) in the plane diagram, and correspondingly the vertical translation will break into three colored ones of 120°, i.e., black–red–blue or white–yellow–green will alternate along the vertical in conformity with the sequence of colors we adopted for the circumference of a circle: white–blue–yellow–black–green–red–white (Fig. 160).

Space mosaics may be varied by making, in the case of a four-fold axis, color translations through 180° rather than 90°; in the case of a six-fold axis, in addition to 60°, also through 120° and 180°. The resulting (monochromatic) groups of symmetry will be, correspondingly, instead of tetragonal $P4_1(4_3)$: only monoclinic $P2_1/m$; and instead of $P6_1(6)_5$: $P2_1/m$ (180°) and $P3_1$ (120°). Higher symmetry will be related only to four-fold and six-fold color axes.

According to such a principle, we shall not be able to obtain [new] space mosaics from plane mosaics with a three-fold axis of color symmetry (in Plate I these are mosaics VII—$P3_1$, IX—$R3$, X—$R3m$, XI—$R3c$, XIV—$P6_2$). A horizontal mirror plane may be introduced into the corresponding space mosaics by another means, namely, by the use of additional colors (raising each of the three basic colors 180°). This is most easily achieved in mosaic XI, in which additional colors are already present[107]. On the layer shown in mosaic XI we place a similar layer with different colors according to the principle of superposition and this is repeated with each new layer. The color translation $c_{\frac{1}{2}}'$ appears in the volumetric mosaic but lattice R will be absent. The remaining glide planes, in conjunction with the horizontal mirror plane, generate horizontal two-fold axes, i.e., the uncolored symmetry group will be $P3/mc2 = P6c2 = D_{3h}^2$.

In order to introduce a horizontal mirror plane into the space mosaic constructed according to mosaic X with group $R3m$ (Plate I), we alternate the layers of the latter with layers of a similar mosaic; one which is, however, composed of colors increased by 180° according to mosaics XI and XV. The Fedorov (uncolored) group of the space mosaic obtained will be $P3/mm2 = P\bar{6}m2 = D_{3h}^1$.

In the same fashion, plane m with perpendicular color translation (180°) is simultaneously introduced into the space mosaic on the basis of plane mosaic XIV with color group $P6_2$. The resulting uncolored (Fedorov) group will be, however, only monoclinic $P2/m$.

Literature on Symmetry*

1. R.-J. Haüy, Mémoire sur une loi de crystallisation appelée loi de symétrie: *J. des Mines*, **37**, 215, 347; **38**, 5, 161 (1815).
2. J. Hessel, Kristall, in *Gehlers Phys. Wörterbuch*, **5**, 1023–1340 (1830); *Kristallometrie*, Leipzig (1831).
3. A. Bravais, Mémoire sur les polyèdres de forme symmétrique: *J. de Math.*, **14**, 141 (1849).
4. L. Pasteur, Recherches sur la dissimétrie moléculaire des produits organiques naturels, in *Leçons de chemie professées en 1860*, Paris (1861).
5. A. Bravais, *Études cristallographiques*, Paris (1866).
6. A. Gadolin, Derivation of all crystallographic systems and their subdivision by a single general principle: *Vseross. Mineral. Obshch., Zap.*, **4**, 112 (1869) [in Russian].
7. C. Jordan, Mémoire sur les groupes de mouvements: *Ann. di matem.* (11a) **2**, 167 (1868); 322 (1869).
8. L. Sohncke, *Entwicklung einer Theorie der Kristallstruktur*, Leipzig (1879).
9. P. Curie, Sur la symétrie: *Soc. mineral. France Bull.*, **7**, 418 (1884).
10. B. Minnigerode, Untersuchungen über die Symmetrieverhältnisse der Kristalle: *Neues. Jahrb. Mineral., Beil. B.*, **5**, 145 (1887).
11. E. S. Fedorov, Symmetry of finite figures: *Vseross. Mineral. Obshch., Zap.*, (II), **25**, 1 (1889) [in Russian].
12. E. S. Fedorov, Symmetry in a plane: *Vseross. Mineral. Obshch., Zap.*, (II), **28**, 345 (1891) [in Russian].
13. E. S. Fedorov, Symmetry of regular systems of figures: *Vseross. Mineral. Obshch., Zap.*, (II), **28**, 1 (1891) [in Russian].
14. A. Schoenflies, *Theorie der Kristallstruktur*, Berlin (1891) (2nd ed., 1923).
15. P. Curie, Sur la symétrie dans les phénomenès physiques, symétrie d'un champ électrique et d'un champ magnétique: *J. Phys.*, (3), **3**, 393 (1894).
16. E. S. Fedorov, *Reguläre Plan- und Raumteilung*, München (1900).
17. E. S. Fedorov, *Course in Crystallography*, Saint Petersburg (1901).
18. H. Hilton, *Mathematical Crystallography and the Theory of Groups of Movements*, Oxford (1903).
19. G. V. Vulf, *Handbook of Crystallography*, Warsaw (1904) [in Russian].
20. G. V. Vulf, *Symmetry and its Manifestation in Nature*, Moscow (1908) (reprint. 1919) [in Russian].
21. Ludwig Bieberbach, Über die Bewegungsgruppen der Euklidischen Räume: *Math. Ann.*, **70**, 297–336 (1911).

* Published by A. V. Shubnikov, *Symmetry and Antisymmetry of Finite Figures*, pp. 162–165, Moscow (1951).

22. A. V. SHUBNIKOV, On the question of the structure of crystals: *Akad. Nauk Leningrad Bull.*, (6), **10**, 755 (1916) [in Russian].

23. E. S. FEDOROV, Systems of planigons, which are typical of isohedra in a plane: *Akad. Nauk Leningrad Bull.*, (6), **10**, 1523 (1916) [in Russian].

24. P. NIGGLI, *Geometrische Kristallographie des Diskontinuums*, Leipzig (1919).

25. F. JAEGER, Lecture on *The Principle of Symmetry and its Applications in all Natural Sciences*, Amsterdam (1920).

26. A. V. SHUBNIKOV, Fundamental laws of crystal chemistry: *Akad. Nauk Petrograd*, (6), **16**, 515 (1922) [in Russian].

27. R. W. G. WYCKOFF, *The Analytical Expression of the Result of the Theory of Space Groups*, Washington (1922).

28. H. MARK and K. WEISSENBERG, Röntgenographische Bestimmung der Strukturgewalzter Metallfolien: *Zeit. Physik*, **14**, 328 (1923).

29. G. POLYA, Über die Analogie der Kristallsymmetrie in der Ebene: *Zeit. Kristall.*, **60**, 278 (1924).

30. P. NIGGLI, Die Flächensymmetrien homogener Diskontinuen: *Zeit. Kristall.*, **60**, 283 (1924).

31. P. NIGGLI, Die regelmässige Punktverteilung längs einer Geraden in einer Ebene (Symmetrie von Bordürenmuster): *Zeit. Kristall.*, **63**, 255 (1926).

32. A. SPEISER, *Die Theorie der Gruppen*, Berlin (1927).

33. A. V. SHUBNIKOV, Harmony in nature and art: *Priroda*, 610–622 (1927) [in Russian].

34. C. HERMANN, Ketten und Netzgruppen: *Zeit. Kristall.*, **69**, 250 (1928).

35. A. M. GINZBURG (Günzburg), Die Grundsätze der Lehre von der Symmetrie auf Linien und in Ebenen: *Zeit. Kristall.*, **71**, 81 (1929).

36. A. M. GINZBURG, *Construction of Drawings*, Kharkov (1929) [in Ukranian].

37. E. ALEXANDER, Systematik der eindimensionalen Raumgruppen: *Zeit. Kristall.*, **70**, 367 (1929).

38. L. WEBER, Die Symmetrie homogener ebener Punktsysteme: *Zeit. Kristall.*, **70**, 309 (1929).

39. E. ALEXANDER and K. HERRMANN, Die 80 zweidimensionalen Raumgruppen: *Zeit. Kristall.*, **70**, 328 (1929).

40. D. MOTZOK, Substitutionentheorie als Analyse der Symmetrielehre: *Zeit. Kristall.*, **70**, 406; **72**, 249 (1929).

41. A. V. SHUBNIKOV, Über die Symmetrie des Kontinuums: *Zeit. Kristall.*, **72**, 272 (1929).

42. E. SCHIEBOLD, Über eine neue Herleitung und Nomenklatur der 230 kristallographischen Raumgruppen: *Akad. Wiss. Sachs., Leipzig, Math. Phys. Kl., Abhandl.*, **40**, No. 5, pp. 9–204 (1929).

43. H. HEESCH, Zur Strukturtheorie der ebenen Symmetriegruppen: *Zeit. Kristall.*, **71**, 95 (1929).

43a. H. HEESCH, Über die vierdimensionalen Gruppen des dreidimensionalen Raumes: *Zeit. Kristall.*, **73**, 325 (1930).

44. H. Heesch, Über die Symmetrie zweier Art in Kontinuen und Semi-diskontinuen: *Zeit. Kristall.*, **73**, 346 (1930).
45. A. V. Shubnikov (Schubnikov), Über die Symmetrie des Semi-kontinuums: *Zeit. Kristall.*, **73**, 430 (1930).
46. D. Motzok, Komposition und Transformation in der Symmetri-elehre: *Zeit. Kristall.*, **73**, 430 (1930).
47. D. Motzok, Mehrdimensionale Symmetrie und Substitutionstheorie: *Zeit. Kristall.*, **75**, 345 (1930).
48. W. Ludwig, *Das rechts–links–Problem im Tierreich und bei Menschen mit einem Anhang rechts–links Merkmale der Pflanzen*, Berlin (1932).
49. S. Bogomolov, *Derivation of the Regular Systems by the Method of Fedorov*, Leningrad (1932, 1934) [in Russian].
50. A. V. Shubnikov, The crystal as a uniform environment: *Zhur. fiz. Khim.*, **4**, 231 (1933) [in Russian].
51. A. V. Shubnikov, Instruction in symmetry as a fundamental method of natural science: *Trudy, Akad. Nauk SSSR, IUbileinoi Sessii*, 181 (1933) [in Russian].
52. A. M. Ginzburg, *Symmetry on a Plane*, Kharkov (1934) [in Russian].
53. A. M. Ginzburg, *Symmetry on a Sphere*, Kharkov (1935) [in Russian].
54. H. J. Woods, The geometrical basis of pattern design: *J. Textile Inst.*, **26**, 197, 293 (1935).
55. F. Seitz. A matrix-algebraic development of the crystallographic groups: *Zeit. Kristall.*, **88**, 433 (1934); **90**, 289 (1935); **91**, 336 (1935).
56. A. V. Shubnikov, Development of symmetrical figures with paper: *Nauka i zhizn*, No. **7**, 29 (1935) [in Russian].
57. A. V. Shubnikov, Ampère's Rule and symmetry of the universe: *Trudy, Akad. Nauk SSSR., Lab. Kristall.*, **1**, 25 (1939) [in Russian].
58. A. V. Shubnikov, Symmetry of electromagnetic rays: *Trudy, Akad. Nauk SSSR., Lab. Kristall.*, **1**, 31 (1939) [in Russian].
59. A. V. Shubnikov, *Symmetry* (The laws of symmetry and their applica-tion in science, technology and applied art), Moscow (1940) [in Russian].
60. A. V. Shubnikov, Thirty-nine kinds of crystallographic point sym-metry: *Trudy, Akad. Nauk SSSR., Lab. Krist.*, **2**, 7 (1940) [in Russian].
61. I. I. Shafranovskii, On the simplest development of elements of symmetry: *Leningrad Univ., Uchenie Zap.*, **65** (1944) [in Russian; this reference could not be verified].
62. W. Zachariasen, *Theory of X-ray Diffraction in Crystals*, New York–London (1945).
63. A. V. Shubnikov, New methods of instruction on symmetry and its applications: *Akad. Nauk SSSR, Obshchee Sobranie* 14–17 Oct., 1944, Moscow–Leningrad (1945) [in Russian].
64. A. V. Shubnikov, Dissymmetry, in Symposium on questions in mineralogy and petrography: *Akad. Nauk SSSR*, 158 (1946) [in Russian).
65. A. V. Shubnikov, Atlas of Crystallographic Symmetry Groups: *Akad. Nauk SSSR* (1946) [in Russian].

66. F. Fumi, Sugli operatori matriciali di simmetria macroscopica: *Rend. Accad. Naz. dei Lincei*, (8) **3**, 101 (1947).

67. A. V. Shubnikov, On manifold elements of symmetry: *Trudy, Akad. Nauk SSSR, Inst. Kristall.*, **3**, 3 (1947) [in Russian].

68. J. Burckhardt, *Die Bewegungsgruppen der Kristallographie*, Basel (1947).

69. N. V. Belov, Structure of Ionic Crystals and Metallic Phases, *Akad. Nauk SSSR* (1947) [in Russian].

70. E. N. Belova, N. V. Belov, and A. V. Shubnikov, On the number and composition of the abstract groups, corresponding to the 32 crystallographic classes: *Dokl. Akad. Nauk SSSR*, **63**, 669 (1948) [in Russian].

71. A. V. Shubnikov, Tetartohedry of Pasteur: *Trudy, Akad. Nauk SSSR, Inst. Krist.*, **4**, 3 (1948) [in Russian].

72. A. V. Shubnikov, Symmetry of vectors and tensors: *Izv. Akad. Nauk SSSR, Ser. fiz.*, **13**, 347 (1949) [in Russian].

73. A. V. Shubnikov, Symmetry and the geometrical interpretation of second rank polar tensors: *Izv. Akad. Nauk SSSR, Ser. fiz.*, **13**, 376 (1949) [in Russian].

74. S. Bhagavantam and D. Suryanarayana, Crystal symmetry and physical properties: application of group theory: *Acta Crystall.*, **2**, 21 (1949).

75. C. Hermann, Kristallographie in Räumen beliebiger Dimensionszahl. I. Symmetrieoperationen: *Acta Crystall.*, **2**, 139 (1949).

76. P. Niggli, Die vollständige und eindeutige Kennzeichnung der Raumsysteme durch Charaktertafeln: *Acta Crystall.*, **2**, 263 (1949); **2**, 429 (1950).

77. J. Nicolle, *La symétrie et ses applications*, Paris (1950).

78. N. S. Akulov and IA. I. Feldshtein, Application of the theory of groups in the analysis of anisotropic crystals: *Dokl., Akad. Nauk SSSR*, **70**, 593 (1950) [in Russian].

79. S. Bhagavatam and T. Venkatarayudu, *Theory of Groups and its Application to Physical Problems*, Valtair (1951).

80. A. V. Shubnikov, Perspectives on the evolution of teaching of crystallography (Crystallography Symposium): *Akad. Nauk SSSR, Fedorovskoi nauchnoi sessii* 1949 (1951) [in Russian].

Supplementary References*

1928-1949

81. E. ALEXANDER and K. HERRMANN, Zur Theorie der flüssigen Kristalle: *Zeit. Kristall.*, **70**, 328–345 (1928).
82. J. J. BURCKHARDT, Zur Theorie der Bewegungsgruppen: *Comm. Math. Helv.*, **6**, 159–184 (1933, 1934).
83. B. N. DELONE, N. N. PADUROV, and A. D. ALEKSANDROV, *Mathematical Foundations of the Structural Analysis of Crystals*, Leningrad (1934) [in Russian].
84. *Internationale Tabellen zur Bestimmung von Kristallstrukturen*, Berlin (1935).
85. A. V. SHUBNIKOV, *Piezoelectric Textures*, Moscow (1946) [in Russian].
86. E. S. FEDOROV, Theory of the structure of crystals, in *Collected Works of E. S. Fedorov on the Structure and Symmetry of Crystals*, Moscow (1949) [in Russian].
87. P. NIGGLI, Die geometrischen Grundlagen der Auswahlregeln der Eigenschwingungen und Termaufspaltungen in Molekül- und Kristallverbindungen: *Helv. Chim. Acta.*, **32**, 770–783; 913–924; 1453–1469 (1949).
88. K. L. WOLF, Symmetrie und Polarität: *Studium Generale*, **2**, 213–224 (1949).

1951

89. P. S. ALEKSANDROV, *Introduction to the Theory of Groups*, 2nd ed. Moscow (1951). [See the English transl. (via German) of the first Russian ed. publ. by Hafner, New York (1959), pp. 4–5.]
90. N. V. BELOV, Classroom method for the derivation of space groups of symmetry: *Trudy, Akad. Nauk SSSR, Inst. Kristall.*, **6**, 25–68 (1951) [*Leeds Phil. Literary Soc. Proc., Sci. Sect.*, **8**, 1–46 (1957)].
91. N. V. BELOV, *Structural Crystallography*, Moscow (1951) [in Russian].
92. A. C. HURLEY, Finite rotation groups and crystal classes in four dimensions: *Cambridge Phil. Soc. Proc.*, **47**, 650–661 (1951).
93. A. V. SHUBNIKOV, *Symmetry and Antisymmetry of Finite Figures*, Moscow (1951) [this vol., p. 1].

1952

94. W. COCHRAN, The symmetry of real periodic two-dimensional functions: *Acta Crystall.*, **5**, 630–634 (1952).

* A complete list of the literature on colored symmetry through 1962, plus a few other papers referred to in this volume.

94a. C. HERMANN, Translationsgruppen in n-Dimensionen, in H. O'Daniel, *Zur Struktur und Materie der Festkörper*, Springer–Verlag, Berlin, pp. 24–33 (1952).

95. W. COCHRAN and H. B. DYER, Some practical applications of generalized crystal structure projections: *Acta Crystall.*, **5,** 634–636 (1952).

96. *International Tables for X-ray Crystallography, Vol.* 1, Birmingham (1952).

97. H. WEYL, *Symmetry*, Princeton Univ. Press (1952).

1953

98. A. M. ZAMORZAEV, Generalization of the space groups: Dissertation Leningrad Univ. (1953) [in Russian].

1954

99. N. V. BELOV, Space groups of cubic symmetry: *Trudy, Akad. Nauk SSSR, Inst. Kristall.*, **9,** 21–34 (1954) [in Russian].

100. G. B. BOKII, *Introduction to Crystallography*, Moscow (1954) [in Russian].

100a. A. V. SHUBNIKOV, Correction to the book "Symmetry and Antisymmetry of Finite Figures": *Trudy, Akad. Nauk SSSR, Inst. Kristall.*, **9,** 383 (1954).

100b. A. V. SHUBNIKOV (CHOUBNIKOV), Antisymétrie des figures finies: *Trudy, Akad. Nauk SSSR, Inst. Kristall.*, **10,** 10–12 (1954).

1955

101. N. V. BELOV, N. N. NERONOVA, and T. S. SMIRNOVA, 1651 Shubnikov groups: *Trudy, Akad. Nauk SSSR, Inst. Kristall.*, **11,** 33–67 (1955) [this vol., p. 175].

102. A. V. SHUBNIKOV, I. S. ZHELUDEV, V. P. KONSTANTINOVA, and I. M. SILVESTROVA, *Investigation of Piezoelectric Textures*, Moscow (1955). [French transl: *Étude des textures piezoelectriques*, Dunod, Paris (1958)].

103. B. K. VAINSHTEIN and G. N. TISHCHENKO, Generalized projections in *F* and *f²* series: *Trudy, Akad. Nauk SSSR, Inst. Kristall.*, **11,** 68–74 (1955) [in Russian].

1956

104. N. V. BELOV, The one-dimensional infinite crystallographic groups: *Kristall.*, **1,** 474–476 (1956) [this vol., p. 222].

105. N. V. BELOV, Mediaeval Moorish ornaments: *Kristall.*, **1,** 609–610 (1956) [in Russian].

106. N. V. BELOV, Three-dimensional mosaics with colored symmetry: *Kristall.*, **1,** 621–625 (1956) [this vol., p. 238].

107. N. V. BELOV and T. N. TARKHOVA, Groups of colored symmetry: *Kristall.*, **1,** 4–13, 615 (1956) [this vol., pp. 211, 228].

108. N. V. BELOV and T. N. TARKHOVA, On groups of colored symmetry: *Kristall.*, **1,** 619–621 (1956) [this vol., p. 228].

109. K. DORNBERGER–SCHIFF, On order-disorder structures (OD-structures): *Acta Crystall.*, **9**, 593–601 (1956).

110. M. A. PORAI–KOSHITS, Derivation of working formulae for electronic density and structure amplitude on the basis of characteristic symmetric and antisymmetric trigonometric functions: *Kristall.*, **1**, 4–48 (1956) [in Russian].

111. B. A. TAVGER amd V. M. ZAITSEV, Magnetic symmetry of crystals: *Zhur. Eksp. Teor. Fiz.*, **30**, 564–568 (1956) [*Sov. Phys. JETP* **3**, 430–436].

1957

112. N. V. BELOV and E. N. BELOVA, Mosaics for 46 plane (Shubnikov) antisymmetry groups and for 15 (Fedorov) color groups: *Kristall.*, **2**, 21–22 (1957) [*Sov. Phys. Crystall.*, **2**, 16–18 (see also this vol., pp. 220, 228)].

113. N. V. BELOV, N. N. NERONOVA, and T. S. SMIRNOVA, Shubnikov groups: *Kristall.*, **2**, 315–325 (1957) [*Sov. Phys. Crystall.*, **2**, 311–322].

114. A. L. MACKAY, Extensions of space-group theory: *Acta Crystall.*, **10**, 543–548 (1957).

115. V. A. MOKIEVSKII and I. I. SHAFRANOVSKII, Symmetry, antisymmetry and pseudosymmetry of nucleation surfaces: *Kristall.*, **2**, 23–28 (1957) [*Sov. Phys. Crystall.*, **2**, 19–23].

116. A. M. ZAMORZAEV, Generalization of Fedorov groups: *Kristall.*, **2**, 15–20 (1957) [*Sov. Phys. Crystall.*, **2**, 10–15].

117. A. M. ZAMORZAEV and E. I. SOKOLOV, Symmetry and various kinds of antisymmetry of finite bodies: *Kristall.*, **2**, 9–14 (1957) [*Sov. Phys. Crystall.*, **2**, 5–9].

1958

118. N. V. BELOV, E. N. BELOVA, and T. N. TARKHOVA, More about the color symmetry groups: *Kristall.*, **3**, 618–620 (1959) [*Sov. Phys. Crystall.*, **3**, 625–626 (see also this vol., p. 228)].

119. H. CURIEN and Y. LeCORRE, Notations des macles à l'aide de symbolisme des groupes de couleurs de Choubnikov: *Soc. franc. minéral. cristall. Bull.*, **81**, 126–132 (1958).

120. G. DONNAY, N. V. BELOV, N. N. NERONOVA, and T. S. SMIRNOVA, The Shubnikov groups: *Kristall.*, **3**, 635–636 (1958) [*Sov. Phys. Crystall.*, **3**, 642–644].

121. G. DONNAY, L. M. CORLISS, J. D. H. DONNAY, N. ELLIOTT, and J. M. HASTINGS, Symmetry of magnetic structures: magnetic structure of chalcopyrite: *Phys. Rev.*, **112**, 1917–1923 (1958).

122. W. T. HOLSER, Relation of symmetry to structure in twinning: *Zeit. Kristall.*, **110**, 249–265 (1958).

123. W. T. HOLSER, Point groups and plane groups in a two-sided plane and their subgroups: *Zeit. Kristall.*, **110**, 266–281 (1958).

124. Y. LE CORRE, Les groupes de symétrie bicolores et leurs applications: *Soc. franç. minéral. cristall. Bull.*, **81**, 120–125 (1958).

125. A. V. Shubnikov, Antisymmetry of textures: *Kristall.*, **3**, 263–268 (1958) [*Sov. Phys. Crystall.*, **3**, 269–273; see also this vol., p. 161].

126. L. A. Shuvalov and B. A. Tavger, Symmetry of magnetostrictive properties of crystals: *Kristall.*, **3**, 756–768 (1958) [*Sov. Phys. Crystall.*, **3**, 765–768].

127. B. A. Tavger, The symmetry of ferromagnetics and antiferromagnetics: *Kristall.*, **3**, 339–341 (1958) [*Sov. Phys. Crystall.*, **3**, 341–343].

128. B. A. Tavger, Symmetry of piezomagnetism of antiferromagnetics: *Kristall.*, **3**, 342–345 (1958) [*Sov. Phys. Crystall.*, **3**, 344–347].

129. A. M. Zamorzaev, Derivation of new Shubnikov groups: *Kristall.*, **3**, 399–404 (1958) [*Sov. Phys. Crystall.*, **3**, 401–406].

1959

130. N. V. Belov, On the nomenclature of the 80 plane groups in three dimensions: *Kristall.*, **4**, 775–778 (1959) [*Sov. Phys. Crystall.*, **4**, 730–733].

131. H. Curien and J. D. H. Donnay, The symmetry of the complete twin: *Amer. Mineral.*, **44**, 1067–1070 (1959).

132. L. M. Corliss and J. M. Hastings, Symmetry of magnetic structures [abs.]: *Jour. Appl. Phys.*, **30**, 2795 (1959).

133. J. D. H. Donnay and Gabrielle Donnay, Tables de groupes spatiaux magnétiques: *Compt. rend. Acad. sci., Paris*, **248**, 3317–3319 (1959).

133a. Gabrielle Donnay and J. D. H. Donnay, Symmetry of Magnetic Structures: *Carnegie Inst. Washington, Geophys. Lab., Ann. Rept.* 1958/59, pp. 189–192 (1959).

134. K. Dornberger-Schiff, On the nomenclature of the 80 plane groups in three dimensions: *Acta Crystall.*, **12**, 173 (1959).

135. V. L. Indenbom, Relation of the antisymmetry and color symmetry groups to one-dimensional representations of the ordinary symmetry groups. Isomorphism of the Shubnikov and space groups: *Kristall.*, **4**, 619–620 (1959) [*Sov. Phys. Crystall.*, **4**, 578–580].

136. J. S. Kasper and J. S. Kouvel, The antiferromagnetic structure of NiMn: *Phys. Chem. Solids*, **11**, 231–238 (1959).

137. N. N. Neronova and B. V. Belov, Ferromagnetic and ferroelectric space groups: *Kristall.*, **4**, 807–812 (1959) [*Sov. Phys. Crystall.*, **4**, 769–774].

138. N. N. Neronova and N. V. Belov, Symmetry in ferroelectrics: *Dokl., Akad. Nauk SSSR*, **129**, 556–557 (1959) [*Dokl., Sov. Phys.*, **4**, 1179–1180].

139. A. Niggli, Zur Systematik und gruppentheoretischen Ableitung der Symmetrie-, Antisymmetrie- und Entartungssymmetriegruppen: *Zeit. Kristall.*, **111**, 288–300 (1959).

140. I. I. Shafranovskii, Geometrical varieties of face forms for crystals falling in the classes of low symmetry: *Kristall.*, **4**, 293–301 (1959) [*Sov. Phys. Crystall.*, **4**, 274–280].

141. A. V. Shubnikov, Symmetry and antisymmetry of rods and semi-continua with principal axis of infinite order and finite transfers along it: *Kristall.*, **4**, 279–285 (1959) [*Sov. Phys. Crystall.*, **4**, 261–266].

142. O. Wittke and J. Garrido, Symétrie des polyèdres polychromatiques: *Soc. franç. minéral. cristall. Bull.*, **82**, 223–230 (1959).

143. L. A. Shuvalov, Ferromagnetic phase transitions and the symmetry of crystals: *Kristall.*, **4**, 399–409 (1959) [*Sov. Phys. Crystall.*, **4**, 371–380].

1960

144. J. D. H. Donnay, Early contributions to the theory of symmetry (abs.): *Acta Crystall.*, **13**, 1083 (1960).

145. M. C. Escher, Antisymmetrical arrangements in the plane and regular three-dimensional bodies as sources of inspiration to an artist (abs.): *Acta Crystall.*, **13**, 1083 (1960).

146. C. Hermann, The interpretation and nomenclature of coloured space groups (abs.): *Acta Crystall.*, **13**, 1084–1085 (1960).

147. W. T. Holser, Relation of pseudosymmetry to structure in twinning: Spain. *Consejo Superior de Investigaciones Geologicas Lucas Mallada. Cursillos y Conferencias*, **7**, 19–30 (1960).

148. V. L. Indenbom, Phase transitions without change in the number of atoms in the unit cell of the crystal: *Kristall.*, **5**, 115–125 (1960) [*Sov. Phys. Crystall.*, **5**, 106–115].

149. V. L. Indenbom, Irreducible representations of the magnetic groups and allowance for magnetic symmetry: *Kristall.*, **5**, 513–516 (1960) [*Sov. Phys. Crystall.*, **5**, 493–496].

150. V. L. Indenbom, N. V. Belov, and N. N. Neronova, The color symmetry point groups: *Kristall.*, **5**, 496–500 (1960) [*Sov. Phys. Crystall.*, **5**, 477–481].

151. A. L. Mackay, Later contributions to the theory of symmetry groups (abs.): *Acta Crystall.*, **13**, 1084 (1960).

152. A. Niggli, Cryptosymmetry and tensors (abs.): *Acta Crystall.*, **13**, 1084 (1960).

153. A. Niggli and H. Wondratschek, Eine Verallgemeinerung der Punktgruppen. I. Die einfachen Kryptosymmetrien: *Zeit. Kristall.*, **114**, 215–231 (1960).

154. W. Nowacki, Überblick über "zweifarbige" Symmetriegruppen: *Fortschr. Mineral.*, **38**, 96–105 (1960); **39**, 152 (1961).

155. I. M. Rumanova, Symmetry of weighted electron-density projections for crystals falling in the groups of lowest symmetry: *Kristall.*, **5**, 180–193 (1960) [*Sov. Phys. Crystall.*, **5**, 166–179].

156. I. M. Rumanova, Formulas for modulated electron density projections for plane oblique-angled and rectangular black-white groups having a center of symmetry (antisymmetry): *Kristall.*, **5**, 831–863 (1960) [*Sov. Phys. Crystall.*, **5**, 793–825].

156a. CLEMENTE SAENZ GARCIA, Pequeñas dosis de cristalografia hiper-spacial: *Ciencias-Revista Trimestral*, **25**, 321–334; 571–588 (1960).

157. I. I. SHAFRANOVSKII, An extended study of crystal forms and the crystal morphology of twins: *Kristall.*, **5**, 525–529 (1960) [*Sov. Phys. Crystall.*, **5**, 504–508].

158. I. I. SHAFRANOVSKII, *Lectures on the Crystallography of Minerals*, Lvov (1960) [in Russian].

159. A. V. SHUBNIKOV, Time reversal as an operation of antisymmetry: *Kristall.*, **5**, 328–333 (1960) [*Sov. Phys. Crystall.*, **5**, 309–314].

160. B. A. TAVGER, Limiting magnetic symmetry of physical systems: *Kristall.*, **5**, 677–680 (1960) [*Sov. Phys. Crystall.*, **5**, 646–649].

161. B. K. VAINSHTEIN, Antisymmetry of transformation of Fourier forms: *Kristall.*, **5**, 341–345 (1960) [*Sov. Phys. Crystall.*, **5**, 323–327].

162. A. M. ZAMORZAEV and A. F. PALISTRANT, The two-dimensional Shubnikov groups: *Kristall.*, **5**, 517–524 (1960) [*Sov. Phys. Crystall.*, **5**, 497–503].

163. I. S. ZHELUDEV, Similar and dissimilar features of antisymmetry, magnetic symmetry and complete symmetry: *Izv., Akad. Nauk SSSR, Ser. fiz.*, **24**, 1436–1439 (1960) [*Acad. Sci. U.S.S.R. Bull., Phys. Sci.*, **24**, 1425–1428].

164. I. S. ZHELUDEV, Complete symmetry of scalars, vectors, and tensors of rank two: *Kristall.*, **5**, 346–353 (1960) [*Sov. Phys. Crystall.*, **5**, 328–334].

165. I. S. ZHELUDEV, Complete limiting symmetry groups of scalars, vectors, and second-rank tensors and their combinations: *Kristall.*, **5**, 508–512 (1960) [*Sov. Phys. Crystall.*, **5**, 489–496].

1961

166. E. F. BERTAUT, Configurations magnetiques. La methode directe: *Phys. Chem. Solids*, **21**, 295–305 (1961).

167. A. BIENENSTOCK and P. P. EWALD, Structure theories in physical and in Fourier space: *Kristall.*, **6**, 665–667 (1961) [*Sov. Phys. Crystall.*, **6**, 820–824].

168. V. A. FRANK–KAMENETSKII and I. I. SHAFRANOVSKII, The law of crystallographic limits and the principle of close packing: *Kristall.*, **6**, 892–900 (1961) [*Sov. Phys. Crystall.*, **6**, 720–726].

169. W. T. HOLSER, Classification of symmetry groups: *Acta Crystall.*, **14**, 1236–1242 (1961).

170. V. A. MOKIEVSKII and I. I. SHAFRONOVSKII, A graphic method for describing crystal forms: *Kristall.*, **6**, 944–948 (1961) [*Sov. Phys. Crystall.*, **6**, 761–764].

171. N. N. NERONOVA and N. V. BELOV, A single scheme for the classical and black-and-white crystallographic symmetry groups: *Kristall.*, **6**, 3–12 (1961) [*Sov. Phys. Crystall.*, **6**, 1–9].

172. N. N. NERONOVA and N. V. BELOV, Colored antisymmetric mosaics: *Kristall.*, **6**, 831–839 (1961) [*Sov. Phys. Crystall.*, **6**, 831–839].

173. W. Nowacki, Probleme der modernen Kristallographie und Structur-lehre: *Chimia*, **15**, 411–420 (1961).

174. G. S. Pawley, Mosaics for color antisymmetry groups: *Kristall.*, **6**, 109–110 (1961) [*Sov. Phys. Crystall.*, **6**, 87–88].

174a. G. S. Pawley, Symmetry and antisymmetry of irregular tetrahedra in a non-lattice array: *Zeit. Kristall.*, **116**, 1–12 (1961).

175. I. M. Rumanova, Formulas for weighted electron-density projections for two-dimensional oblique and rectangular black-and-white groups lacking centers of symmetry or antisymmetry: *Kristall.*, **6**, 13–30 (1961) [*Sov. Phys. Crystall.*, **6**, 10–26].

176. I. I. Shafranovskii, Extension de la théorie des formes crystallines et de la morphologie des macles: *Soc. franç. minéral. cristall., Bull.*, **84**, 20–24 (1961).

177. I. I. Shafranovskii, Erweiterung der Kristallformenlehre: *Fortschr. Mineral.*, **39**, 187–195 (1961).

178. I. I. Shafranovskii, General forms of twinned structures: *Kristall.*, **6**, 31–42 (1961) [*Sov. Phys. Crystall.*, **6**, 27–33].

179. A. V. Shubnikov, Complete systematics of black–white point groups: *Kristall.*, **6**, 49–495 (1961) [*Sov. Phys. Crystall.*, **6**, 394–398].

180. L. A. Shuvalov and A. S. Sonin, The crystallography of antiferro-electrics: *Kristall.*, **6**, 323–330 (1961) [*Sov. Phys. Crystall.*, **6**, 258–262].

181. B. L. Van der Waerden and J. J. Burckhardt, Farbgruppen: *Zeit. Kristall.*, **115**, 231–234 (1961).

182. H. Wondratschek and A. Niggli, Eine Verallgemeinerung der Punktgruppen, II. Die mehrfachen Kryptosymmetrien: *Zeit. Kristall.*, **115**, 1–20 (1961).

183. A. M. Zamorzaev and A. F. Palistrant, Mosaics for 167 two-dimensional Shubnikov groups (three lowest orders): *Kristall.*, **6**, 163–176 (1961) [*Sov. Phys. Crystall.*, **6**, 127–140].

1962

184. N. V. Belov, *Ferromagnetic, Antiferromagnetic and Ferroelectric groups:* Akad. Nauk, Moscow (Public., in Russian, announced 1962; not seen).

185. Arthur Bienenstock and P. P. Ewald, Symmetry of Fourier space: *Acta Crystall.*, **15**, 1253–1260 (1962).

186. N. N. Neronova and N. V. Belov, Color antisymmetry mosaics: *Kristall.*, **6**, 831–839 (1962) [*Sov. Phys. Crystall.*, **6**, 672–678].

187. Adolph Pabst, The 179 two-sided, two-colored band groups and their relations: *Zeit. Kristall.*, **117**, 128–134 (1962).

188. G. S. Pawley, Plane groups on polyhedra: *Acta Crystall.*, **15**, 49–53 (1962).

189. I. M. Rumanova, *Weighted Electron Density Functions in the Structural Analysis of Crystals.* Akad. Nauk, Moscow (Public., in Russian, announced 1962; not seen).

190. A. V. SHUBNIKOV, Groups of (class) symmetry and antisymmetry in a finite band: *Kristall.*, **7**, 3–6 (1962) [*Sov. Phys. Crystall.*, **7**, 1–4].

191. A. V. SHUBNIKOV, Black–white groups of infinite ribbons: *Kristall.*, **7**, 186–191 (1962) [*Sov. Phys. Crystall.*, **7**, 145–149].

192. A. V. SHUBNIKOV, On the attribution of all crystallograp symmetry groups to three-dimensional groups: *Kristall.*, **7**, 49(495 (1962) [*Sov. Phys. Crystall.*, **7**, 394–398].

193. L. A. SHUVALOV and N. V. BELOV, The symmetry of crystals in which ferromagnetic and ferroelectric properties appear simultaneously: *Kristall.*, **7**, 186–191 (1962) [*Sov. Phys. Crystall.*, **7**, 150–151].

194. IU. I. SIROTIN, Magnetic symmetry of tensors and the energy of magnetic anisotropy: *Kristall.*, **7**, 89–96 (1962) [*Sov. Phys. Crystall.*, **7**, 71–77].

195. J. S. KASPER, The application of magnetic symmetry to neutron diffraction data: *Phys. Chem. Solids.* To be published. Abstract in *Acta Crystall.*, **13**, 1085 (1960).

196. N. V. BELOV, T. S. KUNTSEVICH, and N. N. NERONOVA, Shubnikov (antisymmetry) groups for infinite double-sided ribbons: *Kristall.*, **7**, 805–806 (1962) [*Sov. Phys. Crystall.*, **7**, 651–652].

197. I. I. SHAFRANOVSKII, Varieties of the cube in crystallography: *Kristall.*, **7**, 664–670 (1962) [*Sov. Phys. Crystall.*, **7**, 539–543].

198. L. A. SHUVALOV, Antisymmetry and its concrete modifications: *Kristall.*, **7**, 520–525 (1962) [*Sov. Phys. Crystall.*, **7**, 418–422].

199. L. A. SHUVALOV, Limit groups of double antisymmetry: *Kristall*, **7**, 669–672 (1962) [*Sov. Phys. Crystall.*, **7**, 822–825].

200. OSCAR WITTKE, The colour-symmetry groups and cryptosymmetry groups associated with the 32 crystallographic point groups: *Zeit. Kristall.*, **117**, 153–165 (1962).

201. A. M. ZAMORZAEV, On the 1651 Shubnikov groups: *Kristall.*, **7**, 813–821 (1962) [*Sov. Phys. Crystall.*, **7**, 661–668].

COLORED SYMMETRY
by Shubnikov & Belov

ERRATUM

Due to expansion of the Contents List at a late stage, it was necessary to re-arrange the pagination of the preliminary pages, and the Roman numerals relating to these pages in the Index are incorrect. Please, therefore, when referring to the preliminary pages through the Index, increase by ii all Roman numerals.

Index

ALEXANDER, E.   175
Antiaxes
  mirror   xx, 109
  ordinary   xx, 108
Anti-equality   xvi, 97
  congruent   98
  mirror   98
Anti-identification   101
Anti-inversion   107
Anti-movements   xviii
  mirror   x
Antireflection   104
Antirotations   xviii, 106, 108
  mirror   xviii, 109
Antisymmetry   xviii, 88, 161, 171
  operations of   96, 101
  (*See also* Symmetry, dichromatic)
Asymmetry   171
Axis, infinite-fold   60, 75, 161
  mirror   xx, 7, 73
  ordinary   xx, 33
  screw   229
  symmetry of   6

BELOV, N. V.   175, 211, 220, 222, 228
BELOVA, E. N.   220, 228

Center of symmetry   12
Centering
  color   177
  multiple   237
COCHRAN, W.   175, 213
Crystal
  liquid   161
  structure determination   175

Dissymmetry   171
Domains   4, 148

Enantiomorphic figures   xvi, 22, 102
Equality   24
  congruent   xv, 20, 98
  mirror   xv, 20, 98
Euler's theorem   19

FEDOROV, E. S.   xiii, 176
Figure
  antisymmetrical   150
  asymmetrical   99
  enantiomorphic   102
  of mixed polarity   xviii, 98
  neutral   98
  plane   76
  polar   98
  three-dimensional   3
Fluorite, structure of   239
Form
  general   144
  simple   144
  special   144

Group
  abstract   30
  color   241
  crystallographic   76, 84
  definition of a   xix, 27
  elements of a   xix
  gray   112, 185, 211
  Klein   242
  limit   34, 75, 141, 161
  line   222, 225
    dichromatic   223

Group *cont.*
  of mixed polarity 112, 114, 141
  neutral (See Groups, gray)
  order of a xix, 28
  plane 176
    dichromatic 211, 214, 220
    polychromatic 228
  point
    three-dimensional 31, 72
    two-dimensional 84
  polar 112
  rod 226
  Shubnikov 175, 197
    number of 195
  sub- 44, 75, 226
  symmetry 27, 84
    dichromatic 175
    polychromatic 238
  types of 74

HERMANN, K. 175

Identification 13, 29
Identity xiv
Inversion 11, 14, 81

Lattice
  Bravais 176, 212, 223, 224, 236, 238
  centered 180
  identity of 181
  interpenetrating 240
  primitive 180

Mosaics
  cubic 238
  non-crystallographic 234
  plane
    dichromatic 220
    polychromatic 228
  pseudo-cubic 239
  three-dimensional 238
Movements xviii
  mirror xviii

NERONOVA, N. N. 175
Nomenclature (See Symbolism)

Operation, unit 13
  equivalent 11
  of the first kind xvii
  inverse 29
  non-equivalent 11
  powers of 25
  product of 27
  of the second kind xvii
Optical activity 152
Ornamental patterns 229

Piezoelectricity 151
Planes, identity of 184
Pyroelectricity 150

Reflection 4, 13, 14, 15, 23, 185
  consecutive 16
Reversal 14
Rotation xviii, 5, 6, 31
  double 50
  irrational 37
  mirror xviii, 7, 38, 43, 81

SHUBNIKOV, A. V. xiii, 175
Singular points 8
SMIRNOVA, T. S. 175
Space
  two-dimensional 93
  three-dimensional xxi, 93
  four-dimensional xxi, 103
Sub-group 44, 75, 226
Symbolism 31, 38, 73, 180, 185, 187, 195, 222, 229, 237, 241
Symmetry
  colored 175
  definition of xiii, 3
  dichromatic 175
  element of xix, 45, 185
  operations of 4

TARKHOVA, T. N.   211, 228
Tensor
  axial   158
  polar   157
  symmetry of   153
Texture   161
Transformation   xx, 8, 22, 88, 153
  afine orthogonal   92
Translation
  color, 177, 185, 213, 238, 242
  polychromatic   243

VAINSHTEIN, B. K.   175
Vector
  axial   156
  polar   154
  symmetry of   153

WEBER, L.   175

ZAMORZAEV, A. M.   175, 197